EPO AND A CHANGING WORLD:
CREATING LINKAGES AND EXPANDING PARTNERSHIPS

COVER ILLUSTRATION:

Just as the mass of a spiral galaxy centers around the nucleus, the science of astronomy centers around skillfully teaching and presenting its wonders to the public.

Illustration courtesy of Leslie Proudfit

ASTRONOMICAL SOCIETY OF THE PACIFIC CONFERENCE SERIES

A SERIES OF BOOKS ON RECENT DEVELOPMENTS IN ASTRONOMY AND ASTROPHYSICS

Volume 389

EDITORIAL STAFF

Managing Editor: J. W. Moody
Assistant Managing Editor: Jonathan Barnes
Publication Manager: Lisa B. Roper
Editorial Assistant: Amy Schuff
E-book Specialist: Jeremy Roper
Web Developer/Technical Consultant: Jared Bellows
L^ATEX Consultant: T. J. Mahoney (Spain) – tjm@iac.es

PO Box 4666, Room C454 – ESC, Brigham Young University, Provo, Utah, 84602-4666
Phone: 801-422-2111   Fax: 801-422-0553
E-mail: aspcs@aspbooks.org   E-book site: http://www.aspbooks.org

PUBLICATION COMMITTEE

Recent ASPCS Volumes may be found as e-books with color images at
http://www.aspbooks.org

A listing of recently published volumes may be found at the back of this volume.

For a complete listing of ASPCS and IAU Volumes published by the ASP see
http://www.astrosociety.org/pubs.html

ASTRONOMICAL SOCIETY OF THE PACIFIC
CONFERENCE SERIES

Volume 389

EPO AND A CHANGING WORLD:
CREATING LINKAGES AND EXPANDING PARTNERSHIPS

Proceedings of a conference held in
Chicago, Illinois, USA
5–7 September 2007

Edited by

Catharine Garmany
National Optical Astronomy Observatory, Tucson, Arizona, USA

Michael G. Gibbs
Astronomical Society of the Pacific, San Francisco, California, USA

and

J. Ward Moody
Brigham Young University, Provo, Utah, USA

SAN FRANCISCO

ASTRONOMICAL SOCIETY OF THE PACIFIC
390 Ashton Avenue
San Francisco, California, 94112-1722, USA

Phone: 415-337-1100
Fax: 415-337-5205
E-mail: service@astrosociety.org
Web Site: www.astrosociety.org
E-books: www.aspbooks.org

ISBN: 978-1-58381-648-6
e-Book ISBN: 978-1-58381-649-3

Library of Congress (LOC) Cataloging in Publication (CIP) Data:
Main entry under title
Library of Congress Control Number (LCCN): 2008924893

Printed in the United States of America by Sheridan Books, Ann Arbor, Michigan

Contents

Part 1. Innovative Partnerships and Delivery Methods

Part 2. Broadening the Audience

Part 3. Linking Research with EPO

Part 4. The Changing EPO Profession

Part 5. International Year of Astronomy 2009

Part 6. Summaries

Preface

The Astronomical Society of the Pacific (ASP) was founded in 1889 by a group of Northern California professional and amateur astronomers. The ASP's earliest purpose was to disseminate astronomical information, and that purpose has not significantly changed in more than 100 years. The ASP has, however, become much more diversified both geographically and demographically and is now an international organization with members from over 40 nations. The ASP membership and Board of Directors are now comprised of members of the research astronomy, education, and amateur astronomy communities.

The mission of the ASP is to increase public understanding and appreciation of astronomy, to advance science literacy, and to facilitate scientific exchange between scientists, educators, enthusiasts, and the public. The means that the Society uses to fulfill this mission include:

- uniting the interests and expertise of scientists, educators, amateur astronomers, and astronomy enthusiasts.

- providing resources and tools to assist educators of all types.

- recognizing and honoring extraordinary contributions to astronomy and astronomy education.

- disseminating the results of astronomical research to the astronomical community.

- communicating the excitement of astronomy to educators and the general public.

To advance science literacy through engagement in astronomy, recent annual meetings have focused on astronomy and space science education and public outreach. The three day meeting held in Chicago, Illinois in September, 2007 included 48 interactive workshops and 78 posters centered on the themes "Innovative Partnerships," "Towards Broadening the Audience," "The Evolving Nature of Astronomy Research and Implications for EPO," and "The EPO profession: a Changing World." The overarching conference theme, "Creating Linkages and Expanding Partnerships," provided a focus for this national conference on building and supporting a vibrant and connected community of individuals and groups engaged in education and public outreach (EPO) in the disciplines of astronomy, astrobiology, space, and earth science.

The Editors

Support and Sponsorship

The following organizations have contributed significant support to the success of this conference.

Adler Planetarium

~

Education Office of the American Astronomical Society
Evans & Sutherland
Sky-Skan, Inc.

~

Ball Aerospace & Technologies
DePaul University
Meade Instruments Corporation
University of Chicago Press

~

Interstellar Boundary Explorer
University of Arizona, CAPER Team
Carl Zeiss and Seiler Instrument

Digitalis Education Solutions, Inc. • MWT Associates • Starry Night Education
Slooh.com • Swinburne Astronomy Online • You Can Do Astronomy

Part I

Innovative Partnerships and Delivery Methods

EPO and a Changing World
ASP Conference Series, Vol. 389, © *2008*
C. Garmany, M. Gibbs, and J. W. Moody

EPO and the Big Education Reform Picture

George D. Nelson

Western Washington University, Science, Math, and Tech Ed., 516 High St. Bellingham, WA 98225-9155

Abstract. This paper is a summary of the keynote talk delivered at the conference. I have tried to keep the sense of the spoken presentation. Some of the ideas are my own, some are borrowed from colleagues. The biases, and whines are my own.

1. Introduction

There are three topics that I would like to talk about.

1. How can we realize our fantasy that someday every American will be literate in astronomy?

2. Some lessons I have learned that might be helpful.

3. How partnering with each other and other education experts is critical to achieving our goals.

To begin, there are some kudos to hand out. Understand that these are personal and I am sure that I am missing some very worth folks, but some of us have done extraordinary things and should be recognized. First, I want to recognize Barbara Morgan, she "paid the dues and got the views". Barbara persevered after the loss of the Challenger to become NASA's Teacher-in-Space this year. Had she not hung in there, there would be no Educator Astronaut program, a loss to the agency. We can (and should) expect great things from Barbara.

Next, I want to recognize Jacqueline Barber, Isabel Hawkins, Greg Schultz and their colleagues at Berkeley and the Lawrence Hall of Science for setting an example of effective partnership. They assembled a number of NASA forums and education experts to produce *Space Science*, a terrific new curriculum for grades 3-5, soon to be followed by a grade 6-8 addition. These instructional materials responded to the challenge that I made a few years ago to produce something that incorporates the best of NASA's cutting edge research to help children learn grade-level appropriate ideas in astronomy in the time available. By incorporating the latest findings from learning and cognitive science research and tackling a small set of important ideas they have produced a realistic and realizable curriculum. We would do well to become familiar with these materials and promote them to teachers and schools rather than trying to create something else. At the same time, we can learn from teachers and students using *Space Science* and provide feedback to Jacqueline Barber and her team.

Other kudos go to Tim Slater and the CAPER team and to Phil Sadler and others for helping us learn what we need to know and to Sidney Wolff and Andy Fraknoi for starting and sustaining the Astronomy Education Review. It will serve us all well to pay close attention to the growing quality and quantity of astronomy education research. Others are making huge contributions to public outreach, raising the interest in things astronomical. Neil deGrasse Tyson, Larry Krauss and many others are providing an articulate public face for astronomy. Finally, the Astronomical Society of the Pacific and all of you in the EPO world are making a difference. It is an honor to be one of your peers.

2.   A Challenge

A few years ago I was having a conversation about education with a friend who is a very accomplished astronomy researcher at a major American university. At one point while we were talking about the state of undergraduate education and teaching today's crop of students my friend said, "I would say that twenty percent of my students can learn on their own. All I have to do is order the book, show up, and give the tests." Then, amazingly, about five minutes later, as we were talking about students who go on to major in physics or astronomy, my friend said, "You know, I teach to the top twenty percent of my classes..." This conversation highlights one of the real challenges that the schools and universities are facing. Who is our audience and what are our goals?

In elementary schools, it is pretty clear that it is basic literacy and interest for all kids and all teachers. By middle school, there is usually some separation based on who is or isn't taking or succeeding in algebra. High schools cater strongly to those students (and their parents) who are striving to get into "good" colleges and universities. The majority of students in most schools, those who will drop out or find a job after graduation or even those who go on to a local community college, are tolerated by the system, but garner much less of the resources than their numbers ($\sim$80%) would suggest they should receive. Of course, there are exceptions, and there are always wonderful teachers whose heart and soul is dedicated to serving "the forgotten majority", but the system is not. In higher education it is not much different. We treat future majors differently than future elementary teachers, for example. There has been some wonderful work trying to optimize the economic model of huge classes (efficiency = students/faculty), but little work in trying to implement educationally sound models for those who need effective instruction most. In this area, community colleges are at the forefront because they can afford to teach smaller classes. The issue is teaching them well.

Then there is the general public, the great masses of adults and their children who primarily live near cities with museums, colleges or universities with astronomers on the faculty, or those connected to the Internet. And we need to be strategic about choosing our target audiences to maximize the impact of the resources that we are using. A small percentage of adults, teachers, and students are "space groupies" who will be thrilled with anything we do. The majority have other primary interests and commitments and must be convinced of the merit of our offerings. If we are serious about our fantasy, we cannot EPO just to the choir.

So the first challenge is to decide, are you focusing on contributing to the astronomical literacy of generic elementary, middle, or high school students, exciting highly capable students (including girls and under-represented minorities) who might become scientists or engineers, increasing the content knowledge of current or future teachers, increasing adult literacy or appreciation of NASA, or engaging our professional peers in rethinking teaching and learning? The second challenge is to set measurable goals and gather credible evidence of successes or failures. As scientists we owe the community more examples of thoughtful work and good research.

3.   A Focus on Teaching

My own bias is that we will get the biggest bang for our buck by focusing on helping teachers become effective teachers of astronomy. As stated by the Education Trust in their Winter 2004 newsletter,

> "... teacher effectiveness is the single biggest factor influencing gains in achievement, an influence bigger than race, poverty, parent's education, or any of the other factors that are often thought to doom children to failure."

This is not a trivial undertaking. It starts in future teachers' homes and K-12 experiences, continues through their higher education astronomy classes and teacher training. It includes the resources and support that teachers receive in their school districts and buildings.

We should start by asking, what is effective teaching? This is a question that has a strong research base in science, if not specifically in astronomy. First, effective teaching engages students with relevant and important content. It takes place in an environment conducive to learning within the classroom, museum, or laboratory. It provides all students appropriate access to content, uses questioning strategies to monitor and promote thinking, and takes the time to help students make sense of the content.

Next we can ask what does it take to teach effectively? Teachers must have deep content and pedagogical knowledge. They need the best instructional materials available. Instructional materials are tools that enable a skilled practitioner to build a learning environment much like quality tools enable a skilled craftsperson to build a fine piece of furniture. Effective teachers have instructional flexibility, the skills to incorporate new research and adapt for their classroom context. New research is affirming the importance of participation in learning communities, teachers committed to improving their instruction by examining their students' learning collaboratively. This collaboration requires creative support by the administration and careful training.

4.   Four Generations of Instruction and Instructional Materials

This is a brief diversion, because I think curriculum materials are such critical tools for teachers, and so much EPO effort has gone into preparing and disseminating materials. Since Sputnik, there have been many different changes proposed and implemented in instructional materials and materials in schools today reflect a broad spectrum of thinking about students and teaching. This simple model identifies four generations of materials, organized by the underlying instructional approach that reflects the belief of how students learn best.

Generation I: Stand and Deliver   Students as empty vessels The traditional textbook, full of wonderful information, skillfully organized, is still the most common instructional material used in higher education and high schools. It works well for those students who are already motivated self-learners. It works poorly for everyone else unless supplemented with effective instruction by hard working teachers. Every classroom should have one as an encyclopedia in case the Internet goes down.

Generation II: Activity Mania   Students as born scientists Science as Inquiry kits such as FOSS, STC, SEPUP and the materials designed in the 60's and 70's. These materials are in common use in many elementary schools, are gaining market share in middle schools, but rarer in high schools and higher education. They engage students in well-conceived activities that are connected to the big ideas of science though the connections are rarely made explicitly. The kits typically are motivating, and do a nice job of providing authentic experiences. There is little coherence in content among the kits, even those that deal with the same discipline like Earth Science, so there is little scaffolding of ideas from year to year. The kits are also generally weak in helping the teacher identify and address prerequisite knowledge or common student preconceptions. Assessments, both formative and summative are also generally weak.

Generation III: Supported Teachers and Students   These emerging materials, often kit-based, incorporate the research from the past 15 or so years that has been synthesized by the National Research Council in books like *How People Learn* and *Taking Science to School*, and from physics and astronomy education research. Examples include *Interactions in Physical Science*, *Aries*, and *Space Science*. They supplement activities with support for the teacher and student to draw out and examine initial ideas in light of evidence, engage in thinking about phenomena scientifically, and confront their own learning. They generally lack any support for teachers to collaborate around student learning as a means to improve instruction for those students.

Generation IV: Collaborative Inquiry   All the properties of Generation III plus support for administrators and teachers collaborate to improve instruction (no materials yet).

The research is compelling that Generation IV instruction is effective for all students. Our goal in working with teachers then, is to help them deliver Generation IV instruction either by providing the professional development that will help them acquire the knowledge and skills to use their existing materials effectively, or developing new materials like *Space Science*, that will help well prepared teachers deliver Generation IV instruction with minimal professional development. In the long view, we need to work towards a time when new teachers graduate from our institutions with the knowledge and skills and expectations to find and use these materials well.

Realizing Effective Instruction for All Students Realizing effective instruction is more than providing teachers and students unlimited access to information. Access to information is critical, but information doesn't teach itself. That's why I am so skeptical of things like Google Sky and the World Wide Telescope. (Though the WWT developer is making a concerted effort to learn about effective instruction and use the WWT as a tool for real learning.) When Carol Christian says "Sky in Google Earth will foster and initiate new understanding of the universe by bringing it to everyone's home computer," I have to disagree. Just like Google Earth is having minimal impact on students' abysmal understanding of geography, Google Sky will neither "foster" nor "initiate" increased student "understanding of the universe" unless it is incorporated into a sound instructional model. And that is hard to do, but it is what we should be working on. The question now is how can we realize Generation IV or effective instruction in every classroom? An interesting conversation to have with an elementary principal is to ask, "Are you committed to the goal that every lesson for every student, every day, every year, every subject be taught effectively?" Of course they are. But think about this from the elementary teachers perspective. They know that some are better at teaching reading, or science, or math than others, that some really don't know much about science or math, not because they are dumb or don't care, they have been and continue to be, poorly served by the K-16 system. So if you know that a certain third grade teacher, for example, is a poor science teacher, isn't there a moral responsibility to do something about it - now?

So the first step in realizing effective instruction is to agree to the shared vision outlined above, every student taught well all the time. There is no one best way to achieve this vision. There is one sure way not to, that is maintain the status quo. Here are some other steps. We can start with a collaborative professional development plan for existing teachers. Who needs to learn what to become more effective? One size never fits all. Schools can also engage in strategic hiring. Ask your district if they look at the math and science grades in the transcripts of new teacher applicants, then ask them if they might.

We can create, and schools can adopt and implement with adequate professional development and support, 3rd or 4th generation instructional materials. We can also support administrators, teachers, and students to be part of professional learning communities. It is critical to adopt Richard Elmore's Principle of Reciprocity that basically says there will be no unsupported mandates, but that real support merits accountability.

Some Reform Examples from the Field Over the past four years, we have been working with about 150 schools and five higher education institutions in northwest Washington State in a Math and Science Partnership program funded by NSF. I hope these examples will show you what can be accomplished through intentional, research-based work. Our most important finding is that we can take average teachers and through carefully designed and implemented professional development help them to become effective science teachers.

One of the activities of the project is to work intensively with at least one teacher from each school, first to increase their capacity to teach effectively in their own classroom, then to help the teachers become leaders in facilitating instructional improvement in their buildings. Here are two examples from

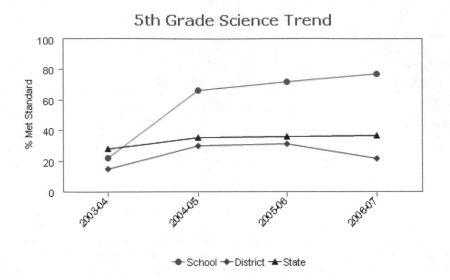

Figure 1.   The percentage of Big Lake Elementary School students passing
the 5th grade state science test by year compared to the state and district
average.

buildings that took the shared vision discussed earlier to heart. Both buildings
restructured their teaching to meet the goal of effective instruction in all subjects
for every student every year. In one case, the principal led the restructuring,
in the other, the initial ideas came from the teachers, but in both cases the
teachers and principals functioned as a team. We call this the "Collaborative
Specialist" model because, it is not the typical "science specialist" model of an
isolated teacher responsible for teaching a single subject like middle and high
school. Rather, the teachers, two in one school and three in the other became
collaborative teams that shared students and the responsibility for their learning. The principals were able to provide, through creative scheduling and at no
extra cost, time everyday for the teachers to meet to discuss their students, their
assignments, and their plans.

Big Lake Elementary School started their collaboration in the 2004-2005
school year following the first summer of intense professional development. Figure 1 shows how the percentage of the school's students passing the 5th grade
state science test changed over time compared to the state and district average.
Larrabee Elementary School began their model in the 2006-2007 school year. A
similar jump in the passing rate on the 5th grade science test occurred(Fig. 2).

Another example comes from the science content courses we designed for
preservice and inservice elementary and middle school teachers. Working with
our partner science faculty in the community colleges, we developed a life and
Earth science curriculum using the Physics and Everyday Thinking materials
developed by Fred Goldberg and collaborators at San Diego State University as
a template. The materials took two years to bring to the pilot stage and are still
undergoing revision. They were taught in teams to approximately 150 inservice

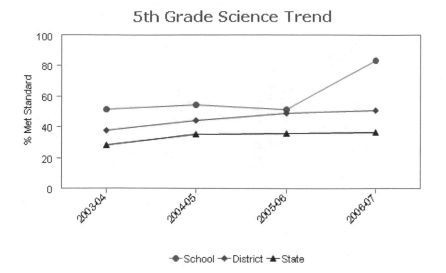

Figure 2.   The percentage of Larrabee Elementary School students passing the 5th grade state science test by year compared to the state and district average. The jump in percentage for 2006-2007 occurred when Larrabee used the collaborative specialist model.

teachers during summer academies at Western Washington University by all of the twenty-five science faculty that are part of the project. For example, the first summer, the physics faculty led teams of biology, chemistry, and geology faculty. The next summer, the biologists were the lead instructors, followed by the geologists. The teachers not only learned science during these courses, they were intentionally engaged as partners in understanding the pedagogical approach and actively critiquing and providing feedback on the design. The courses are currently being taught on all five participating campuses to future elementary teachers. Results from pre- and post-tests and one-year delayed post-tests are shown in figure 3. We would like to have a similar course in astronomy based on the common themes of the transfer and transformation of energy in interactions, but did not have the time or resources to develop it ourselves. Here is an opportunity to make a contribution.

5.   What Can EPO Do?

These few examples are not only a chance to brag a bit, they are intended to illustrate the key point of this presentation. To have the biggest impact we must partner, partner, partner! We can promote the use of materials like Space Science in schools where we work as part of a coherent curriculum. We can partner to design and deliver professional development to teachers using the new Space Science curriculum, even if we were not involved in the development. We can design, carry out and publish solid research on the materials and the implemen-

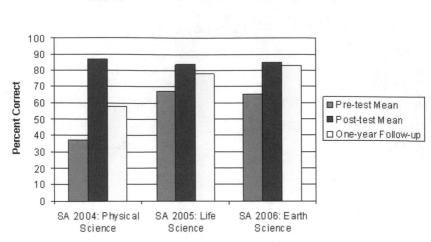

Figure 3.   Results from pre- and post-tests and one-year delayed post-tests given to approximately 150 inservice teachers during summer academies at Western Washington University.

tation models and provide feedback. We can partner to design and implement a new course for future elementary teachers so they don't need to take Astronomy 101 with 500 of their closest friends. We can work with World Wide Telescope to help it realize its potential as an educational tool. No one institution or organization has all the knowledge and expertise they need to be successful. Only by working and learning together, by sharing our resources and acknowledging our needs will we achieve our fantasy of universal astronomical literacy. I am optimistic that this powerful group of dedicated astronomy educators will make can make it happen. We are making a difference. There is still much to learn and do.

EPO and a Changing World
ASP Conference Series, Vol. 389, © 2008
C. Garmany, M. Gibbs, and J. W. Moody

Partnering with Nontraditional Out-of-School-Time Networks

Heather Gibbons

Pacific Science Center, 200 Second Ave N, Seattle, WA 98109

Julie Lutz

University of Washington, Box 351580, Seattle, WA 98195-1580

Abstract.   Who do you partner with in your outreach efforts? Are there groups in your area that can provide the infrastructure you need to deliver your content to a larger audience? In this session we will explore the possibilities of partnering with out of school time networks to disseminate science education materials and content. We will use, as examples, the partnerships that Pacific Science Center and the NASA Education Resource Center at University of Washington have built with Schools Out Washington (SOWA) and Washington State MESA (Math Science and Engineering Achievement). SOWA and MESA have statewide professional development and program infrastructures to serve their direct service providers. By leveraging the statewide provider network that these groups serve, Pacific Science Center and NASAERC have been able to deliver content more efficiently and to a much broader audience. Utilizing a "train the trainer" model, as well as direct delivery, these partnerships allow science organizations to reach the underserved audiences they wish to reach and the OST Service Groups to offer more services and trainings for their constituencies. In examining the successes and challenges faced by Pacific Science Center and NASAERC in building these partnerships, we will launch brainstorming and discussion with you. There will be time for participants to share similar experiences and to develop plans of their own. If you have unique partnerships to share or want to gain insights to develop new ones, come join this lively discussion!

1.   Structure of the Session

In this session, participants were broken into groups of four to six seated at round tables. They were then given discussion points to consider in a break out within their groups. Below you will find a an introduction and a section for each of the breakout discussions with the ideas raised in the groups.

2.   Introduction of the Session

As we seek to engage a diverse public in astronomy activities and ignite an interest in science, many of us have worked with individual day cares, Boys and Girls Clubs, community centers and other out of school time (OST) providers. The difficulty is that, as one person or organization, we can only reach so many individual OST groups, which can limit the impact we may wish to have. This session is intended to explore ways in which forming partnerships with larger "umbrella" organizations can be a more effective way to reach a broader audience.

Julie Lutz, with the NASA Education Resource Center (NASAERC) at the University of Washington, and Heather Gibbons with Pacific Science Center in Seattle, WA, developed partnerships with Schools Out Washington (SOWA) and Washington State Math Engineering and Science Achievement (MESA) among other networks. These partnerships have allowed them leverage the existing training and communication infrastructures they have with OST providers across the state in order to deliver astronomy content to more children. This session explores the benefits of and how to develop these types of partnerships.

3.   Breakout Discussions

3.1.   Breakout I - Discussing Partnerships

What defines a partnership?

- Mutually beneficial relationship to reach a common goal
- Win - win situation
- Mutual understanding of why you are both there
- Joining networks together
- Unified outcomes
- Synergy
- Each brings something and takes something away
- Each side has needs that are addressed

What are the differences and similarities within and between the short-term and long-term partnerships?

Short term:

- Event centered with limited time
- Specific program interaction
- Could be a pilot for another potential program
- Time limited
- A workshop
- Collaborations between artists and professionals with an outcome

Long term:

- With a national or local established organization

- Involves top leaders on both ends
- Common goal
- Continuing support of the infrastructure built between partners
- Ongoing
- Includes training
- Needs planning for the future
- Depends on resource availability
- Needs commitment of administrations

3.2. Breakout II - Potential Partners

Based on the information from the previous breakout, brainstorm additional groups you could partner with to increase your reach.

- Corporations for family days
- Libraries
- Centers for people with disabilities
- Senior Centers
- Look at City and State levels
- Do more networking
- Do a needs assessment
- Need funding

4. Breakout III - Developing the Partnership

Brainstorm how you might develop the relationship with these OST groups that would create a "long-term, sustainable partnership" How do approach the partnership?

- Do a needs assessment
- Need to define audience before approaching the partnership
- Offer to meet needs
- Find mutual focus and look for growth
- Build strong connections
- Start small

- Get to know how to work with the individuals and structure of each organization
- Work together to set expectations
- Make sure the program fits with both systems and structure of organizations

What are obstacles or challenges you might face?

- Pre-work is unfunded to find the partner
- Long term partnerships with different kids each week
- Managing kids in an outreach situation
- No supervision from park/club staff
- Lack of framework for some audiences to build on to understand astronomy
- "Babysitting" falls on your staff
- Egos of other organizations - not attentive to your needs
- Organization rules and identity are rigid
- Setting expectations
- Locations in the field
- Resources (staff, funding...)
- Training needed
- Understanding how to work with diverse audiences
- Personnel are busy and have high turnover

How do you create a sustainable partnership?

- Transferring power from EPO to partners
- Overcoming obstacles, like staff turnover
- Keeping the relationship going
- Foster cultural bridges
- Show science in your community
- Memorandum of understanding through time and compromise
- Establish credibility

5. Sample Partner Checklist

5.1. Partnering with Nontraditional OST Networks: A Checklist for Forming Partnerships

You probably already know all you need to know to form solid long term partnerships with outside groups. You may have already engaged in some very successful partnerships. This checklist is meant to capture some of the steps you may have automatically followed in an easy to use tool. This could prove useful as you seek to pursue partnerships and collaborations that are outside of your traditional networks. Please feel free to add to the checklist to make it even more useful. The results of this session will be published in the conference proceedings and your input will make the results all the more useful to your colleagues who did not attend this session.

Identify a New Potential Partner.

1. Why are you interested in partnering with this group?

2. Do you know of a reason they might want to partner with you?

3. If you find that there seems to be a good enough reason to partner, identify a contact person with the group and set up an initial meeting.

4. The first meeting should be about only one thing, getting to know each other. This includes gaining a good understanding each other's organizational missions and goals. Consider this a first date and a lunch date at that. You do not propose on the first date.

5. Once you have established that you have some things in common and something unique to bring to the partnership, you can start a conversation about actual things you can do together.

6. You should start out with very small projects together. This will give you both a chance to learn how each organization functions. When partnering with non-traditional groups, like out of school time groups, you need to be sure that both organizations' procedures and business practices are compatible. You do not want to discover incompatibilities on a large or highly visible project.

7. Then overtime you will need to maintain the relationship with the group regardless of funding or the size of project. It is very important to maintain the trust with your partners so that when the larger, funded opportunities arise, you are ready to take advantage of it. In fact, having a long-term sustained partnership regardless of money can help you to get funding for projects.

Other Tips:

1. Multiple Contacts: It is helpful to have multiple contacts on both sides of the partnership that have consistent interactions. This helps when there is staff turnover. I find three people on each side to be effective. Rarely will three people leave at once and three is a manageable number of people to work with.

2. Communication: Talk about worries and difficulties openly and honestly. This prevents small problems from becoming "deal breakers."

3. Service: Think in terms of meeting the needs of your partner as much or more than you think of your own needs being met. This will ensure that you are constantly evaluating needs and relevancy of the partnership.

5.2.   Participant Thoughts on the Checklist

- Perhaps expand existing programs to new groups similar to groups with whom you already work

- Would not do #1 first, but instead would assess audience and goals first

- Might approach multiple networks first to seek ideas and assess needs

- Assessment throughout

EPO and a Changing World
ASP Conference Series, Vol. 389, © *2008*
C. Garmany, M. Gibbs, and J. W. Moody

Videoconferencing: Is It Out of My League?

Daniel Zevin

Astronomical Society of the Pacific, 390 Ashton Ave., San Francisco, CA 94112

Janice Harvey

Gemini Observatory, 670 A'ohoku Place, Hilo, HI 96720

Anna Hurst and Paul "Pablo" Nelson

Astronomical Society of the Pacific, 390 Ashton Ave., San Francisco, CA 94112

Abstract. There are a variety of videoconferencing technologies that EPO providers can use for their projects and programs. Applications, to name just a few, include teacher professional development, classroom presentations, and project team meetings. Prices range from completely free for simple web-based (IP network) systems (excluding start-up costs such as computers, webcams, and Internet access) to a few to many thousands of dollars for systems that run over the Integrated Services Digital Network (ISDN), which provides the highest quality video and audio conferencing available today. Browser-based systems provide multi-user viewing and chatting capabilities, although video/audio is mostly one-way and quality is the major limiting factor for employing such a system. Each system investigated should be judged based on provider and user needs and rated for both pros and cons regarding reliability and quality, setup, ease of access and use, and overall value vs. costs.

1. Introduction

Like jet packs and meal pills, videoconferencing was once the promise of the future when it comes to delivering live education and public outreach (EPO) content from afar. Yet unlike the former examples, videoconferencing is now an everyday reality in the EPO world, and thanks to technological advances like the Internet, it is also affordable. However, more EPO professionals could be taking advantage of video-conferencing today if they knew more about what services are available, what they cost, and how they can be used.

There are a variety of videoconferencing technologies that EPO providers can use for their projects and programs. Applications, to name just a few, include teacher professional development, classroom presentations, and project team meetings. Prices range from completely free for simple web-based (IP network) systems (excluding start-up costs such as computers, webcams, and Internet access) to a few to many thousands of dollars for systems that run over the Integrated Services Digital Network (ISDN), which provides high quality video and audio transmission over standard telephone lines.

Figure 1.   *iChat AV* is an example of a free "video-chat" service that provides relatively good quality video/audio (for an IP network system).

2.   Three Examples of Videoconferencing Formats and Services

2.1.   Inexpensive "Video Chat"

Examples of free and low-cost video conferencing systems (often called "video-chat" or "instant messaging" with video conferencing capabilities) abound, and in many cases, one or two such systems are included as part of the standard software package provided with the purchase of any personal computer. A simple Internet search on "free video conferencing" will reveal a multiplicity of inexpensive video chat services available for download.

One example of such a system is *iChat AV* (http://www.apple.com/macosx/features/ichat/), which comes standard today with most Apple^{TM}computers and currently allows for up to four separate video feeds (i.e., participants from four different locations) for a given chat session (and up to 10 feeds for audio only chats). Pros include no monthly subscription costs, simple controls, text messaging options, and relatively good quality video/audio (for an IP network system) if each user is on a high-speed Internet connection and using a high-performance computer. Cons include limited participation, required software and account registration, the inability to work across platforms (e.g., with a Windows based PC), limited use for transmitting video of groups of people (e.g., students in a classroom), and bad quality video and audio when used over low-speed Internet connections and/or on older, low-performance computers.

2.2.   Browser-compatible Videoconferencing

Web-based video chat services are great if users are looking for free or low-cost options and communication is needed between only a few different locations.

Figure 2. Browser-compatible video conferencing systems like those at http://www.influxis.com allow multiple users at any location with high-speed Internet access and a web browser to connect to a live presentation without the need of complicated downloads and installations.

But what if you need to connect with multiple and widespread users? For example, what if you wanted to have a real-time guest speaker for a distance learning professional development workshop with participants located across the country? Such a videoconferencing system was required for the Astronomical Society of the Pacific's *Astronomy from the Ground Up* (AFGU) project (http://www.astrosociety.org/afgu), a modestly budgeted distance learning professional development program for informal science educators at science centers, nature centers, museums, and other informal science education institutions. The AFGU team realized they needed videoconferencing capabilities that allowed presenters to be seen and heard clearly enough to be understood, allowed participants to ask questions, and were relatively easy for participants to start using (e.g., downloads were not necessary or minimal, and system operation was simple). Since most people have access to the Internet these days and are quite comfortable using a web browser, the AFGU team decided to search for a browser-compatible videoconferencing system. They ended up choosing the *Flash*[1]/streaming media-based [2] Influxis system (http://www.influxis.com).

---

[1] http://en.wikipedia.org/wiki/Flash_Video

[2] "Streaming video" is a sequence of 'moving images' that are sent in compressed form over the Internet and displayed by the viewer as they arrive. "Streaming media" is

Pros of the browser-compatible Influxis system include its ease of integration into the host's website server (through source files access), the ability of multiple users at any location with high-speed Internet access and a web browser to connect to a live presentation without the need of complicated downloads and installations, and its relatively low cost (price ranges from $9.95 to $920 per month depending on number of connections needed and size of bandwidth desired). Cons of such a system, however, are many and include limited screen size, relatively low quality video/audio as bandwidth and Internet reliability issues abound (although higher priced plans do improve video and audio to some degree), and mostly one-way video communication (options for additional video screens are few, and for the most part participants, except for presenters, communicate via text chatting/messaging - although this can also be a pro [3]).

2.3. ISDN-based Videoconferencing

The Integrated Services Digital Network (ISDN) has been around since the early 1990s and runs on what is called a "circuit switched" network over standard telephone lines, although special equipment is necessary to make it work. Since it runs on a much more direct "source-to-source" system, it can provide very high quality video and audio. However, because there are setup fees and fixed fees per month for each ISDN line used, it is also much more costly than the other videoconferencing systems previously discussed.

The Gemini Observatory's *Live From Gemini* (LFG) program, which brings live video and audio presentations by professional astronomers direct from the Gemini Control Room straight into the classroom, is an example of an ISDN-based videoconferencing system used for EPO purposes. LFG employs software and hardware by Polycom (http://www.polycom.com), a videoconferencing industry leader that caters primarily to business. Students and astronomers can communicate in real time while astronomers move about the Control Room explaining their observing projects and point out the Gemini Observatory's state-of-the-art equipment.

Cons of ISDN-based systems center mainly around costs, which can climb into the tens of thousands of dollars depending on system type, hardware (e.g., they tend to lean toward more sophisticated cameras), and number of end users. Other cons include possible difficulties due to installation issues and dealing with local telecommunications carriers. But if budget is not a problem, then there is no beating the video and audio quality of ISDN-based systems. They are also best for transmitting video and audio for a large group of people at one time (e.g., from a classroom, a meeting room, and even large auditoriums), and because they operate over basically private channels, they are much more

---

streaming video with sound. With streaming video or streaming media, a Web user does not have to wait to download a large file before seeing the video or hearing the sound. Instead, the media is sent in a continuous stream and is played as it arrives" (http://www.cesa8.k12.wi.us/media/digital_dictionary.htm).

[3]Limiting participants to text chatting allow presentations to go on uninterrupted if desired with moderators (or presenters themselves) fielding questions as they see fit. It also eliminates the need for the audience to have access to webcams to participate, which also ensures that they are focused almost solely on the presenter

Figure 3. The Gemini Observatory's *Live From Gemini* program is an example of an ISDN-based videoconferencing system used for EPO purposes. It transmits live video and audio presentations by professional astronomers direct from the Gemini Control Room straight into the classroom

reliable. Through its new high definition (HD) product line, Polycom now offers "pure clarity and rich detail to deliver the most life-like conferencing experience possible."

3. Summary

The numerous choices of videoconferencing systems available today should encourage any EPO practitioner interested in employing videoconferencing to explore his or her options for delivering educational programming, providing professional development training, and/or offering improved team/partner communications. Each system investigated should be judged based on provider and user needs (e.g., video quality vs. system flexibility), and rated for both pros and cons regarding reliability and quality, setup, ease of access and use, and overall value vs. costs. Web/IP network-based systems are usually cheaper and simpler to install and use, but ISDN-based systems almost always provide higher quality video and audio.

James G. Manning, ASP Executive Director, welcomes participants

EPO and a Changing World
ASP Conference Series, Vol. 389, © *2008*
C. Garmany, M. Gibbs, and J. W. Moody

Providing Professional Development from a Distance: The Opportunities and Challenges of Reaching Educators through Online Astronomy Courses

Anna Hurst,[1] Katy Garmany,[2] Robert V. Steiner,[3] Rachel Connolly,[4] Sanlyn Buxner,[5] and Edward Gomez[6]

Abstract.   Online distance learning can be the perfect way to reach educators who often have busy schedules and small budgets that prevent them from attending traditional training workshops. Session participants will discuss the benefits and challenges of online learning and share their own experiences as online learners and/or moderators, as well as learn about practical approaches to the challenges of program administration, course design, marketing, and evaluation. Panelists will present the latest research in the field and the lessons learned from a few established programs.

1.   Case Studies

1.1.   AFGU from the ASP, NOAO, and ASTC (Hurst)

Program Overview   Astronomy from the Ground Up (AFGU) is a NSF-funded program that provides materials and training for informal educators from small museums, science centers, and nature centers who want to bring the excitement of modern astronomy to their visitors through hands-on activities and programs. Professional development workshops are offered in both in-person and online formats, with the ultimate goal of the project being the comparison of these two delivery methods. Participants of all workshops join an ever-growing online community of practice, which now numbers over 160 educators in 40 states. By the end of 2008, around 100 additional educators will have joined the AFGU community through participation in either an online or in-person workshop. Members of the community participate in ongoing learning opportunities and exchange ideas and information through online forums. Partners include the Astronomi-

[1]Astronomical Society of the Pacific, 390 Ashton Ave., San Francisco, CA 94305, USA

[2]National Optical Astronomy Observatory, 950 N. Cherry Ave, Tucson, AZ 85719, USA

[3]National Center for Science Literacy, Education and Technology, American Museum of Natural History, New York, NY 10024, USA

[4]College of Education and Human Development, University of Louisville, Louisville, KY, 40292, USA

[5]University of Arizona Lunar and Planetary Lab, 1629 E. University Blvd., Tucson, AZ 85721, USA

[6]LCOGT, Faulkes Telescope Operations Centre, School of Physics and Astronomy, Queens Buildings, The Parade, Cardiff, CF24 3AA, UK

cal Society of the Pacific (ASP), the National Optical Astronomy Observatory (NOAO), and the Association of Science-Technology Centers (ASTC).

The online workshops allow the educators, who often wear many hats, to fit professional development into their busy schedules and to immediately apply what they learn at their institutions during the course of the workshop, while still promoting the personal connections and networking opportunities that occur at more traditional in-person workshops. The first workshops have been encouragingly successful, with high participation rates and participants reporting use of the new materials and content with their audiences immediately following, and sometimes even during, the workshop.

The workshops last four weeks, with a main "core" time of three weeks and an additional few days at the beginning for orientation and again at the close of the workshop for wrap-up. During the main three-week period, participants are expected to devote about six hours per week to the workshop. Participants receive a "toolkit" with most of the materials necessary to try the hands-on activities associated with the workshop, along with a binder with information and workshop materials.

The workshop is moderated by an astronomy educator at the ASP, with support from an "astronomer-in-residence" from NOAO to answer in-depth content questions and a workshop coordinator from ASTC to handle logistics. Leading up to the workshop, participants also receive considerable personal attention from a project coordinator at the ASP, including a one-on-one technical orientation over the phone, in order to ensure that they are comfortable with the website and other technology for the course. The environment for the online community and individual online workshops is created using Moodle (http://moodle.org/), a free, open-source course management system.

Each week during the workshop focuses on a specific theme. The three themes include: *How Big? How Far? The Scale of the Universe*, *Change in the Universe: What's Predictable? What's Not?*, and *Light & Color: Breaking the Cosmic Code*. Each week consists of four components, outlined in a one-page checklist. The components include the following:

- **Warm up discussion**: Participants watch a short video about an issue in astronomy education and complete a quick card sorting activity, discussing both in the workshop forum.

- **Hands-on activities**: Each participant is responsible for trying out one of the three featured activities for the week and reporting back in the forum by describing his/her experience, suggesting ideas for improvements or adaptations, and sharing photos. Many participants often try more than one activity.

- **Investigation**: This short hands-on assignment is designed to encourage deeper exploration of the week's theme. Participants may, for example, search their museums and centers for examples of models, observe a day-time moon or the movement of shadows throughout the day, or experiment with lenses to build a simple telescope.

- **Videochat**: Once per week, all participants and facilitators come together at the same time for a videochat, which typically includes a short presentation on some more in-depth astronomy content by the "astronomer-in-residence", followed by an activity demonstration by the facilitating educator. Participants can see and hear the presenters in real time, follow along in a slide show built into the videochat window, and type questions or comments into a chat window, where presenters can read them and then respond.

AFGU partners are planning future workshops covering topics beyond the basic astronomy of these initial workshops. The ASP is interested in collaborations with other institutions wanting to reach informal science educators and welcomes suggestions. More information about AFGU is available at: http://www.astrosociety.org/afgu

Lessons Learned At the time of this writing, only three online AFGU workshops had been completed. While we feel we have learned a great deal through developing and facilitating these first few three-week sessions, the lessons learned are at this point anecdotal. After the completion of several more workshops, a full analysis will be carried out and reports will be disseminated by the project partners and by the project evaluator, the Institute for Learning Innovation (http://www.ilinet.org/). That said, we feel relatively confident about the following initial findings:

- Online workshops take more staff time than comparable in-person workshops. We had initially made the false assumption that facilitating a three-week online workshop would take significantly less time than organizing and running a three-day in-person workshop. In fact, the main facilitator of the workshops spends about 15 hours per week during the main three weeks, in addition to development time and logistics prior to the start of the workshop.

- For our purposes, three weeks seems to be an ideal duration for a workshop. It is long enough to allow participants to become comfortable with the online environment and to cover the material in sufficient depth, yet short enough so as not to lose participants' attention. Though most participants seem satisfied with the duration, we have also received some comments that it felt rushed and that a longer period to cover the same material might be preferable. Further experimentation may be useful.

- It is important to hold the workshop during a time period that is convenient for the intended audience. In the case of the informal educators participating in AFGU, the ideal times seem to be September - November and January - early March. This avoids the busy field trip and summer camp seasons.

- The ideal number of participants for an online workshop of this nature seems to be about 20 - 25, though further experimentation would certainly be useful.

- It is crucial to be clear and consistent with expectations beginning prior to the start of the workshop and to reinforce them throughout the course of the workshop. During the short orientation period, we hold a tele-conference with all participants to go over the structure of the workshop and answer any questions they have. Each week, we provide a one-page check list outline all of the tasks for the week, including estimates of how long each task will take and where the relevant materials can be found on the website or in the toolkit. We consistently receive comments that this checklist is extremely helpful.

- The workshop benefits from having a simple, consistent structure. AFGU workshops have four weekly components, as described above, which remain consistent each week. Although individual activities change from week to week, they always fall under one of the four components, which are outlined each week on the checklist.

- The discussions that occurred during the online workshop went into more depth than those that occurred during the in-person workshop, by virtue of the longer time period over which they took place and the ability of participants to reflect before writing their thoughts in the forum.

1.2. The RBSE Program at NOAO (Garmany)

Program Overview The Research Based Science Education (RBSE) program at NOAO has run for 10 years. It recruits high school teachers from across the U.S. who are interested in bringing research-based astronomy projects to their students. Originally teachers spent 4 weeks in Tucson, but there were numerous issues with this model, which led to the idea of presenting some of the material in an online course.

The online component of RBSE has been offered for the past six years. Participating teachers complete a thirteen-week online course to qualify for the concluding trip to Kitt Peak. During this period, they complete units on astronomy content, using the downloadable software. There are five different people who teach different sections of the online portion of the course, so there is an online "moderator" who has no formal astronomy training but is very knowledgeable about the online system. This has proved very important. Currently Blackboard serves as the workshop platform, but in past years it has been D2L (Desire 2Learn) and WebCT.

A major issue with most online courses is motivation. In principal teachers are not invited to the summer workshop if they do not complete the online work: in practice the laggards generally excuse themselves. The course requires them to work in teams of four or five people, and this is a great motivator. Not only do they help each other, thus taking some burden from the instructor, but they also encourage and motivate one another to stay on schedule.

As part of the online course we use numerous software packages. ImageJ is a free downloadable software for quantitative image processing and analysis. We provide Graphical Analysis, from Vernier Software, for spectroscopic plotting and analysis. We also make use of various java animations and other web tools like http://astro.unl.edu/naap/blackbody/animations/blackbody.html.

The payoff for completing the course is a ten-day workshop including four full days/nights at Kitt Peak National Observatory: each teacher takes data at the 2.1m, Coude, solar and 0.9m telescopes, with a concentration on their selected research project. The projects, first introduced in the online course, include a nova search in M31, open cluster color magnitude diagrams, spectroscopy of variable stars, AGN spectroscopic identification, and solar magnetic fields. For more information on RBSE, please see the program website: http://www.noao.edu/education/arbse

Lessons Learned

- It is important to choose the right e-learning platform. There are many platforms, or course management systems, available. WebCT, Blackboard (which has purchased WebCT and is phasing it out) and Desire2Learn are the systems with which we have experience. These platforms are not cheap, and require IT people behind the scenes. A popular "free" system is Moodle: a course management system (CMS) which, according its website (http://moodle.org/), is "a free, Open Source software package ... to help educators create effective online learning communities." Each has its own learning curve, for both the teacher and the student. All have systems for a syllabus, different email and chat options, document download, etc. Each of these has its own suite of features: once you learn them, it is simple, but for the novice, it can be very frustrating trying to find a way to access material and navigate the various features.

- The goal for RBSE is for the students (teachers in real life) to work together online, so that when they arrive at the workshop they are already an effective team of about 4-5 people. This requires a very special online atmosphere. Different platforms offer a variety of options to make this work. In the case of RBSE, the participants must first complete an online quiz to demonstrate that they have explored the e-learning platform. They will also be using software which they must download, which presents various issues. If your goal is only to present content, you will have different needs. It is important to carefully consider your needs before deciding on a format and tools for the course.

- It is particularly important to have all material online and tested well before the course begins. No last minute prep for these classes! We have several instructors contributing their individual sessions to the class, which works well for the students but only if each instructor is ready to play their part when the time arrives.

- The relationship between instructor and participants is crucial. The instructor's personality is electronically filtered in ways that may not always be evident. We have found it very helpful to have a course facilitator: this is someone who understands the e-environment, and can help participants with technical issues. He also serves to encourage participants who aren't playing an active role.

1.3. Seminars on Science from the AMNH (Steiner and Connolly)

Program Overview In order to improve the content knowledge of K-12 teachers, the American Museum of Natural History has developed an online teacher professional development program called Seminars on Science. The program currently includes ten online courses in the life, earth and physical sciences including a new course on the Solar System. The courses are co-taught by an experienced classroom teacher who has been prepared to teach in the online environment as well as by a research scientist.

The Seminars on Science courses are authored by one or more Museum scientists working in conjunction with the educators, professional developers and educational technologists of the Museum's National Center for Science Literacy, Education and Technology. Through the leveraging of its extensive resources - including more than 200 full-time scientists, its exhibitions, expeditions and laboratories, as well as a large staff of educators and professional developers - the Museum has sought to create cutting-edge experiences that not only deepen scientific understanding but also an understanding of the process of scientific inquiry. Online courses include original essays, images, and videos, as well as data-based animations, simulations and links to other Web-based resources.

Each week is typically framed by a guiding question (e.g. "How did the Earth's atmosphere evolve?" or "How does speciation occur?") for which the essays and other media serve as resources. Participants have an opportunity to reflect upon their understanding, to pose questions and to post additional resources in discussion forums in which the course instructor, the course scientist and other participants interact. These rich forums allow for a level of participation that often cannot be accommodated within the time constraints of a traditional course.

Through partnerships with eight higher education institutions, the International Baccalaureate Organization and the National Science Teachers Association, the American Museum of Natural History is able to offer the courses for graduate credit and to disseminate them to a wide audience.

While online courses typically lack the spontaneity and immediacy of face-to-face experiences, they offer new opportunities for curricular and pedagogical innovation - particularly when combined with more traditional educational settings.

There are currently about seven course sessions offered per year. During the coming year, the program expects approximately 1,000 participants. Approximately 65% of these participants come from the Northeast region of the United States. About one half of the participants are high school teachers, with the balance from elementary and middle schools.

The program's newest course, The Solar System, is co-authored by Neil deGrasse Tyson and Denton Ebel, both of whom are distinguished curators at the Museum. Course topics include the Sun, as well as the origin, differentiation and distinguishing characteristics of planets, comets and other bodies of the Solar System. Other topics covered include atmospheres, the Solar Wind, magnetic fields, planetary life and their interrelationships. Each week of the six week course will also provide a special focus on a current space research mission.

Other Seminars on Science courses that may be of particular interest to educators and professional developers in astrophysics include *Earth: Inside and Out*; *Space, Time and Motion*; and *The Ocean System*. Descriptions of these offerings along with sample resources, assessment rubrics, evaluation information and correlations to the National Science Education Standards can be found on the program website at http://learn.amnh.org.

Lessons Learned   Extensive coverage of lessons learned from the Seminars on Science project is found in the independent evaluation by Inverness Research Associates (http://www.inverness-research.org). Among the findings in that report, and those buttressed by our subsequent experience, are that:

- teachers report a deepening of their understanding of science and of the process of scientific inquiry;

- online courses can provide teachers with useful digital resources for the classroom;

- an instructional model that combines an experienced educator and a scientist can be a powerful one that combines content expertise with classroom application;

- a process of educational engineering involving course design, development, implementation, evaluation and revision over an extended period of time provides a strong knowledge base for future efforts;

- partnerships, while sometimes challenging to create and maintain, provide unique, often unforeseen opportunities to extend program power and reach;

- institutions that have traditionally considered themselves to be geographically based can utilize online programs to leverage their staff expertise and scientific and educational resources to a far-flung audience.

1.4. Invisible Universe Online (Buxner)

Program Overview   The Invisible Universe Online is a class that has been offered through the Montana State University's Extension Service (MSES) and National Teachers Enhancement Network (NTEN) programs since 2002 and is sponsored by the SOFIA and SPITZER EPO programs. It is a 15-week online class geared towards teachers interested in learning more about multi-wavelength astronomy and resources to do astronomy with their students with special emphasis on materials available online. The course serves as an elective for the graduate program as well as an interest course for those outside the program. Timely completion of assignments and regular participation in discussion are required elements of the course and are graded weekly. Enforcement of on time completion and discussion keeps participants on schedule for completing a challenging set of materials and maintains active discussion throughout the semester. The course is delivered through WebCT and is taught by a primary instructor who dedicates 20 hours per week to the course and teaching assista nts who dedicate 10 hours per week to the course. Students are required to participate in a weekly discussion in a small group (8-10 people) as well as complete homework and lab assignments. A midterm and final are used during the semester as well as a semester curriculum project. All interaction is conducted within the WebCT course management environment, including all email interaction.

For more information on NTEN, please see: http://www.scienceteacher.org/. For more on the Invisible Universe Online, please visit the course website: http://www.scienceteacher.org/courses/phys583.htm

Lessons Learned

- An effective way to create a sense of community is to create an area of the course that gives each participant a personal profile where they can post pictures, hobbies and other information about themselves. This allowed participants in discussion groups to get to know each other in a non-academic setting and put a face with a name.

- Maintaining a non-content related discussion board allows participants to continue long-term conversations that do not relate to the material being discussed. In this way, the formal discussions do not get off track but there is a dedicated forum for participants to talk about other issues that are important to them.

- Establishing a clear rubric for grading participation in discussion helps promote meaningful, active, and consistent participation in discussion. Keeping the small discussion groups intact for at least half a semester is beneficial to promote richer discussions where participants can refer back to previous shared discussions.

- Initial assignments can be used for participants to familiarize themselves with the course management system early on in the semester. These initial assignments are low stakes tasks that help participants navigate the course management system. For example, participants are asked to upload a survey in the same way that homework will be submitted and to post a welcome message in a discussion board. These assignments help reduce anxiety about the course management system so that participants' energy can be spent on the content of the course and not on learning the logistics of the course. In online courses many technical problems can arise throughout the semester. We alleviate many of these issues by having participants upload and verify all the software that is to be used for the course before the semester starts. This course includes a "Week 0" as a non-content week to take care of technical and initial familiarizing assignments.

- Instructors for this course collect over one hundred individual files per week, therefore it is essential to enforce standardization of file naming and file format. Getting participants to comply with this standardization reduces the logistical workload for the course instructors.

1.5.   Faulkes Telescope Online Training (Gomez)

Program Overview   This program has been running for UK teachers for 18 months. Initially it was created to accompany face-to-face training run at a variety of locations across the UK. The purpose the training is to show teachers how to plan an observing session, what they can do with telescope data, familiarity with planetarium and data analysis software, and some basic astronomy.

In the UK, there is no official requirement for teachers to be involved in any sort of professional development. Because of this, teachers often meet with opposition when seeking to take time out of the classroom for this purpose. It became evident that teachers who were able to come to training events would also have liked some activity outside of the event which would help reinforce what they had learned (but might not have been able to use immediately and so had forgotten, for example).

With these two requirements in mind we created our online training program. It was created with Moodle, because it is open source and freely available.

At first, offerings included online courses for all the topics covered in training events. These have been popular with teachers who wanted to refresh their memories of training they have done. As a result, all research-based activities and projects are now available as Moodle courses. Moodle provides a clear way of providing an overview, course objectives, and ways which subscribers can manage their own participation in different courses. Administrators can follow the progress of different participants and set quizzes which are automatically marked by Moodle.

Around 100 teachers are now subscribed to the online training. They have access to all courses, but have to sign up to a particular course to participate. Everyone has participated in the core course and the advanced courses have had approximately 30 participants each. This is not surprising because the advanced courses are more involved, requiring the participants to make observations, perform data analysis, etc.

Previously resources for advanced activities were posted on the Faulkes Telescope/LCOGT website, but Moodle made it much easier to organize in way suited for procedural learning. Whether it was the ease of use, methodology or the interactive nature of the online learning environment or some other reason which has appealed to teachers, is difficult to say. Since introducing the online training, we have been able to interact with the teachers in a more organized and, hopefully, more productive way.

For more information on the Faulkes Telescope Online Training, please visit the website at: http://faulkes-telescope.com/education/online_training

Lessons Learned

- Moodle developers often write new modules (extending the features Moodle comes with). Be careful about using any modules that have not been tested fully. Also, stay away from patches which have not been fully tested. If you have full backups before committing any changes or upgrades, you can save yourself many hours of frustration.

- Moodle provides a discussion forum, but our users found email more convenient, so we set up a discussion group for the advanced courses. This made for logistical problems and a forum would have been easier to manage, mostly because then only the participants of a particular course could contribute.

2. Conclusions

Most of the twenty or so members of the audience of this session were in some way involved in producing an online astronomy / space science course. Two of them (Buxner and Gomez) contributed case studies for this article. When presented well, an online course can be an effective medium to provide professional development, and even provides certain advantages over traditional in-person workshops. When done poorly, however, the experience can be frustrating for both the students and the instructor. Although effective strategies vary depending on the audience and the aim of the course, the following points seem consistent across the board, as illustrated by the case studies presented here and by the anecdotes shared during the session by the audience.

- Carefully consider the goals of the course and the needs of the learners before deciding on a structure and format for the course. Consider timing, duration, materials, group size, and the platform and additional tools you will use.

- Expect a significant investment of staff time. Do not offer a workshop online in order to save on staff time!

- Prepare and test materials well before the start of the course.

- Consider having multiple staff members fill different roles in a course: facilitator, instructor, content expert, etc.

- Be clear and consistent about expectations, on the part of both the instructor and the students.

- Make efforts to orient the students to the online environment and allow time for them to become comfortable with it.

- Consider breaking larger groups into smaller discussion groups.

- Create a supportive atmosphere and do not let individual personalities get lost through the online medium.

3.   Resources

The following resources may be useful when designing an online course:

- Concord Consortium
  http://www.concord.org/work/themes/online_learning.html

- TERC - Facilitating Online Learning: Tips and Suggestions
  http://scienceonline.terc.edu/facilitating_online_learning.html

- Innovate Online - journal of online learning
  http://www.innovateonline.info/

- Virtual Center for Online Learning Research
  http://www.ncolr.org/

EPO and a Changing World
ASP Conference Series, Vol. 389, © *2008*
C. Garmany, M. Gibbs, and J. W. Moody

Astronomy Professional Development Workshops for After-School Program Providers

Julie Lutz

Department of Astronomy, University of Washington, Box 351580, Seattle, WA 98195

Kristine Washburn

Department of Physics, Everett Community College, 2000 Tower St., Everett,WA 98201

Anita Krishnamurthi

University of Maryland/GSFC, Code 660.1 NASA Goddard Space Flight Center, Greenbelt, MD 20771

Heather Gibbons

Pacific Science Center, 200 Second Avenue North, Seattle, WA 98109

Abstract. Increasingly after-school programs are looking to sciences like astronomy for content and activities that are suitable for the kids who attend their programs. Astronomy has some excellent things to offer, but the after-school realm is really different than the classroom. This workshop featured group discussions of some of those differences and how they translate in offering appropriate professional development of after-school program personnel. The intent of the workshop was to provide a "networking with a focus" experience for participants who wanted to learn about after-school programs and to contemplate how the work that they (the participants) do might contribute to after-school. Thus the role of the presenters was to provide some structure (including imposing some limits on discussion times) and to moderate the sharing of ideas and information that came out of the small group discussions. The highlights of the discussions and some information about after-school programs are included in this paper.

1. Introduction

Millions of children participate in after-school programs of one type or another. Included in the realm of "after-school programs" are the classic programs that children attend after the school day ends (and sometimes also before the school day begins), either in their school building or at another site (e.g., community center, commercial enterprise). After-school organizations include a multitude of other organizations and programs: Boys and Girls Clubs, 4-H, Campfire, Girl and Boy Scouts, after-school clubs, and summer camps, to name just a few examples.

"After-school" is a term that is used interchangeably with "out-of-school" time (OST). The names of some of the leading professional organizations in the field reflect the "can't quite decide what to call it" ambiguity. For example, the National AfterSchool Association is an organization that includes everyone from commercial learning centers, to summer camps, to youth organizations such as 4-H and Campfire to the programs operated in cities to provide after-school care for youth. The National Institute for Out-of-school Time (NIOST) is an organization that does research and position papers on the after-school field. The NIOST web site has excellent information about the characteristics of quality after-school programs, the difference that being a part of a quality after-school program can make in fostering positive youth development, and desirable traits of those who work in after-school programs, be they volunteer or paid. The Coalition for Science After School (CSAS) is a strategic alliance among individuals and organizations from STEM education, youth development and out-of-school time programs. The CSAS mission, as articulated on their web site, is to "coordinate and mobilize community stakeholders to strengthen and expand opportunities for young people to do and learn science in after-school settings."

Over the last several years, more attention is being paid to after-school programs for various reasons that are beyond the scope of this paper to examine in detail. The NIOST and After School Alliance web sites have information on the political and sociological issues involved in this trend. In addition, there is increasing interest in incorporating science learning and discovery into OST programs. The CSAS web site has position papers and information on this subject.

2.   Goal and Objectives of the Workshop

Our goal was for participants to learn some new things about after-school programs and to reflect on how they might work with after-schools settings. Our objectives were for participants to brainstorm ideas on the following topics: desirable characteristics of astronomy materials for after-school programs and providing professional development experiences for people involved with after-school programs. The thoughts of the workshop participants and organizers are summarized in the following sections of this article.

3.   Astronomy Materials for After-school Programs

Participants discussed in small groups some of the factors that make for good after-school astronomy materials and activities. A "top factors" list was made from a brief whole-group discussion and displayed for all the participants to keep in mind.

Characteristics mentioned by multiple groups:

- Activities should be fun for the kids in the program to do. In many after-school programs, the kids have a choice about whether or not to participate and/or a choice of things to do, so the "fun factor" is important.

- Activities should be more active rather than passive. Kids sit still a lot during the school day, so active engagement (moving around, hands-on) is considered a desirable characteristic of after-school activities.

- Activities should incorporate and model good youth development practices (collaboration, sharing, listening).

- Suite of materials/activities must address a variety of learning styles, including special needs children.

- Materials that are re-used multiple times must be durable and inexpensive. Consumables associated with the activities must be inexpensive and easy to obtain. After-school programs usually operate with modest budgets, so these factors are important in whether or not particular materials get adopted and used by programs.

- Activities/materials could be linked by a theme but must also honor the reality that program participants may not attend every day.

- Materials and activities must be easy to use (ready to go, easy to setup) be-cause after-school program staff do not have a lot of preparation time and may not be very familiar with the content addressed by the materials and activities.

- Safety is an important factor in all materials and activities.

Other factors discussed by the groups:

- Materials and activities should be easily obtainable and inexpensive. No copyright issues.

- Materials and activities should be age and audience appropriate, even if this means having a variety of things for the kids to do, depending upon their interests and abilities.

- Level and depth of the program materials should be expandable according to audience interest. For example, further exploration should be available if child is interested.

- Activities should be easy to train others to use and shouldn't require a lot of expertise or prior knowledge on the part of the program providers.

- No grades.

- Materials don't necessarily have to follow state or national standards.

- After-school programs require the use of different kinds of assessments than are used in K-12 programs. The people who fund and support after-school programs need evidence that the program is benefiting the participants.

- Some of the NASA Science Mission Directorate education, Project Astro and other materials developed for K-12 classrooms are adaptable to after-school settings using the principles given above.

- Many after-school programs have "free choice learning" which requires that there be a selection of projects/activities for the participants.

4.   Professional Development of After-school Personnel

The small groups discussed factors that should be considered when designing professional development for after-school program providers. Again a "top factors" list was made and displayed.

- The trainers should not assume that participants have a uniform level of content or background knowledge. After-school program providers often do not have much of a background in science. Their educations and work experiences are much more diverse than for a group of K-12 classroom teachers.

- Trainers should model an active learning environment during the professional development. Actually doing the activities rather than discussing the write-ups of materials helps the OST providers to envision how the activities can be used in their programs.

- Good facilitator guides are essential materials for participants to take away from professional development workshops.

- Trainers must be competent in content and must understand the after-school program providers' needs, constraints and audiences.

- The trainer should be aware of trainee constraints (time, language difficulties, etc.) and provide incentives (money, clock hours, materials) for attendance at the trainings.

- There should be some provision for follow-up support from the trainer or a mentor if the participant has questions or issues after the professional development workshop is complete.

Other considerations mentioned by discussion groups:

- The professional development workshop should include suggestions for how to conduct assessments. What assessments are meaningful will vary with the nature of the after-school program and its goals and objectives. Assessments can help to establish how the offerings meet the program's goals and objectives and/or how the offerings can be improved. Assessments are also needed to satisfy program sponsors such as agencies, foundations and parents.

- The trainers should seek advice on methods of delivery for the professional development if they are not familiar with the world of after-school.

- Professonial development workshops for after-school providers should give more attention to program management, time management and/or equipment use issues than in formal education settings. Classroom teachers have train-ing on these issues, but they likely should be brought up specifically when doing trainings for after-school program providers.

- Participants want to know about resources (web, books) for further information on the workshop topics in case they have kids who are curious and want to find out more. They generally don't want lots of resources for themselves because they don't have preparation time to develop programs and activities.

- Professional development should include consideration of community and family involvement.

- Consideration should be given to offering mentoring programs associated with professional development experiences.

5. Developing Workshops

Given the principles and issues discussed above, the groups then went into a brief discussion of what sort of professional development offerings they might design for after-school providers in a specific scenario chosen by the group members. Part of the brainstorming was directed at using additional sources of information such as web sites of professional organizations and existing programs. The ideas that surfaced include the following:

Workshop Topics:

- Solar System workshops-activities and content adapted for kids ages 5-12

- How to form an after-school astronomy club for kids in middle or high school

- Workshops on stars and constellations

Organizations for after school programs and providers and their web sites:

- **National After School Association:** The NAA mission is to be the leading voice of the after-school profession dedicated to the development, education and care of children and youth during their out-of-school hours. http://www.naaweb.org.

- **Coalition for Science in After School:** The CSAS is a strategic alliance among individuals and organizations from STEM education, youth development, and out-of-school time programs. The Coalition's mission is to coordinate and mobilize community stakeholders to strengthen and expand opportunities for young people to do and learn science in after-school settings. http://qt.exploratorium.edu/csas.

- **National Institute on Out of School Time:** The NIOST mission is to ensure that all children, youth, and families have access to high quality programs, activities, and opportunities during non-school hours. http://www.niost.org.

- **After School Alliance:** The Afterschool Alliance is dedicated to raising awareness of the importance of after-school programs and advocating for quality, affordable programs for all children. It is supported by a group

of public, private and non-profit organizations that share the Alliance's vision of ensuring that all children have access to after-school programs by 2010.
http://www.afterschoolalliance.org.

A few examples of science (particularly astronomy) materials, programs and reports developed for after-school settings:

- The Consumers Guide to After-school Science Resources features reviews of high-quality, hands-on science content for after-school programs. Developers began by asking after-school practitioners to recommend programs or materials that they themselves had used or seen in action. A panel of after-school and science content experts then carefully reviewed the resources identified as most promising.
http://www.sedl.org/afterschool/guide/science/index.html

- The Beyond Einstein Explorers' Program (BEEP) is an after-school program for middle school students. This program introduces participants to basic tools of astronomy (such as using light to gather information about objects) and to the universe outside the solar system.
http://beyondeinstein.nasa.gov/education/BEEP/

- MIT/Chandra After-school Astronomy Project was designed to provide high school youth in out-of-school time programs with an opportunity to reinforce learning in physics and space science through activities that also develop students' computer skills.
http://space.mit.edu/EPO/ChandraAsap.html

- The report "NASA and Afterschool Programs: Connecting to the Future" contains a wealth of useful information on adapting formal education materials for afterschool settings, as well as useful perspectives on the after-school world.
http://education.nasa.gov/pdf/113900main_NASAAfterschool_508_3_reduced.pdf

- Lowes et al. (2005) describe their work with Girl Scout USA trainers of troop leaders over several years in order to increase the number of troops working on astronomy, space and other science-related merit badges.

- The National Institute for Out-of-School Time publishes a yearly statement (8 pages) called "Making the Case: A Fact Sheet on Children and Youth in Out-of-School Time". Many interesting studies and links are also found on this site.
http://www.niost.org

- The National AfterSchool Association's mission statement begins with "To be the leading voice of the after-school profession...". The NAA provides accreditation for after-school programs and they have a large annual confer-ence for after-school professionals.
http://www.naaweb.org

- Coalition for Science After School is a recently-founded umbrella organization that seeks to keep a focus on incorporating more science content and activities into all types of after-school programs.
http://qt.exploratorium.edu/csas/about.html

- The Educational Equity Center has recently released a report titled "After-school, Science and Equity" which demonstrates the role that appropriate science activities can play in influencing attitudes and career aspirations.
http://www.edequity.org

6. Conclusions

Opportunities abound for astronomers and astronomy education and public outreach specialists to work with after-school programs. Understanding the nature of OST programs is crucial to the success of such collaborations.

Acknowledgments. J. L. would like to thank NASA for support of Space Science Network Northwest through NCC5-605.

References

Lowes, L., Betrue, R., Allen, J., Tobola, K., and Hailey, M., "The NASA-GSUSA Collaboration: Together We Inspire Young Women to Explore, Discover, Understand", in Walker, G., Wahl, E., and Rivas, L. M. *NASA and After-school Programs: Connecting to the Future.* (American Museum of Natural History, New York, 2005)

Lucy Fortson of Adler Planetarium receiving the traditional co-host cap from
ASP Executive Director Jim Manning

General plenary session

EPO and a Changing World
ASP Conference Series, Vol. 389, © 2008
C. Garmany, M. Gibbs, and J. W. Moody

Current and Potential Partnerships between NASA and the National Park Service

Michele Bahr

Marine Biological Laboratory, 7 MBL St, Woods Hole, MA 02543

Cherilynn Morrow

SETI Institute, 515 N. Whisman Road, Mountain View, CA 94043

Catherine Tsairides

NASA Ames Research Center, MS 240-1 Moffet Field, CA 94035

Susan Kelly

Montana State University, 607 Leon Johnson, P.O. Box 173142, Bozeman, MT 59717-3142

Abstract. NASA and the National Park Service are engaged in a variety of partnerships intended to preserve and interpret natural resources as a living laboratory. The purpose of this workshop was to initiate a conversation among participants about audiences, the meanings of place, and professional interpretation within the context of this partnership. Our first objective was to examine successful collaborations. We then explored potential partnerships that could be developed at locations throughout the US and considered our collective experience to make future partnerships successful.

1. NASA Projects in National Parks

1.1. *Earth to Sky Institutes*

The first ASP workshop session to focus on NASA and the National Park Service (NPS) was "How to be a Space Ranger: Taking a Page from NPS Informal Education Methodology", presented by Anita Davis, NASA GSFC, Ruth Paglierani, NASA SMD/UC Berkeley, and Dave Hutson, National Park Service. The *Earth to Sky Institutes* involve workshops for NPS rangers, and the creation EPO products, thereby enabling rangers to bring NASA Space and Earth science to millions of park visitors. It also exposes many NASA scientists and EPO specialists to NPS's informal education methodology, known as *interpretation*. The Interpretive Model and interpretive techniques were the focus of the session.

1.2. NPS Structure

The second session began with the parallel between NPS Goals of Interpretation "Through interpretation, appreciation; through appreciation, understanding; through understanding, protection" and NASA Education Goals to excite people about science, increase science literacy and engage the next generation of scientists. Another parallel is the hierarchical nature of both organizations. Park management includes Interpretive, Natural Resource, Law Enforcement and Maintenance Divisions, and may in larger Parks also include Natural History Associations, Wilderness Institutes, Public Affairs, Concessions, Foundation Groups and Amateur Astronomy Clubs. Goals and priorities of the different divisions can conflict and affect EPO projects. Understanding the Interpretive Division structure as outlined in Fig. 1 can be an aid in developing working relationships.

1.3. Successful Collaborations

One example of a successful collaboration involves NASA's Astrobiology Institute, Lockheed Martin and the Ames Research Center Astrobiology team. They developed outdoor Astrobiology exhibits in locations throughout Yellowstone National Park that best illustrate the most compelling aspects of astrobiology research in Yellow-stone, describe how the Park's hydrothermal features are extreme habitats for amazing life forms that may help explain the history of the Earth and provide clues in the search for life on other planets. In addition to telling the story of Yellowstone's hid-den treasures and greatly improving visitor experience in the world's first national park, the study of Astrobiology in Yellowstone is a model for interpreting complex scientific information in other national parks and public spaces throughout the United States and serves as an example to visitors that science is not only important and accessible but interesting and fun.

2.   Developing a New Collaboration

Identifying the synergy is critical in any collaborative effort. Finding a direct connection between missions and making a long term commitment are essential first steps in building credibility and trust. EPO coordinators can learn the art of interpretation from extensive NPS experience and how it might be applied to NASA resources. Develop sensitivity about Park culture, identify a positive person in the structure and clarify expectations from both sides, while remaining alert to competing interests. A handbook on Park rules and procedures can be useful for scientists doing research in a park setting. Above all, value your own passion! It's shared by many in the National Park Service.

Acknowledgments.   The authors acknowledge and are grateful for support from the NASA Astrobiology Institute EPO Collaborative Fund.

EPO and a Changing World
ASP Conference Series, Vol. 389, © 2008
C. Garmany, M. Gibbs, and J. W. Moody

Amateur Astronomers: Secret Agents of EPO

Marni Berendsen and Vivian White

Astronomical Society of the Pacific, 390 Ashton Avenue, San Francisco, CA 94112

Edna DeVore

SETI Institute, 515 North Whisman Road, Mountain View, CA 94043

Michael Reynolds

Florida Community College, 3939 Roosevelt Boulevard, Jacksonville, CA 32205

Abstract.   Amateur astronomers prime the public to be more interested, receptive, and excited about space science, missions, and programs. Through recent research and targeted programs, amateur astronomy outreach is being increasingly recognized by professional astronomers, educators, and other amateurs as a valued and important service. The Night Sky Network program, administered by the ASP, is the first nationwide research-based program specifically targeted to support outreach by amateur astronomers. This Network of trained and informed amateur astronomers can provide a stimulating introduction to your EPO programs as Network members share the night sky with families, students, and youth groups.

1. Amateur Astronomers and Their Impact on Their Audiences

Amateur astronomers can be found volunteering their time in classrooms, science and nature centers, community fairs and events, libraries, parks, and parking lots. They bring their knowledge and their telescopes, as well as educational hands-on activities, to inspire families, students, and community groups to better understand the universe.

Evidence for their ability to inspire is both anecdotal and backed by research. One report from an amateur astronomer in Texas illustrates the impact they make: "One student said that she could see a lot of pictures in her textbooks, but it was nothing like the feeling of reality that she got when looking through a telescope."

As reported by Gibbs and Berendsen (2007), teachers partnered with astronomers in the Project ASTRO program were asked "Did Project ASTRO change your students' attitudes towards science?" Sixty percent of the teachers who were partnered with amateur astronomers reported a large positive change. Only 7% reported no perceptible change.

A book recently published by the Astronomical Society of the Pacific, *Science Educators Under the Stars* (Gibbs, Berendsen, & Storksdieck 2007), summarizes much of the current research on amateur astronomers as science educators. Stories from the amateur astronomers themselves illustrate the motivation and personal satisfaction of sharing astronomy with the public.

2. Increasing Recognition and Support for Amateur Astronomy Outreach

Amateur astronomy outreach has, until recently, been almost exclusively an individual or club effort, largely undocumented, informal, and with little outside support or recognition. The ASP's experience with Project ASTRO, formal research on amateur astronomers and their outreach, and the establishment of the Night Sky Network (http://nightsky.jpl.nasa.gov) have helped initiate a trend toward increasing support, visibility, and recognition of amateur astronomy outreach.

2.1. Increasing support through programs

ASP's Project ASTRO was established in 1994 to partner astronomers with teachers in the classroom. Many of these partners were amateur astronomers. The keys to the success of this program were matching the astronomer to the needs and interest of the teacher and an intensive two-day training workshop where the partners actively participated in classroom-tested hands-on activities as well as coming to an understanding of the importance of communication and mutual planning between the partners. Activities and resources are detailed in *Universe at Your Fingertips*, an ASP publication that is provided to each partnership.

From this program, the ASP recognized a potential need to expand support for amateur astronomy outreach to the wider amateur community. In 2002 the ASP conducted a survey on outreach among amateurs. The results (Storksdieck *et al.* 2002) revealed three primary areas where amateurs expressed a need for support:

- Targeted and themed materials and activities

- Training in astronomy content, outreach techniques, and relating to audiences

- Contact with like-minded amateurs

The Night Sky Network, with extensive cooperation and support from JPL's Navigator Public Engagement Program, was established in 2004 to meet these needs. Thousands of events are logged each year into the Night Sky Network, providing extensive insights into the practices, impact, and effectiveness of amateur astronomers engaged in public outreach.

2.2. Increasing visibility among professional astronomy educators and scientists

Since the success of the first "Outreach ToolKit" issued to the Night Sky Network members, several other NASA missions and education professionals have recognized amateur astronomers as a many-thousand-strong nationwide coalition who regularly reach large numbers of the general public in ways that other types of educators cannot. In a partnership of the ASP, NASA, and the Night Sky Network members, six Outreach ToolKits have, as of this writing, been developed on the science behind a variety of NASA missions.

NASA's *Kepler Mission* (http://kepler.nasa.gov/) is one such mission that saw the opportunity of supporting amateur astronomy outreach to disseminate information about the mission. The SETI Institute, in charge of EPO for the *Kepler Mission*, partnered with the ASP to produce the Outreach ToolKit, Shadows and Silhouettes: Phases, Eclipses & Transits, featuring the *Kepler Mission* and its objective of searching for transits of Earth-size planets orbiting other stars.

The reasons for the *Kepler Mission* participation were many:

- Communicates *Kepler Mission* science to the public

- Creates and tests unique activities to demonstrate transits, eclipses, and phases which are all essential astronomy concepts to understand the *Kepler Mission*

- Supports outreach by amateur astronomers

- Based upon thoughtful needs assessment of amateurs

- Demonstrated quality and effectiveness by NSN

2.3. Increasing recognition through awards for outreach

In addition to the ASP's annual amateur outreach award and a number of annual awards granted by astronomy-themed magazines, the Astronomical League (AL) established a new individual award for outreach in 2006.
http://www.astroleague.org/al/obsclubs/outreach/outreach.html.

Patterned on the Astronomical League's Observing awards, also referred to as "Observing Clubs," the Outreach awards have three levels of achievement. A pin and certificate are issued to awardees. In its first year, over 100 AL members were issued this award.

What makes the AL's Outreach award unique is that in the past, recognition of achievement as an amateur astronomer was primarily based on one's ability to observe and document those observations. The AL has over 25 different categories of observing awards.

The Outreach award helps to expand the idea that outreach is another valued way for amateur astronomers to pursue their hobby.

3. Conclusions

The role of amateur astronomers as informal science educators is becoming more widely understood, supported, respected, and recognized. Recent research has documented the impact and effectiveness of these dedicated volunteers. We look forward to the expansion of the Night Sky Network and other programs to support and recognize amateur astronomy outreach.

References

Gibbs, M., Berendsen, M., and Storksdieck, M. (Eds.) *Science Educators Under the Stars: Amateur Astronomers Engaged in Education and Public Outreach* (Astronomical Society of the Pacific, San Francisco, CA, 2007)

Gibbs, M. and Berendsen, M., "Effectiveness of Amateur Astronomers as Informal Science Educators," Astronomy Education Review **5**, 2 (Association for Universities for Research in Astronomy, Inc., Washington, D.C., 2007)
http://aer.noao.edu/cgi-bin/article.pl?id=228

Storksdieck, M., Dierking, L.D., Wadman, M., and Cohen Jones, M., *Amateur Astronomers as Informal Science Ambassadors: Results of an Online Survey*, Technical Report (Institute for Learning Innovation, Annapolis, MD, 2002)
http://www.astrosociety.org/education/resources/ResultsofSurvey_FinalReport.pdf

EPO and a Changing World
ASP Conference Series, Vol. 389, © *2008*
C. Garmany, M. Gibbs, and J. W. Moody

Astronomy After-School Programs: Effective Pathways to Success

Anita Krishnamurthi

CRESST/University of Maryland & NASA Goddard Space Flight Center, Astrophysics Science Division, Greenbelt, MD 20771, USA

Irene Porro

MIT Kavli Institute for Astrophysics and Space Research, 77 Massachusetts Avenue - NE80, Cambridge, MA 02139, USA

Abstract. We discuss our experiences with developing and implementing two astronomy after-school programs. Afterschool Universe, formerly called the Beyond Einstein Explorers' Program, is targeted at middle school students and the Youth Astronomy Apprenticeship is directed at high school students. For the benefit of those readers interested in developing their own astronomy OST program, we summarize here how to get started, implementation challenges and lessons learned.

1. Introduction

Young people spend a large percentage of their time out of school and many of them do so in unstructured and unsupervised ways. It has also been shown that low in-come and underserved minorities are enrolled in after-school programs in greater percentages than the general population (Afterschool Alliance 2004). Thus, after-school programs reach those who most need additional help and do so in a setting with fewer constraints than a classroom. There is a tremendous potential for teaching science and astronomy in these settings.

After-school programs or out-of-school-time (OST) programs are run in a variety of settings and serve a diverse range of students. In contrast to programs targeted at students in a school setting, there is more flexibility in program design. This freedom is a great strength in working with OST programs, but it also generates a list of questions and issues to consider carefully before proceeding. We address some of these issues as we discuss two independent astronomy OST programs and the lessons learned from their implementation.

2. Case Studies: A Tale of Two Astronomy OST Programs

2.1. Afterschool Universe[1]

Afterschool Universe, formerly called the Beyond Einstein Explorers' program (BEEP), was developed by the Astrophysics Science Division at the NASA Goddard Space Flight Center to teach middle school students in OST programs

---

[1]The Beyond Einstein Explorers' Program (BEEP) was renamed Afterschool Universe in December 2007.

about the Universe beyond the solar system. Students at this age are very interested in complex topics (such as the life cycles of stars and black holes) but rarely have an opportunity to explore that interest as the middle school curriculum does not typically address these topics. A quick survey of available astronomy OST programs showed that there were no programs even in that setting on this content for the middle school age group.

Recognizing the need, we decided to develop a program for the middle school audience where they could be introduced to these topics in a hands-on, engaging manner. We strongly believed this to be important as the middle school years are a critical time in shaping students' attitudes to science, particularly in girls.

Afterschool Universe (AU) begins by having participants explore their current ideas of the Universe and creating models of the Universe as they understand it. They then learn about some fundamental topics in astronomy such as light and how it can be used to obtain data about far away objects. Next, they proceed to study the tools astronomers use, such as telescopes and spectroscopes, and build examples of these tools. The next set of sessions explores specific objects in the Universe such as stars, black holes, and galaxies and how they fit into the Universe. A visit by a scientist or engineer is built into the program to allow participants to clarify any questions that may have arisen during the program. This visit also provides the students an opportunity to interact with a scientist or engineer and learn about careers in space science. Participants re-create a model of the Universe at the end of the program and this allows a measure of perspective changes that occurred as a result of the program. AU currently has 12 sessions that are structured very flexibly to allow program leaders to split them into modules if necessary. We also expect to add more sessions in the coming years. Every session of AU includes hands-on activities to engage the participants and ensure an active learning experience.

A comprehensive manual provides background information and detailed descriptions of how to conduct each activity. We also offer an intensive two-day training at NASA Goddard for all participants who can travel to the location. The training allows program leaders who are unfamiliar with the content to become comfortable leading the sessions. The OST program is responsible for obtaining all the materials needed. We are now exploring options for training methodologies that will allow us to increase our reach across the country.

We conducted a pilot with a small group of participants from inner-city Washington, DC in summer 2006. Based on feedback from this effort, we refined the program and conducted a second test of the program with a larger group of participants across the country in summer 2007. This effort was conducted with the aid of a Chandra EPO grant and was formally evaluated by an external evaluator. We expect to make AU widely available to the OST community in 2008.

The basic goals of AU are to inspire participant interest, curiosity, and excitement in astronomy and science. By the end of this program, we expect students to begin gaining an appreciation for the scale of the Universe and how the various components fit into it. Preliminary evaluation reports indicate that we have succeeded in meeting these goals.

2.2. Youth Astronomy Apprenticeship

The Youth Astronomy Apprenticeship (YAA) program is a project from the MIT Kavli Institute (MKI) Education and Outreach Group, run in collaboration with the Smithsonian Astrophysical Observatory (SAO), the Timothy Smith Network (TSN), and the Institute of Learning Innovation (ILI). The target audience for YAA is urban teenage youth and after-school professionals.

The MKI education and outreach group has been promoting initiatives for Boston OST programs since 2000 funded by several Chandra EPO grants. The target audience was originally chosen (and has remained) to be urban teenage youth, a group that is typically both underserved and underrepresented in STEM (NSF 2005). Over the years we also kept the same simple but ambitious goal: to generate a fresh interest in science among urban teens from underrepresented groups and to motivate and prepare them to pursue STEM learning and eventually STEM-related careers.

The experience built up from these prior efforts allowed us to design YAA as a new comprehensive project grounded in past initiatives and lessons learned from them. We understand now that to encourage and support youth to pursue STEM learning, and eventually STEM career paths, it is important to promote the development of an environment that supports the same goals. This is why YAA specifically aims to reach out also to the families of the youth who participate in the program and eventually to the local urban communities the YAA teens belong to.

The main desired impact for YAA is to empower teens to develop new science understanding but also develop personal and interpersonal skills needed to fully participate in the life of our society. In addition, we want to encourage the development of personal interest in astronomy and science for all YAA audiences. Our aim is to eventually have all YAA audiences participate in some science learning experiences and become advocates for new STEM learning initiatives in their communities.

YAA is funded through a NSF ISE grant and is built on two main programs. First, youth attend an after-school program that is run over the school year at community-based centers. YAA and after-school professionals from centers lead high school students in an astronomy training program. The 12-14 week YAA curriculum is designed to promote effective reasoning and communication, computer skills and science learning. During each session youth engage in a combination of hands-on activities and youth-led explorations of the Universe, from the solar system to far away galaxies, based on the images they take with MicroObservatory, a network of robotic telescopes. Youth learn to use software tools to process astronomical images, and produce reports and presentations about their projects. The curriculum is de-signed to promote youth's project ownership as they practice some of the professional skills used in the sciences.

Youth who complete the after-school component are then eligible to attend the summer apprenticeship program at MIT, the core element of the YAA model. During the summer program youth train in a variety of disciplines, in addition to working on astronomy content, and develop community outreach events. In summer 2007 for example, YAA teens worked on three main projects: they wrote and produced a play on the life cycle of stars; they designed activities to introduce a lay audience to the use of the telescope; and they created three components for a museum exhibit on black holes that will open in 2009. Later the same teens will bring these projects on the road and they will perform at various venues in their communities across the city.

Additional information about AU can be obtained on the website at http://universe.nasa.gov/afterschool/ and additional information about YAA can be obtained on the website at http://epo.mit.edu.

3.   Getting Started With OST Programs

As with the design of any program, the first step is to articulate and define expectations for the effort. Identifying the target audience as specifically as possible, the impact you want the program to have on that audience, and the resources that you have or may need to acquire to implement the program are all issues to explore at the beginning. During this process, challenges to the implementation of the program will surface and potential solutions can be discussed. Eventually as the program is implemented, new issues may arise and solutions to such issues are produced as a result of the analysis of the lessons learned during each implementation.

3.1.   Defining the Audience

It is extremely important to articulate upfront the rationale guiding the choice of a target audience. In the two case studies discussed above, the target audiences were chosen for clearly defined reasons.

Questions to consider for a detailed definition of the audience one wishes to work with include: Is the program targeted at urban youth, suburban youth or rural youth? What age level do you wish to target? Where will the program be implemented (school or community-based center)? Who will be your point-of-contact and what sort of resources are available at that location? What are the constraints of the location? Do you wish to offer a set of activities that may fit science clubs or summer programs, or do you want to develop a full curriculum for year-round OST programming? Asking these questions early on and understanding the implications is a key first step in the project design.

3.2.   Setting Goals

The intended impact that program designers want their program to have is obviously related to the target audience previously identified. But it is also affected by several other factors such as the availability of resources, existing partnerships and collaborations, and specific funding requirements.

The basic question to ask when defining a goal for your program is "What do I want to accomplish through this OST program?" Answers may range from providing engagement with science in a setting that allows exploration of topics not possible in a standards-driven science classroom, supporting the learning that occurs during the school day and offering help with homework, teaching participants details of one particular topic, or building up a particular set of skills (for example data reduction or communications skills). All of these are worthwhile goals but it is important to articulate them early so that you know what success should look like.

3.3. Identifying and Forming Community Partnerships

Partnerships with organizations active in the specific community targeted by the program are critical for long-term success of OST programs. They are crucial allies in recruiting participants and are key in developing the conditions for the sustainability of the program over time.

AU was developed in close collaboration with the non-profit DC Children and Youth Investment Trust Corporation (CYITC). This organization sponsors about one hundred OST programs in the Washington, DC area. The Associate Director for Curriculum Development at this organization was very interested in working with NASA to bring space science programming to his grantees and was especially enthusiastic about a program that would go beyond what the middle school curriculum typically covered. He was responsible for recruiting all the groups that participated in the initial pilot and initiated a conversation between the OST programs and the program developers about needs and constraints on both sides before program development got underway. Additionally, he sponsored the purchase of the materials for his grantees and was the key to getting the program off the ground the first year. He continues to be a staunch supporter and AU has now become a core part of his organization's programming portfolio.

Similarly, the MKI Education and Outreach Group early on established a collaboration with the Boston 2-to-6 After-School Initiative, an initiative by the City of Boston created to support the expansion of high-quality, affordable, and accessible after-school programs across the City of Boston. Through this collaboration the MKI team was able to connect with programs and community centers that are usually attended by urban teenagers. Some of these programs, such as GEAR UP, a federally funded program designed to increase the number of low-income students who enter and succeed in postsecondary education, are available across the nation. We were particularly encouraged though to look at local efforts, such as health community centers. The teens who attend these centers indeed represent a meaningful percentage of all participants in our programs. Eventually the most important partnership we developed through the 2-to-6 Initiative was with the Timothy Smith Network (TSN). The TSN Centers, located in community agencies, churches and schools, represent the primary technology access point for predominantly low-income Boston residents from a broad range of racial, ethnic and cultural backgrounds. These TSN Centers provide after school locations throughout the most disadvantaged city neighborhoods.

3.4. Resources

Once you have identified target audience and goals for the program, it is time to take stock of the resources on hand to apply to your effort. Resources can include ongoing efforts that can be adapted for the OST environment, educational materials, staff time, existing contacts or partnerships that lend themselves to initiating such an effort, and funding. In particular, funding will determine the scope of the program as it affects the number of program staff and after-school professionals that can be involved in the program. Staff availability in turn will have a major impact on the program design and quality of program outcomes.

3.5. Developing a Curriculum

When developing a curriculum, the first question to consider is whether you want to develop new materials from scratch or use or adapt existing materials. For example a small team will most likely welcome existing materials and will focus on how to adapt them. Astronomy educational resources based on the most current astronomy data and tools are widely available today, but how to choose what to use for an after-school program may not be a simple task. Decisions need to be based on the goal of the program, the target audience, and the science expertise available. Sometimes the funding source may have some say in the choice of materials used.

For AU, we began by doing a comprehensive survey of available educational materials on the topics we wished to cover. We utilized the skeleton of the curriculum developed for the After-School Astronomy Project (ASAP) from MKI as a starting point. Partnering in-house with the *Imagine the Universe!* program, an outreach effort of NASA's HEASARC program, we adapted several of their materials initially developed for high-school classroom use. We also adapted available formal-education materials from a variety of other sources including the Universe Education Forum, the Chandra EPO program, etc.

The YAA team also looked for existing educational materials that promoted open-ended investigations. Over the years MKI and SAO have developed a productive partnership that allows MKI's programs access to the MicroObservatory, a net-work of robotic telescopes created by the Science Education Department at SAO. The telescopes are operated remotely so youth in our after-school programs can plan observations any time during the day. These observations are then carried out at night and an image is sent to each user within three minutes after it was taken. Because our partners at SAO had already developed a classroom curriculum based on the use of MicroObservatory, their "From the Ground Up!" curriculum became our main source for activities for our after-school programs.

4.   Challenges and Potential Solutions

Both AU and YAA faced several of the typical challenges that affect OST initiatives directed at urban youth: participant recruitment and retention, limited awareness of programs among families and parental involvement, after-school staff turnover, wide variance in the professional attitudes, knowledge, and skills among after-school staff, fragmented urban communities and lack of coordination among after-school programs, lack of continuity in funding, etc. (Technical Development Corporation 2004). Incidentally, all of these factors directly or indirectly affect youth retention which ultimately determines the degree of success of an OST program. Additional challenges to our programs included adapting educational materials created for the traditional classroom environment and/or created for different age groups, designing an effective professional development for after-school professionals and sustaining the program over time.

4.1.   Recruitment and Retention

The partnerships with community-based organizations were critical to our recruitment efforts. Such organizations have a sound record of effective programming with our target audiences and can bring participants to the table.

Retention or regular attendance is a different issue than recruitment. In general, OST programs cannot assume continuity of attendance from participants that join them on a volunteer basis. For this reason both YAA and AU are based on modular curricula that allow flexibility for youth who may not attend all the sessions to still have a meaningful learning experience. Participants who attend the sessions regularly will benefit from the progressive build-up of knowledge, and in the case of YAA this is also a requisite to participate in the summer youth apprenticeship program.

4.2. Curriculum Adaptation

The adaptation of existing curriculum materials presents two main issues. The first has to do with the fact that most of the astronomy educational activities available to us were designed for the regular classroom. Some of the basic changes that need to be implemented for use in OST include: removing work sheets with extensive calculations that "feel like schoolwork", including participant interactions at each step of the activity, building in flexibility for implementation in non-ideal space configurations, making the activity as self-contained as possible, including moderate physical activity (even if just exchanging seats), and including opportunities to practice proper verbal, written and visual communication by incorporating elements from the arts and forms of expression familiar to youth.

The second challenge is that school materials are designed to focus on astronomy topics highlighted by education standards. In the free-choice learning environment typical of OST, these restrictions to standards-based topics do not apply. The freedom afforded by this has to be balanced by a careful analysis of the relevance and value of the topic to the overall goal.

In the case of AU, most of the materials available on the topics we wished to cover had been developed for a high-school science classroom. The pilot in summer 2006 with a small number of groups provided valuable input that allowed us to refine the program for the second test in summer 2007.

4.3. Professional Development for OST Staff

Professional development for OST staff is a key element both to implement a current program and to support program sustainability. In this respect the OST community has some unique characteristics that must be borne in mind. Unlike teachers in schools, OST program leaders come from a wide variety of backgrounds. A few of them may be school teachers who have taken on this role for the summer, others are college students who have taken on a summer job, while most of them are community-based employees who may have taken their last science class when they were in high school. Their degree of familiarity and comfort with facilitating science activities varies greatly. There is also a high degree of transience in the leader population. While some program leaders are full-time staff with community-based organizations that offer OST programming, most are temporary staff. This implies that training schedules must take the start dates of the employees into account. In order to build up any institutional memory on running the program, one must work with upper-level program staff so that your program can be established as one of the core components of their portfolio of programs.

5. Lessons Learned

In summary, some of the lessons learned from our experience with developing and disseminating BEEP and YAA can be briefly described as below

- Partner with someone who works with the target community. They will be critical allies in the long-term success and sustainability of your program.

- Discuss the basic philosophy of your OST program at the very beginning. Some OST programs provide support for schoolwork, while others focus on developing other aspects of a child's development.

- Design the programs to be flexible as the program leaders will each implement the program as best suits their situation. Provide them with a set of tools to form a basis for success but accept that they will adapt it as best suits the population and schedule they have to work with.

- OST programs are not additional school hours! The program has to be engaging and hands-on. Keep lecturing to a minimum, ensure that there are opportunities for hands-on learning, and provide opportunities for different types of learners (by incorporating kinesthetic activities, elements of art, music, etc.).

- Wherever possible, include youth's input in the program design, implementation, and advertisement as they are the best science ambassadors to their own communities.

- The OST community is a professional community with its own culture and pressures. Becoming familiar with the rich OST literature and attending OST conferences is very valuable.

- Do not assume that because science is important and exciting for you, it is the case for everybody. Through your program, contribute to creating an environment that is supportive of the youth's science learning experience: build in your program opportunities to connect to the families and the larger communities to which the youth belong.

- Evaluation in a free-choice learning arena can be a challenge. It is best to design the program so that the evaluation is as self-contained as possible and the session activities themselves provide feedback on whether they worked and achieved the goal of the program.

References

Afterschool Alliance, *America After 3 PM: A Household Survey on Afterschool in America* (2004)

Technical Development Corporation, *Coming of Age in Boston: Out-of-School Time Opportunities for Teens* (2004)

NSF, *Pathway to STEM Careers: Preparing the STEM Workforce of the 21st Century, Final Workshop Report* (2005)

EPO and a Changing World
ASP Conference Series, Vol. 389, © 2008
C. Garmany, M. Gibbs, and J. W. Moody

Vodcasting for Everyone

Robert Hurt

Spitzer Science Center, MS 220-6, Pasadena, CA 91125

Lars Lindberg Christensen

ESA/Hubble, ESO Office 010, Karl-Schwarzschild-Strasse 2, D-85748 Garching bei München, Germany

Abstract. Video podcasting, or vodcasting, is the latest evolution of the podcast revolution. The market for on-demand content spans the gamut, ranging from portable media players to computers, and increasingly to televisions through home media centers. This new mode of accessing video content is rapidly growing in popularity, particularly among younger audiences. Because it allows a direct link between consumer and content producer, bypassing traditional media networks, it is ideal for EPO efforts. Even modest budgets can yield compelling astronomy vodcasts that will appeal to a large audience. Gateways like the *iTunes Music Store* and *YouTube* have created new content markets where none existed before. This paper highlights the key steps for producing a vodcast. The reader will see how to make (or improve) a video podcast for science communication purposes learn about some of the latest developments in this rapidly-evolving field.

1. Introduction

Up through the 1970's virtually all video content in the United States was produced by one of three networks, and could only be seen during specific time slots. By the 1980's this "TV 1.0" era gave way to a fundamentally new paradigm of flexibility and choice. In the "TV 2.0" era viewers now had dozens, even hundreds, of niche-market networks offering a much broader variety of programming. The advent of the VCR, and more recently the digital video recorder (DVR), has also increased flexibility by "time-shifting" content from its *broadcast* time to a *convenient viewing* time.

Widespread broadband internet access is enabling a new revolution, dubbed "TV 3.0." Viewers now have the option of bypassing networks and schedules altogether, instead downloading content on-demand for viewing on their computer, portable media player, or television. There is no longer a network executive and programming schedule standing between the content producer and the audience; it has become a direct relationship!

The instrument of change is the podcast. The "Personal On-Demand broadCAST" is really no more than an online media file posted alongside an XML file (a feed), that is updated as new content becomes available. Media aggregators (such as *iTunes*) allow subscriptions to the feed and will automatically download new content to their computers in the background as it becomes available.

Figure 1.   Who needs convincing? After introducing a high definition format, the *Hidden Universe* briefly reached the top spot in the US rankings
of all podcasts in September, 2007, ahead of major players such as National
Geographic, ESPN and HBO. New episodes are routinely downloaded 80,000
times in their first month online.

While the roots of podcasting are in the audio MP3 format, video has
become overwhelmingly common in recent years. The video podcast, or vodcast,
has become a competitor for traditional television viewers, thus defining the TV
3.0 revolution.

2.   Why Vodcast?

Vodcasting allows producers of compelling content to connect directly to an audience. This opens up incredible opportunities for astronomy outreach. There
are a number of compelling reasons science communicators should consider vodcasting.

Astronomy is Visual: Of all the sciences, astronomy is arguably the
most visual and is responsible for some of the most memorable images of our
time. Video is a natural medium for astronomy communication because of the
readily available image, illustration, and animation resources for production.
Astronomy vodcast content is highly appealing to audiences and is a natural fit
to the medium.

Easy to Produce: The standards for online video content are dramatically
more forgiving than for broadcast television. The "Do-It-Yourself style" of many
of the established vodcasts lowers the technical expectations among the audience,
and puts emphasis on the content - the idea and the messages. While a broadcast
documentary can cost tens of thousands of dollars or more to produce, effective
vodcasts can be made on a shoestring and thus are within reach of even the
smallest EPO groups.

It's The Future, Not Just a Fad: The explosion of downloaded content
over recent years makes it clear this is an inescapable trend, not just a fad of
the moment. It is supported by powerful industries such as *Apple, Google*, and
video community websites such as *Veoh* and *YouTube*; vodcasting is not going
away anytime soon.

Connect to Large Audiences: There are increasing numbers of people
actively searching for compelling online content. This is particularly true for

younger audiences including children who are growing up online rather than in front of the TV. Astronomy vodcasts can attract large audiences simply by existing; viewers will find the content without having to be told about it ("pull" as opposed to "push").

3. Vodcasting Examples

As examples of vodcasts we will examine the production of two successful video podcast series: *Hidden Universe* and *Hubblecast*.

The Hidden Universe of the Spitzer Space Telescope, produced by NASA's Spitzer Science Center, was the first astronomy video podcast. The first episode went online in May 2006, and one year later it became the first astronomy vodcast to also offer a high definition (HD) version. The focus is science, not human interest stories. It uses two show formats: *Showcase* episodes are mini-documentaries (∼5 min) featuring a host, rich visuals, and interviews, and *Gallery Explorer* episodes (∼2 min) that display one or more related images with simple overlay text for background.

The *Hubblecast* is produced by the European Space Agency's Hubble group and started in March 2007. It features the latest news and images from the NASA/ESA Hubble Space Telescope. The host is Dr. Joe Liske a.k.a "Dr. J" from ESO, who was selected at a screening session from ten other very promising scientists by a panel consisting of several men and women from different backgrounds in a 'reality television' casting session. The production time for an episode is roughly five working days. The duration of an episode is five to six minutes. *Hubblecast* has three channels: SD (Standard Definition), HD (from June 2007) and Full HD (possibly the first Full HD Vodcast in the world). In addition eight other video formats are made available online on spacetelescope.org. Further information about *Hubblecast* is available in Christensen et al. (2007) and online [1].

4. Production Design & Resources

In a vodcast production where manpower is often restricted, it is vital to manage resources and make the best of existing assets. These assets include (but are not limited to) images, animations, a host and scientists. In designing a vodcast, one should identify which assets are available and develop a show format to use as much in-hand material as possible. Minimizing custom production needs is critical for maintaining a sustainable production.

Images: Astronomy images are abundant and are a key resource for any vodcast. Most of the third-party astronomy images on the web are free to use for educational and communication purposes. Even static images can be fantastic for video by adding slow zoom and/or pan effects.

Animations: One or two well-chosen animations, either artistic or derived from science data/simulations, can help communicate a difficult science concept. While they can be time-consuming or expensive to produce, many institutions

---

[1] http://www.spacetelescope.org/videos/hubblecast.html

have broadcast-quality content available online that may eliminate the need for custom work.

Host: A recurring host can give a personal touch and can help establish an identity for a vodcast. A host can also provide a visual focus when images or animations are not available to illustrate a point. Her or she can even make low resolution content less obvious if it is presented as a "newscaster" style inset. It is critical to cast someone with clear speech patterns and good presentation skills with technical material; it is even better if they can memorize material rather than read off of cue cards.

Interviews: Scientists can bring a personal angle to technical results, and can be a great resource for video. By interviewing them several times on the subject it is often possible to get a good, clear "take" that gets across key ideas. Plus, anything covered in an interview does not have to be written into the script, simplifying production. Note that not all scientists are equally suited to appear in front of a camera and it is good in advance to screen a potential scientist guest for his or her ability to present the material in a lively, concise way.

Both *Hidden Universe* and *Hubblecast* utilize all of these assets for their productions. Typical end-to-end production times are on the order of a week. However, the *Hidden Universe Gallery Explorer* format was specifically designed to include only readily available images and animations to provide a rapid-production option (less than a day) to assure timely updates when a full *Showcase* production is not possible.

5. The Script

Vodcasting is a very "light" medium; the format is short and it is essential to focus on key facts and make them as engaging as possible. The script can make or break a production. It must encompass both the narrative and the visual content and effectively link them.

The first step is to identifying the target audience. Is the product intended for children, laypeople, or the informed public? This determines the number of ideas and the level of background information needed to explain them. The traditional news criteria can help determine the elements that make for interesting stories (see for instance Christensen 2007).

Adapting already existing material, such as a news release, can be a shortcut to researching and writing on a new topic. However, spoken dialog has a significantly different character than written text, and it is important to carefully rewrite such material so it sounds right to an audience. It is also critical to make adjustments to the content if the source material was intended for a different level of audience.

6. Audiovisual Production

Once the script is ready, the visuals for the vodcast must be assessed. Image and animation segments need to be located online or developed using animation software. This process can start even before audio and video footage has been acquired if the timings for the script are recorded; this can be done with timed read-throughs or even by using text-to-speech software.

6.1. Shooting Video

Any production with host or interview segments will need to shoot video. There are many options, ranging from on-location in an office, working in a controlled studio setting, or even using substituted backgrounds by shooting against a green-screen.

Real footage is recorded with a camcorder either in-house or with the assistance of a small hired camera team, depending on the budget. Naturally, the better the real footage is, the more "cinema-like" the final result, and so using the best equipment that fits the budget is helpful. High definition video cameras today start at just a few hundred dollars (US) but the better quality equipment starts in the thousands of dollars.

6.2. Background Removal & Virtual Sets

It is not too difficult to create a completely imaginary set for your host or interview subjects. The backdrop can be as simple as an image, an animated background pattern, or even a "virtual set" constructed in image and 3D graphics editing programs. The technique requires shooting the subject against a distinctively colored backdrop that can be digitally removed, or "keyed" out. Typically these are bright blue or green screens; green is more commonly used as it is less likely to match common clothing or skin tones. Note that these green screen studio installations need not be permanent, but can be set up in about an hour or so. Common editing applications have tools for removing these backgrounds.

Shooting green screen footage does place stronger technical requirements on your video equipment. The least expensive digital video cameras will tend to blur out colors, making it difficult to cleanly separate the subject from the background. This leaves an unnatural border that can ruin the effect. It is useful to check online forums to see what results filmmakers have had with specific video equipment before committing to a particular camera.

6.3. Recording Audio

The audio quality is dramatically better through an external microphone instead of the camera's built-in system. This can include shotgun/boom microphones near the camera or lavaliere microphones that clip onto the shirt (either wired or wireless). Even for narrations without video, using a high quality microphone will make a big difference to how professional the production feels as audio problems are difficult or impossible to fix after the fact. Anyone speaking on camera or in a voiceover must have good pronunciation and clarity. Very strong accents can be distracting. If a speaker is important to a story but is difficult to understand, try to use them to reinforce established points and not introduce new material.

6.4. Music and Sound Effects

Music and sound effects can dramatically improve the impact of a video. Free sound tracks and effects from the web, as well as copyrighted "pay-per-use" stock music are available for the sound. Many so called 'net labels' exist that have favorable conditions for the use of the music. However, it may be interesting to collaborate with artists who can compose music and sound effects that will better fit the specific needs of the project.

7. Editing

The post-production stage follows the recording of the audio and video. At this point the video footage is screened and the best "takes" chosen and trimmed to remove unwanted parts. The remaining video, animation, and audio assets are assembled.

Using the script as a template the project is pieced together in the editing software like a jigsaw puzzle. Video and audio clips are added to the timeline to tell the story. Audio levels are adjusted to be consistent, video colors are corrected, and transitions are added where they improve the storytelling. Finally, extras like music and sound effects are laid into the timeline for the final polish.

Naturally specialized hardware and software is needed for these tasks. Fortunately, both Mac and Windows computers now come standard with incredible computing power and data input/output rates, and basically any new high-end computer can be used for video editing. Key considerations are lots of storage space (7200 rpm drives, internal or Firewire, but not USB). High definition editing is particularly demanding and requires larger monitors and high performance video cards (this technology changes rapidly; it is worth consulting computer experts to find the best current video card options). There are many powerful options for video editing software today. Industry standards now include suites like *Final Cut Studio* and *Adobe®Premiere®*, but even entry-level products like iMovie can produce a solid vodcast.

8. Video Formats

Today the broadcaster is faced with an almost dizzying array of image sizes and formats. Traditional US (NTSC) and European (PAL) formats have different frame rates and dimensions but share a common aspect ratio (4:3). Now a new set of high definition (HD) formats are becoming the new broadcast standard. They are differentiated by two image sizes (both with widescreen 16:9 aspect ratios) and a variety of frame rates.

Table 1 summarizes all of the major video formats. These affect even vodcasters since common production formats mirror those for television broadcast work. Interlacing becomes a key issue in choosing formats; this process is a kind of workaround for limited signal bandwidth in which every other line of an image is sent (a field), and the remaining interlaced field is filled in on the next pass. While this does create a faster refreshing screen, the resulting interlace artifacts create an unpleasant effect for online viewing and should be avoided for all vodcast work.

What is the best format for vodcasting? There is no easy answer. Standard definition (SD) formats and lower frame rates make for smaller files and faster downloads that are compatible with a wider cross section of hardware. However new computers are able to play back and display HD material on the computer screens. Many consumers already have HD or Full HD plasma or LCD screens in their home, and media centers and HD players such as Apple TV are becoming increasingly common. Paradoxically most normal consumers are not able to find much HD content to display on the computers or TVs and this is definitely a niche that can be exploited for science communication purposes.

In the production sense the perhaps most important difference between SD and HD is the change of aspect ratio (the ratio between the two sides of a video frame) from 4:3 of the traditional SD frames to 16:9 for HD frames. As current video production is moving rapidly towards the widescreen 16:9 aspect ratio, even for SD shows, this is arguably the more forward-looking choice today.

The other consideration is the target hardware platform. For instance, video iPods can handle images up to 640 x 480 at frame rates up to 30 fps. The newer Apple TV's have an added potential to handle 1280 x 720 frames at up to 25 fps. Most new computers can display 1920 x 1080 at up to 25 or 30 fps. Of course once a master video file has been created it is easy to downsample it to lower resolutions using encoding tools.

Final distribution videos are far too large in their raw, uncompressed state to distribute and play, so it is necessary to "encode" them into a compressed format designed for easy playback. One of the best video "codecs" in use now is H.264 (MPEG4 part 10). Within the limits stated above, this format is compatible with iPods, many other portable media players, and computers running Quicktime. However, offering vodcasts in multiple formats can reach audiences with older hardware; common choices are MPEG1 and Sorenson 3 Quicktime. Also posting minimally compressed, high quality formats makes it easy for broadcasters to include the content in news and documentary programming for television.

Using a good batch compression tool can simplify the creation of media files. It is simple to take a final source file and create multiple versions using different compression codecs and at different image dimensions. Naturally it makes sense to produce a vodcast at the highest desired dimension and frame rate, and downsample to lower qualities as needed. On Macs *Compressor* which is part of *Final Cut Studio* is used by many. On PCs *ProCoder* is a good tool to batch compress many different formats from the largest format in the workflow.

Table 1.   Summary of video formats

Format	Dimensions [pixels]	Interlacing	Field/Frame Rate [fps]
NTSC (broadcast)	640 [720] x 480	Interlaced	60 (fields)
NTSC	640 [720] x 480	Progressive	24, 30
PAL	720 [768] x 576	Progressive	25
HD (720p)	1280 x 720	Progressive	24, 25, 30, 50, 60
HD (1080i)	1920 x 1080	Interlaced	50, 60 (fields)
HD (1080p, "Full HD")	1920 x 1080	Progressive	24, 25, 30

What is the best distribution format? There is no simple answer in a time of rapidly advancing technology and consumer interests. But with the rapidly increasing marked for HD televisions and related hardware, there is already a surprisingly strong trend towards large-format content. Since introducing both 720p and 1080p formats of *Hubblecast*, recent months have shown these HD options account for about half of the total downloads. For *Hidden Universe* the

720p format produced an even more dramatic ratings spike; it is downloaded about 10 times more frequently than SD!

9.   Distribution - It's all about the ratings!

The final important step is the distribution and promotion of the video. The primary distribution of vodcasts today is through the iTunes Music Store. As the XML feed is updated with information on new episodes, this information is displayed for casual browsers looking through the podcast section. Video community sites such as *You-Tube*, *DailyMotion*, *blip.tv* and *veoh* can be excellent channels for promoting a vodcast. Download numbers from these pages can be substantial (up to 20-25% of the total).

As with TV better visibility will give higher ratings. A good name to the vodcast channel, a sexy description and recognizable icon are critical elements in your success. Learn from other vodcasts - what looks interesting and why? Episode titles and descriptions are important since casual browsers often sample an episode before subscribing. Waste nothing in your description; the first few words can be pivotal in capturing a potential subscriber's interest!

10.   Conclusion

With the experiences from the two successful vodcasts *Hidden Universe* and *Hubblecast* we feel confident in saying that the vodcasts are here to stay. Delivering content in multiple formats to appease both the desires of instant gratification and of premium viewing quality seems to maximize the potential audience. Our experiences show that being one of the first providers of a new format can pay off, so watch for new trends, platforms and formats!

By the time of this writing, ten episodes of *Hubblecast* and 14 episodes of *Hidden Universe* have been released and both vodcasts have been downloaded close to a million times. The two podcasts are - at least for the time being - regularly ranked among the 10 most viewed podcasts in the science category in iTunes, and among the Top 100 podcasts in total. We plan to keep up with the steady stream of exciting vistas of space seen through the eyes of Hubble and Spitzer and presenting the latest science to the young generations as long as the segment of young viewers enjoys our work. Who knows what the next trend will be? Podcasts in 3D HD? Will there be another even more exciting medium that can help us bring the stars to everyone on Earth? Only the future can tell...

Acknowledgments.   The authors would like to acknowledge the two vodcast teams from both *Hidden Universe* and the *Hubblecast*, as well as Will Gater for his editorial contribution to the paper.

References

Christensen, L.L, Kornmesser, M., Shida, R.Y., Gater W., and Liske, J., "The Hubblecast - The World's First Full HD Video Podcast?" in *Proceedings from Communicating Astronomy with the Public* edited by L. Christensen and M. Zoulias (2007)

Christensen, L.L, *The Hands-On Guide For Science Communicators* (Springer, 2007)

EPO and a Changing World
ASP Conference Series, Vol. 389, © 2008
C. Garmany, M. Gibbs, and J. W. Moody

Learning about the Dynamic Sun through Sounds

M. Quinn

Design Rhythmics Sonification Research Laboratory, 92 High Rd, Lee NH 03824

L. M. Peticolas and Janet Luhmann

Space Sciences Laboratory, University of California, 7 Gauss Way, MC 7450, Berkeley, CA 94720-7450

J. MacCallum

Center for New Music and Audio Technology, 1750 Arch Street, Berkeley, California 94720

Abstract.   Can we hear the Sun or its solar wind? Not in the sense that they make sound. But we can take the particle, magnetic field, electric field, and image data and turn it into sound to demonstrate what the data tells us. We present work on turning data from the two-satellite NASA mission called STEREO (Solar TErrestrial RElations Observatory) into sounds and music (sonification). STEREO has two satellites orbiting the Sun near Earth's orbit to study the coronal mass ejections (CMEs) from the Corona. One sonification project aims to inspire musicians, museum patrons, and the public to learn more about CMEs by downloading STEREO data and using it to make music. We demonstrate the software and discuss the way in which it was developed. A second project aims to produce a museum exhibit using STEREO imagery and sounds from STEREO data. We demonstrate a "walk across the Sun" created for this exhibit so people can hear the features on solar images. We show how pixel intensity translates into pitches from selectable scales with selectable musical scale size and octave locations. We also share our successes and lessons learned.

1.   Mapping STEREO Data to Sounds, Sonification

The STEREO Mission has multiple instruments; so many that four suites of instruments each have a principal investigator in charge of each suite. In simple terms the data can be broken down into five data concepts: images, magnetic fields, positively charged particles, electrons, and waves in the electric fields. We are working to sonify all of these types of data. At this time we sonify all the data except the waves in the electric fields.

We are developing a program for the public and science centers that sonifies the STEREO beacon data (e.g. the fundamental aspects of the data useful for real-time space weather forecasting). The software is designed to allow a user to download the data products mentioned above for both STEREO satellites. The user can then both see and listen to the data. We have combined particle data from different instruments to make it easier to view, listen, and explain to non-scientists. A day of extreme ultraviolet images is made into a movie, which can be played back at varying speeds. When a user moves their mouse over a data display, it is explained in a separate text box with an accompanying image.

We are also creating a science center exhibit where visitors can listen to the images of the Sun by interacting with the image while also hearing the solar wind particles and magnetic fields measured by the STEREO satellites. We have developed a number of methods to perceive the Sun through musical sonification. For example, a radar display uses an audio line that spins around the image to listen to a part of the Sun. Spread out along the line are up to 60 audio needles, each of which play the pixel data under them, similar to the way a record needle would play a record. We have found that using the hue, saturation, and brightness color model of the pixel information is much more effective than using the red-green-blue color model. The hue of the color selects one of 18 instruments. The saturation selects one of 30 volume levels from moderate to moderately loud. The brightness selects one of 36 notes spanning 5 octaves of the 7-note per octave Spanish Gypsy scale - the brighter the pixel, the higher the note in the scale.

2.   Conclusions and Lessons Learned

Our major successes can be summarized as follows:

- Creating new image sonification techniques.

- Generalizing the application of solar image sonification to any image.

- Creating and developing new infrastructure and working elements of software programs for displaying and listening to the data.

- Developing new collaborations amongst scientists and musicians and educating the instrument groups about applied sonification.

- Invited image sonification demonstrations at conferences (e.g., the Soundscapes panel of the 2007 Art Education for the Blind Conference sponsored the Metropolitan Museum of Fine Art (Met) and Art Beyond Sight).

We have learned many lessons along the way. Working with data, creating software, and designing sonifications takes longer than one often expects. Sonification results may be subjectively viewed as "beautiful" or "interesting", just like various graphic displays may be considered appealing to some. Thus, appealing to all with a particular sonification is impossible. Evaluations should be developed to ensure that the resulting audio meets scientific and data presentation goals set for the project. Evaluations should include feedback from both sighted and limited-sight people. The lack of access to STEREO instrument suite data in textual formats has slowed development of the particle sonifications. Our work seems to indicate that image sonification may make art work more accessible to those who are blind or visually impaired.

These projects stem from the STEREO-IMPACT (In-situ Measurements of Particles and CME Transients) EPO program and a grant from the IDEAS (The Initiative to Develop Education through Astronomy and Space Science (IDEAS) Grant Program.

EPO and a Changing World
ASP Conference Series, Vol. 389, © 2008
C. Garmany, M. Gibbs, and J. W. Moody

Aurora and Magnetospheric Teacher Guides: Bringing Data into the Classroom

L. M. Peticolas

Space Sciences Laboratory, University of California, 7 Gauss Way, MC 7450, Berkeley, CA 94720-7450

S. Odenwald

Astronomy Café, 9717 Culver St., Kensington, MD 20895

A. Walker

Cornerstone Evaluation Associates LLC, 205 Peddler Place, Pittsburgh, PA 15212-1975

Abstract.   The NASA missions Fast Auroral SnapshoT (FAST) and Time History of Events and Macroscale Interactions during Substorms (THEMIS) study Earth's aurora and magnetosphere. As part of the THEMIS Education and Public Outreach (EPO) program, magnetometers were placed in twelve schools in ten states in the Northern US where auroras are often or occasionally detected. In order to bring the science of auroras and Earth's magnetosphere and the data associated with these missions, we have created several teacher guides with middle and high school teachers. Many of these teachers were the ones we worked with in the twelve schools with magnetometers. These guides cover a wide array of topics including 1) Earth's magnetic field to create electrical current; 2) Earth's changing magnetic field on timescales of hundreds of thousands of years, hours, and seconds; 3) space weather effects on the magnetosphere and aurora; 4) universal time; 5) the creation of aurora, 5) auroral substorms; 6) the calculation of the total magnetic field at a particular location over months and years; and 7) the prediction of whether or not auroras will be visible using magnetometer data. We will share the review feedback about these guides from both teachers and a NASA review panel and explain what we did to address these suggested changes. From our evaluation results, we will reveal the challenges of bringing data into the classroom as well as the enormous capacity of these missions to inspire students to get involved with data and NASA missions.

1.   Developing Successful Teacher Guides

We feel we have developed teacher guides that are used in the classroom and inspire students to learn difficult space science and physics concepts. Below, we outline how we did this. We first started with activities that other EPO missions had developed. Then we elaborated on these activities or added new ones that seemed to fill gaps. Our feedback on the lessons came in several steps. Next, we obtained teacher feedback on our THEMIS teacher guides at our annual THEMIS teacher professional development work-shops when we did the activities with the teachers. We learned what lessons did not work, such as a lesson trying to calculate the effects of aurora on the magnetometer data using a random few days of data - the data was not clear enough. At these workshops, a couple of teachers shared their own lessons, which were incorporated into the guides. This is as far as we have evaluated the FAST aurora lesson.

After we incorporated these changes, we got further feedback from telephone interviews with the teachers. This feedback could be categorized as the teacher's concern in "implementation", "student skill level," "cost of materials," and "teacher's content knowledge." Examples of their concerns in each of these categories were: 1) students get a different answer every time they made a measurement, 2) the math skill level was too high in several of the activities, 3) the orienteering compasses were expensive, and 4) a teacher was not comfortable with his/her own knowledge with regard to magnetic obser- vatories and electrical currents. We addressed all of their concerns either by changing the lesson completely, adding additional lessons to bring student to the right level, offering to pay for the expensive materials, and/or providing additional science background in the guides. In addition, we broke up the guide into several guides, had teachers provide additional lessons doing research topics with the data for better lessons that dealt directly with the data.

NASA offers a free service to evaluate NASA-funded EPO products with a panel of scientists and educators. With the feedback from this panel, we again changed some of the lessons. The biggest changes came from comments that the lessons did not have enough inquiry.

2.   Data in the Classroom, Successes and Challenges

Through these teacher guides and the magnetometer data, we have brought real scientific data into the classroom as part of a larger satellite mission. The process of involving the teachers in such a sustained way in the development of the teacher guides has been a key component to making this program successful. However, even with this level of involvement, it took at least a year and in some cases, two years, just for the teachers to get to the background lessons before they felt comfortable looking at the data. In order to help the teachers feel comfortable enough with the data, many had to do some research of their own with the data. They did this research with the students in mind so they could bring these activities into the classroom. Several teachers have still not reached this point and are only using the background lessons.

To see the effect this program has had in terms of engaging and teaching students about Earth's magnetic field and space weather, visit the PBS News Hour with Jim Lehrer website and do a search for "THEMIS." You will hear and see how the enthusiasm of being part of a bigger picture and working with real data has clearly inspired three rural students to become scientists.

Acknowledgments.   We would like to thank the teachers who have made these guide possible and brought the activities and inspiration to their classroom: Victor Trautman (AK), Cris DeWolf (MI), Wendy Esch (WI), Laura Orr (OR), Terry Parent (NV), Wendell Gehman (SD), Sean Estil (MT), Harriet Howe (ND), Frank Martin (ND), Ray Benson (AK), James Bean (NV), Keith Little (PA), Holly Wyllie (VT).

EPO and a Changing World
ASP Conference Series, Vol. 389, © *2008*
C. Garmany, M. Gibbs, and J. W. Moody

Creating Sister Cities: An Exchange Across Hemispheres

Mark T. Adams

National Radio Astronomy Observatory, 520 Edgemont Road,
Charlottesville, Virginia 22903-2475

Sergio A. Cabezon and Eduardo Hardy

Associated Universities, Inc., National Radio Astronomy Observatory,
Av Apoquindo 3650, Piso 18, Los Condes, Santiago de Chile, Chile

Robyn J. Harrison

National Radio Astronomy Observatory, 1003 Lopezville Road,
Socorro, New Mexico 87801

Abstract. Sponsored by Associated Universities, Inc. (AUI) and the National Radio Astronomy Observatory (NRAO), this project creates a cultural and educational exchange program between communities in South and North America, linking San Pedro de Atacama in Chile and Magdalena, New Mexico in the United States. Both communities have similar demographics, are in relatively undeveloped regions of high-elevation desert, and are located near major international radio astronomy research facilities. The Atacama Large Millimeter/submillimeter Array (ALMA) is just 40 km east of San Pedro; the Very Large Array (VLA) is just 40 km west of Magdalena. In February 2007, the Mayor of San Pedro and two teachers visited Magdalena for two weeks; in July 2007 three teachers from Magdalena will visit San Pedro. These visits enable the communities to lay the foundation for a permanent, unique partnership. The teachers are sharing expertise and teaching methodologies for physics and astronomy. In addition to creating science education opportunities, this project offers students linguistic and cultural connections. The town of San Pedro, Chile, hosts nearly 100,000 tourists per year, and English language skills are highly valued by local students. Through exchanges enabled by email and distance conferencing, San Pedro and Magdalena students will improve English and Spanish language skills while teaching each other about science and their respective cultures. This poster describes the AUI/NRAO Sister Cities program, including the challenges of cross-cultural communication and the rewards of interpersonal exchanges between continents and cultures.

1. The Mission

What does a small rural village in New Mexico, population 900, elevation 6500 feet, have in common with a small rural village in northern Chile, population 3000, elevation 7000 feet? Both are home to cutting-edge radio astronomy observatories: the Very Large Array (VLA) and the Atacama Large Millimeter/submillimeter Array (ALMA), respectively.

So it seemed only natural to introduce the two villages to one another. In the fall of 2006, Associated Universities, Inc., via the National Radio Astronomy Observatory initiated a Sister City program between Magdalena, New Mexico, and San Pedro de Atacama, Chile. Our mission was to explore ways in which the two communities and school systems could help each other culturally and academically.

2.   The Action

For two weeks in February (during the Chilean summer), San Pedro tourism teacher Gabriela Rodriguez and high school principal Myriam Rivera visited Magdalena. San Pedro Alcaldesa Sandra Bernal also visited for a few days, getting to know the students, teachers, and people of Magdalena.

In July, Magdalena second grade teacher Sandra Montoya and fifth grade teacher Jim Sauer, accompanied by NRAO Education Officer Robyn Harrison, visited San Pedro for two weeks.

3.   What We Learned

Many of the problems for teachers and students are the same; San Pedro class-rooms were not heated, even in the midst of winter, but the children came to school dressed appropriately and appeared not to mind, or even to notice; even though classes were huge (40-50) there were fewer discipline problems in San Pedro

4.   The Future

1. We have proposed to AUI the funding of a student exchange for fall semester 2008: two students from Magdalena exchanging with two students from San Pedro.

2. The tourism industry requires English. We propose funding to teach English for two months during the southern summer to students, parents, and tourism industry workers in San Pedro.

3. We hope to continue our alliance with email and video conferencing.

EPO and a Changing World
ASP Conference Series, Vol. 389, © 2008
C. Garmany, M. Gibbs, and J. W. Moody

It Takes an e-Village

Fraser Cain,[1,2] Pamela L. Gay,[2,3] Thomas Foster,[3] and Phillip Plait[4]

Abstract.   Online discussion groups, such as the popular BAUT Forum, bring together astronomy enthusiasts with amateur and professional astronomers to discuss astronomy news, views, and dreams. Within this digital community, we look to discover if an e-village can raise an astronomer. In this pilot study, we follow 3 individuals as they go from forum newbie to community elder. We examine their posting habits to determine if it is possible to quantify learning within the bulletin board-based forum environment. We specifically document how the difficulty levels of user questions and the patterns of their responses to questions can be used to document growth in knowledge base and confidence in material. In this poster, we put particular emphases on the creation, validation, and evaluation of our interpretive rubric used to track the development of our three users along the previously identified dimensions. In effect, can we create an objective tool to measure learning from participation in an e-village?

The rubric will allow EPO evaluators to judge the effectiveness of forums in meeting both educational and community needs given limited finances. The rubric will also open up new avenues for educational researchers exploring the impact of internet-based learning tools. This tool is the first step in a broader study to assess learning within the BAUT Forum, the largest online astronomy forum. We strive to achieve a statistical significant sample of life-long learners.

1.   Introduction

Astronomy inspires everyone with its beautiful images to its thought-provoking philosophical questions. The internet has brought astronomy into the homes and classrooms of anyone with internet access, but it has been decidedly one-way delivery of information. The advent of bulletin boards changed that: they provide interested individuals a place to discuss astronomy and ask questions.

In the Bad Astronomy and Universe Today combined BAUT Forums, thousands of people gather on a daily basis to talk and ask questions about astronomy. Over time, the forum has become more than simply a place to talk; it has evolved into a community of friends, a mutual support network, and, perhaps most importantly, an institution of learning. A vast amount of knowledge about space and astronomy is stored in the discussion threads there, and everyone is free to ask questions, answer them, or just discuss the latest news.

---

[1] Universe Today, http://www.universetoday.com

[2] Astronomy Cast, http://www.astronomycast.com

[3] Southern Illinois University Edwardsville, Department of Physics, Campus Box 1654, Edwardsville, IL, 62026-1654

[4] Bad Astronomy, http://www.badastronomy.com

2. Human Subject Privacy Concerns

US regulations require a subjects' rights be protected (Brogt et al. 2007) in research involving humans. Our data comes from public forums that don't require registration to read. Posters choose their own level of anonymity. The public nature of this forum removes any expectation of ownership of post content. Since poster anonymity is already guaranteed and the data we are mining is free for the taking, this study does not require IRB approval. As a courtesy, we posted a thread about this study. It received 114 posts, and 1,644 views. Feedback was generally supportive, no one asked that we stop the study, and a representative comment stated: "[My posts] are public submissions on a public board. But, if you are interested, I would be willing to be one of your subjects."

3. Selecting Usernames and Strategies

We selected 3 individuals to follow in this initial, rubric-creation study. In designing this experiment, we failed to recognize how many posts individuals might have. Four members of BAUT forum made over 10,000 posts, 23 made over 5000 posts, and 211 made over 1000 posts. Unfortunately, the forum software only displays a user's 500 most recent posts or threads. This challenged us to find individuals with about 500 messages over several years. We selected three subjects who met the following criteria: have about 500 posts (487, 492, 521), have been members since summer 2002 (join dates 06-02, 07-02, 08-02), and who have posted within the past summer (last posts: 05-07, 07-07, 09-07).

Given our focus on learning, we only studied posts in the Q&A sub-forum, and in the Space & Astronomy forums. We also adopted sampling strategies; we read the post in a required sub-forum closest to every sixtieth post. We examined all threads started by posters (15, 31, 85 threads).

4. Looking for Posting Patterns

We identified 3 posting patterns: 1) transformation from primarily asking questions to regularly answering questions, 2) transitioning between preferred sub-forums, and 3) transitioning how information is presented. For instance, one poster went from posting a sentence or two with a link in 2002 to today regularly posting lengthy explanations and participating in conceptual discussions.

To quantify forum participation we developed the following preliminary rubric: Questions are rated Q1 for facts-based and "translate this link" questions, Q2 for application of facts and equations, and Q3 for conceptual questions expressing knowledge and asking aid in synthesis or evaluation. News postings are rated R1 for links without explanations, R2 for links with key points attached, and R3 for links with "Why this is interesting/novel" verbiage attached. We also rated answers A1 for factoids or raw links, A3 for conceptual explanations, and A2 for intermediate answers. Additional sub-division will be needed.

References

Brogt, E., Dokter, E., and Antonellis, J., AER, **6** (2007)

EPO and a Changing World
ASP Conference Series, Vol. 389, © 2008
C. Garmany, M. Gibbs, and J. W. Moody

JINA: Bringing Nuclear Astrophysics to Classrooms and Communities

Zachary Constan

National Superconducting Cyclotron Laboratory, Michigan State University, East Lansing, MI 48824

Abstract. The JINA (Joint Institute for Nuclear Astrophysics) Physics Frontier Center enables swift communication and stimulates collaborations among astronomers, astrophysicists and nuclear physicists. Part of its mission is to introduce those fields into the classroom - from the academy to secondary school students to the public - providing opportunities for meaningful collaboration whenever possible. JINA's outreach goals include contributing to science education at K-12 level, reaching the public primarily through the internet, and increasing diversity in the field of nuclear astrophysics. This poster will present some of the myriad ways JINA achieves those goals, through summer programs, hands-on experiments, and magnetic marbles. For more information, go to http://www.JINAweb.org.

1. The Joint Institute for Nuclear Astrophysics

The Joint Institute for Nuclear Astrophysics (JINA) is supported by the National Science Foundation through the Physics Frontier Center program. JINA's mission is to encourage collaboration and facilitate the exchange of information between observational astronomers, nuclear experimentalists and nuclear astrophysicists. The core JINA institutions are the University of Chicago, Michigan State University, and University of Notre Dame. JINA's outreach programs share the science of its member institutions with students and the general public. These initiatives share the unified goal of educating the public, and employ a variety of pedagogies. The primary efforts in this regard will be to enhance science education in K-12 classrooms (with a particular focus on encouraging nuclear astrophysics), providing resources for the public via the web portal http://www.JINAweb.org, and enhancing diversity in the field of nuclear astrophysics.

1.1. Physics of Atomic Nuclei (PAN/PIXE-PAN)

PAN and PIXE-PAN are two-week nuclear science camps for high school/middle school science instructors and high school students. PAN is hosted by the National Superconducting Cyclotron Laboratory (NSCL) at Michigan State University, while PIXE-PAN takes place at Notre Dame's Nuclear Structure Laboratory (NSL).

Both programs offer many advantages due to their positioning within research laboratories at major universities. Participants hear daily lectures on nuclear science and related fields from leading researchers. PIXE-PAN allows them access to the NSL's accelerator to study microscopic structure through the

Proton-Induced X-Ray Emission (PIXE) technique, while PAN lets them build a Berkeley Lab-designed detector from scratch and find creative ways to test the nature of cosmic rays with it.

With the experiences and teaching materials gained in the PAN programs, each teacher participant can return to school and pass on knowledge of nuclear astrophysics to dozens of students each subsequent semester. Also, PAN is an opportunity for high school students to realize what scientific research truly evolves at the university level, helping them plan their academic careers and presenting possible future goals.

1.2.   Marble Nuclei

The Marble Nuclei project is intended to give teachers the option to teach nuclear astrophysics to students in grades 6-9. The project centers around nuclear models constructed from magnets. Downloadable lesson plans help the teacher guide students using this tool to investigate nuclear properties, unstable isotopes, decay modes, nuclear reactions, and so on. The lessons can be taught with simply a supply of marbles, but there are related pieces of equipment that can also be used to demonstrate further concepts. These lesson plans can also be used in conjunction with a field trip to a nuclear research laboratory such as NSL or NSCL.

1.3.   Sensing Our World

This one-week day camp lets students ages 12 to 14 learn the scientific principles behind sensors used in everyday life through hands-on activities. Participants work with lasers and electronics, while studying about polymers, cryogenics, and electrical generators. This program is a collaboration among departments at Notre Dame, which contribute faculty, staff and graduate students to run specialized laboratory experiences. JINA's contribution emphasized nuclear astrophysics through student interaction with Marble Nuclei and the associated educational materials.

1.4.   Art-to-Science

This program combines artistic expression with scientific exploration for children. JINA provides content-specific books, art supplies, and instructors to special needs programs and after-school programs for at-risk students. In turn, the children create art and written/ oral reports about their understanding of the science based on the theme "Made of Star Stuff," from a famous quotation made by astronomer Carl Sagan. The artwork is displayed at JINA Physics Frontiers centers, on the JINA web-site, and as part of a traveling exhibit available to schools and public libraries.

1.5.   Other Programs

JINA also provides "mini-grants" for new classroom demonstration equipment, funds student visits to the NSL and NSCL, and offers a "CNO cycle card game" for download that teaches players one process of stellar energy generation.

Acknowledgments.   The author would like to thank Mary DeWitt, Hendrik Schatz, Remco Zegers, David McCreight, Lindsay Hebeler and John Raguse.

EPO and a Changing World
ASP Conference Series, Vol. 389, © 2008
C. Garmany, M. Gibbs, and J. W. Moody

Fredrickson Park: From Toxic Hazard to Community Science Education Center

Ruth P. Craft and Jesse Warren

South Bend Community School Corporation, 215 South St. Joseph Street, South Bend, IN 46601, USA

Patrick J. Bridges

LaSalle Council, Boy Scouts of America, 1340 South Bend Avenue, SouthBend, IN, 46617, USA

Gary Gilot[1] and Phil St. Clair[2]

City of South Bend, [1]Department of Public Works and [2]Department of Parks, 227 W. Jefferson, South Bend, IN 46601, USA

Philip J. Sakimoto

Department of Physics, 225 NSH, University of Notre Dame, Notre Dame, IN 46556-5670, USA

Abstract.   Fredrickson Park is an on-going venture, the result of collaborative planning and development in South Bend, Indiana. This city park lies within a low-income residential neighborhood not far from the University of Notre Dame and until recently was a casual dump, an eye-sore, and a toxic hazard. Through a unique coalition of community organizations, the area has been converted to a prairie-ecosystem park available for community use, has become the home of the administrative offices of the Boy Scouts of America-LaSalle Council, and is the pilot site for curriculum-based field trips for children in the South Bend Community Schools with Notre Dame, Saint Mary's, and Indiana University-South Bend students assisting. Priority plans include enhanced nature and physical fitness trails with expanded earth and space science inquiry stations for school, Scout, and community use. In addition, a scale model of the Solar System is planned to start at the park and extend into the heart of the city. Fredrickson Park is a community success serving South Bend students and families through formal and informal science education.

1.   Background and Problem

South Bend, like other cities, has expanded over time to include former wilderness areas, swampland, and run-off ravines once commonly considered of little value except as convenient casual dumps for industrial or over-sized waste. By the 1970s one such ravine was surrounded by a lower-income residential neighborhood in the northeastern part of the city near Notre Dame University and adjacent to a major city thoroughfare.

The area was purchased in 1986 by the City of South Bend with the intent to clean it up and reclaim it as a neighborhood park. At the time of the purchase, the degree of contamination was underestimated. The industrial waste, decomposition, and methane production were far deeper and more widely spread than originally thought; excavation was not feasible. The projected park area was an ecological liability.

2.   Plan and Progress

A two-part plan was initiated by the City of South Bend Department of Public Works. The first phase would involve remediation of the environmental problem, upgrading the site status from negative to neutral. The second phase would be the creation of an environmental education center, taking the situation from neutral to positive.

Remediating the toxic waste situation included reshaping the landfill, installing a two-foot clay cap and an active gas control system. Additional topsoil and seeding the new surface completed this first phase. Work began in July of 2003 and was completed a year later, funded by a Brownfield Revolving Loan provided by the U. S. Environmental Protection Agency and administered by the State.

The second phase of the project, creation of an environmental education center, is a cooperative venture involving a number of local agencies and institutions. Neighborhood groups met to offer input. The LaSalle Council of the Boy Scouts of America constructed an administrative building adjacent to the park which now houses the environmental education center as well as the headquarters for the regional Scouting program. South Bend Community School personnel assisted in developing hands-on activities that encourage interaction with nature and development of science skills. Fredrickson Park is currently a pilot site for curriculum-based field trips for children in the South Bend Schools with Notre Dame students assisting. By working together, these diverse groups have created a valuable community resource.

Plans for future development include additional science inquiry and physical fitness stations in the park for school, Scout, and community use. The City of South Bend intends to purchase an adjacent wooded plot for a picnic site. Other groups have proposed enhancements such as outdoor classrooms and bike trails. Funding is being sought for a scale model of the Solar System to begin at Fredrickson Park and extend along a proposed linear park into the heart of South Bend.

3.   Conclusion

The goal of converting a neighborhood ecological liability into a positive community resource has been achieved and development continues. The creative energy of an innovative partnership of local agencies and institutions has sparked the ongoing development of an exemplary community resource for environmental and science education, Fredrickson Park.

Acknowledgments.   The educational activities at Fredrickson Park are developed and implemented in their entirety by the volunteer efforts of the staffs of the Boy Scouts, Notre Dame, and South Bend Community Schools.

EPO and a Changing World
ASP Conference Series, Vol. 389, © 2008
C. Garmany, M. Gibbs, and J. W. Moody

Mini-Partnerships: Successes of "Just Asking"

Alice Altair Gift Enevoldsen

Pacific Science Center, 200 2nd Ave N, Seattle, WA 98109

Abstract. Partnerships between scientists and educational institutions are usually complex: involving overhead, management, grant applications, responsibilities, and a mutually-beneficial arrangement. Though this is very powerful, it is not the only way for scientists and educators to work together and share new science with the public. We should also explore mini-partnerships: partnerships that have a minimal time commitment and no ongoing responsibilities.

For example: five times between January and May, when I was writing various curricula or articles, I found I was missing some piece of information, usually on a very recent discovery. The lack of published information on these recent finds led me to directly contact the team making the discovery, with a carefully-worded, pertinent question. Every time I asked, I received a prompt, cheerful reply, with an answer to my question and an offer for assistance in the future.

The key to the success of these mini-partnerships has been politeness, understanding of time constraints, knowing what question to ask, and being able to interpret the answer.

1. Educator—Make the Cold Call

- Be polite: E-mail is fun and easy, but this use of it counts as a business letter and should take a similar format. Have someone proofread it for you, even if it's only two sentences.

- Be succinct: short and to the point.

- Do your research: don't ask a question that's already been answered, especially if Google has the answer as its first hit, or the listserv you're e-mailing has this question posted to it twice a week.

- Don't pester. Interpret the answer yourself—don't keep going back and asking your source to "dumb it down" for you. If you're not able to interpret the answer; that may indicate that it is time for a more in-depth partnership.

- Assume that your partner has as little time as you do. Aim to keep your interaction under 5 minutes. E-mail if you can: it's less intrusive—but provide your phone number in case the scientist prefers to talk directly.

- Ask the right person, or ask them to point you to the right person. Don't waste the time of someone who doesn't know the answers, or has to spend an hour looking them up.

2.   Researcher—A Useful Reply

- Write back—even if you just say "I don't know" or "I don't have time." (We all understand both sentiments).

- The best ways to help: answer the question, point to an accessible resource, forward the e-mail to a colleague.

- Try to avoid jargon and acronyms. We'll be better able to interpret your answer ourselves, without calling you again, if the answer is in common English. The internet is great for telling me what a "Three-Letter Acronym" is, but not so hot on "TLA" (is that the Texas Library Association?).

- Be polite. I know your time is limited, and we're sorry if you think we wasted it. If you're upset, delete the e-mail—we're not adding you to a spam listserv. (Oh, and speaking of listserves, don't add us to your listserv without asking, either.)

3.   What You Gain as a Researcher:

- Masterfully spinning words can turn a few quick interactions like this into the education and public outreach (EPO) section of a grant, and rightfully so. By using 5 minutes of your own time and answering the questions of an educator, you are passing that knowledge about your research to between 15 and 1000 people, depending on what format the educator uses to teach.

- You can ask to be listed in the credits of the curriculum, lesson plan, handout, or article. This gives you renown, and the educator credibility.

- Now this educator owes you a 5-minute favor—try e-mailing them next time you need to rephrase something from academic-paper-format into freshman-level-lecture format. Or call and ask them to let you into their museum for free (it might work).

4.   Quick Information an Educator Can Give Back to a Researcher:

- How many people this knowledge will be disseminated to

- The format this knowledge will be disseminated in

- The city/country/or number of locations in which the knowledge will used

- A credit in the curriculum listing the name and institutional affiliation

- Permission to list the educational institution in the EPO section of papers and grant proposals

Acknowledgments.   Thank you to Heather Gibbons, Dennis Schatz, Beth Amsbary and Holly Csiga at the Pacific Science Center, and to everyone at the Astronomical Society of the Pacific.

EPO and a Changing World
ASP Conference Series, Vol. 389, © *2008*
C. Garmany, M. Gibbs, and J. W. Moody

Space Science Core Curriculum Sequence: A GEMS and NASA Collaboration

John Erickson

University of California Lawrence Hall of Science #5200 Berkeley, CA 94720-5200

Abstract. GEMS has collaborated with NASA to produce core curriculum sequences in space science for elementary school and for middle school. This text describes the design process and some of the features of the curriculum.

1. Space Science: A Familiar Topic For GEMS in a New Format

Great Explorations in Math and Science (GEMS) is a program at the Lawrence Hall of Science, a math and science education center at the University of California in Berkeley. Since the mid 1980s GEMS has produced curriculum guides for teachers that have been used as supplemental curricula or as building blocks for a core curriculum. Space science has always been well represented among the GEMS guides, beginning with Earth, Moon, and Stars (Cary Sneider 1986) and continuing with several guides that were developed with NASA partners.

With the resources of existing space science GEMS units, and a successful history of relations with NASA, the GEMS program embarked on the creation of a comprehensive curriculum that would satisfy criteria for adoptability by schools, such as manageable time frame, content linked to standards, and an assessment system. These are the NASA partners in the creation of the Space Science Sequences:

- Ibex Mission EPO

- Kepler Mission EPO

- Origins Education Forum/Hubble Space Telescope

- Solar System Education Forum

- Sun-Earth Connection Education Forum

2. The Development Process

A survey of teachers in the GEMS Network found that about 30 class sessions each for elementary school and middle school would realistically fit into teaches' time frames if they could be flexibly implemented across the grade levels. Using National Standards and Benchmarks, a survey of state standards, common misconceptions, and current and historical research in space science, we generated the big ideas that would be the topics for each unit.

Space Science Sequence for Grades 3 to 5

    Unit 1: How Big and How Far?
    Unit 2: Earth's Shape and Gravity
    Unit 3: How Does the Earth Move?
    Unit 4: Moon Phases and Eclipses

Space Science Sequence for Grades 6 to 8

    Unit 1: How Does the Sun Affect the Earth?
    Unit 2: Why Are There Seasons?
    Unit 3: The Solar System
    Unit 4: Beyond the Solar System

Because of teachers' time constraints, only a limited number of concepts can be taught for full understanding. Concepts were sorted into three groups: "Key Concept" "Good to Know," and "Worth Being Familiar With." The key concepts were the ones to be assessed, and the others would be included according to how they sup-ported the key concepts. This was a difficult process.

Pre- and post-questionnaires were developed for each unit. These are used as assessments by teachers, but they are also launching points for discussions and investigations, and opportunities for students to reflect on how their thinking has changed. For developers these questionnaires focus the creation of activities and assess their effectiveness.

During numerous meeting, GEMS developers and NASA partners sequenced the concepts and matched them to activities, existing and newly developed, to create the curriculum. GEMS developers pilot-tested them in classrooms and authored drafts for national field-tests. Feedback from field-test teachers and NASA partners was incorporated into a final version. Retesting of revised activities was conducted as necessary.

3.   Some Features of the GEMS Space Science Sequences

Evidenced-Based Learning Students are given scaffolded opportunities to engage in discourse and build evidence-based explanations. They are presented with alternative claims and asked which they agree with and why.

Concept Wall As instruction progresses, the teacher posts concepts. This makes explicit to the student what they are expected to learn. Concepts include space science content as well as concepts about the nature and methods of science.

Student Readings Informational readings on various topics, including current missions, enhance student understanding.

Supplementary CD-ROM Activities and explorations on CD-ROM provide extra experience and give an alternative platform for some of the core activities.

EPO and a Changing World
ASP Conference Series, Vol. 389, © *2008*
C. Garmany, M. Gibbs, and J. W. Moody

The Black Hole Experiment Gallery

Roy Gould, Mary Dussault, Alex Griswold, Erika Reinfeld, and Simon Steel

Science Education Department, Harvard Smithsonian Center for Astrophysics, 60 Garden St., Cambridge, Massachusetts 02138, USA

Abstract. We report preliminary findings from the development and proto-typing of the *Black Hole Experiment Gallery,* a NASA and NSF-funded national traveling exhibition and related educational materials on black holes. Among the innovations described are partnerships with community-based programs that enable culturally diverse youth to collaborate in exhibit development; and computer-networked technology that helps personalize visitors' exhibit experiences through the creation of a "digital diary," that extends learning beyond the gallery, and that collects embedded evaluation data.

1. The Project

The Harvard-Smithsonian Center for Astrophysics (CfA) is leading a project to engage museum-goers in exploring the recent breakthroughs and outstanding mysteries in our scientific understanding of black holes, through a 2500-square-foot national traveling exhibition; a portfolio of educational materials and programs; and an associated website. Due to open in 2009, The Black Hole Experiment Gallery benefits from the expertise of many collaborators: The Association of Science-Technology Centers (ASTC); the design firm, Jeff Kennedy Associates; evaluators from Good-man Research Group; an advisory team of leading astrophysicists and free-choice learning experts; and researchers and educators from the CfA, universities, and NASA.

The project's overall goals for visitors are: 1) to increase engagement, awareness and interest in current astronomy research among diverse audiences; and 2) to increase participants' knowledge, understanding, and personal meaning-making around ideas of gravity, black holes, tools and techniques of astronomers, and theory and evidence in science.

2. Preliminary Findings

2.1. Engaging Visitors Through Predictions is Important

Black holes are so far beyond the realm of direct experience, and so counter-intuitive in their theoretical and observed behaviors, that we felt it important to provide a context for visitors' explorations by asking them to make simple predictions in advance of their observations: "Do you think a black hole is hot or cold?" "Do you think a black hole swallows everything in its path?" "Do you think a black hole has weight?" On exit interviews, we found that visitors indeed phrased their learning in terms of their prior ideas and predictions: "Outer space is so cold, so I thought black holes were cold, but they're not." "I didn't know about spinning black holes. I thought they only suck things in, not that they have jets."

These opportunities to make predictions and confront them with observations enable visitors to share the surprise that scientists themselves had when they confronted theoretical ideas about black holes with the first, counter-intuitive observations of candidate black holes in nature.

2.2.   Exhibit Connectivity Can Increase Visitor Engagement and Learning

With XhibitNet, Inc. we began testing a recent innovation that uses bar-code technology to keep track of visitors' progress through the exhibit-helping visitors to make sense of their observations, and ultimately to create a personal, secure web diary that captures the highlights of their experience and that links to additional activities and resources about black holes. The system allows visitors to record comments and video. Our preliminary results show a remarkably high degree of acceptance and enthusiasm about the process of documenting their activities. "I liked it-it's like getting your space badge... and when home [we can] show what we collected, like a virtual museum." "It makes me feel involved because it asks for comments...[I] feel like part of the exhibit."

Not all visitors expressed enthusiasm. Concerns were voiced about the added complication, about being camera-shy, and about the security of the eventual web-based product. These are concerns that will be addressed in exhibit development.

2.3.   Teen Involvement

During summer 2007, we partnered with the Youth Astronomy Apprenticeship program at the MIT Kavli Institute, where a group of high school age apprentices created three prototype exhibit components for our August formative evaluation session at Boston's Museum of Science. Marysabel and Abdirashid created "Got Gravity?," a hands-on activity that used "event-horizon" nets and floating Styrofoam "stars, gas, and dust" to encourage visitors to find out how black holes can grow in size and mass. Lourdes and Jackie produced "Hollywood Presents Black Holes," an interactive multimedia piece that allowed visitors to view movie clips, rate those clips as being true, partly true, or false, and compare their responses to those of scientists. Kenneth, Kymberlee, and Ashley created "Days of Our Lives," a "South Park"-like animated soap opera of the lives of an aging neutron star and his twin black hole.

Our collaboration with the YAA teens resulted in numerous lessons learned, three of which have immediate implications for our continued exhibit development: 1) Teens' questions about black holes are visitors' questions, so using youth as visible guides through the exhibition may be an important strategy. 2) Teens are very creative and articulate about the kinds of immersive and interactive experiences they want, but need considerable support and scaffolding to implement them in scientifically accurate, pedagogically sound, and technically feasible ways. 3) Teens know pop culture and they know media, so high-quality media pieces created by teens have great potential to provide visitors with accessible routes into black hole content.

EPO and a Changing World
ASP Conference Series, Vol. 389, © *2008*
C. Garmany, M. Gibbs, and J. W. Moody

Don't Reinvent the Wheel!

Suzy Gurton and Michael Bennett

Astronomical Society of the Pacific, 390 Ashton Ave., San Francisco, CA

Abstract. The ASP develops training and resources for amateur astronomers, informal science educators, and K-14 formal educators. All continue to thrive as we work to provide ongoing and updated resources and recognition for their efforts to serve their audiences in exemplary ways. If you'd like to reach these audiences, don't reinvent the wheel, partner with us to leverage your efforts.

1. Network of Amateur Astronomers

Programs
The NASA Night Sky Network (NSN): This is a coalition of amateur astronomy clubs whose members actively engage their communities in exploring the skies through outreach events. The ASP, under contract to NASA, develops themed outreach toolkits, training DVD's for the outreach materials and provides ongoing support through telecoms, web casts with NASA scientists, and monthly newsletters.

Sharing the Universe: This is an NSF funded study of amateur astronomy clubs to develop additional support mechanisms that will help establish a culture of outreach within NSN clubs and others.

Recognition
The ASP awards yearly the **Amateur Achievement Award** for significant observational or technical achievement by an amateur astronomer, and the **Las Cumbres Amateur Outreach Award** for outstanding outreach by an amateur.

2. Network of Informal Science Educators

Programs
Astronomy from the Ground Up: This NSF-funded program is creating a growing community of informal educators in small science and nature centers who are bringing more astronomy to their audiences. The community is supported by materials and training developed by the ASP and others and ongoing learning communication through a web portal.

Recognition
The ASP presents yearly the **Klumpke-Roberts Award** for outstanding contributions to the public understanding and appreciation of astronomy.

3. Networks of Formal Educators (K-14)

Programs
Project ASTRO/Family ASTRO: Project ASTRO is an inquiry-based national science education program that pairs volunteer professional and amateur astronomers with educators, their students and families. Project ASTRO partnerships are in both classroom and after school settings. Since 1993, the program has brought the excitement of astronomical discovery to nearly 200,000 children. The spin-off from this program, Family ASTRO, has brought the same activities to thousands of families. There are 13 active sites around the country participating either in Family or Project ASTRO or in some cases both. Those coordinators meet annually to exchange innovations and resources at the Project ASTRO National Network Site Leaders' Meeting.

Cosmos in the Classroom: Approximately every three years, the ASP organizes a hands-on symposium on teaching astronomy to undergraduate, non-science majors. The proceedings of the 2000, 2004 and 2007 symposia are available through the ASP AstroShop.

SOFIA Education and Outreach: In partnership with the SETI Institute, the ASP manages the educational and public outreach program for NASA's Stratospheric Observatory for Infrared Astronomy. This program has a goal of flying high school teachers with researchers on the observatory.

Recognition
The ASP awards yearly the **Richard H. Emmons Award** for excellence in college astronomy teaching; the **Thomas J. Brennan Award** for exceptional achievement related to teaching astronomy at the high school level; and the **Pricilla and Bart Bok Award** for an astronomy award at the Intel Science and Engineering Fair.

4. Resources

Universe in the Classroom: The ASP's newsletter for teachers of grades 3-12 is now hosted on the web and looking for international translators. Each issue features astronomy articles, classroom-ready activities, and resources. You may now register to be notified by e-mail when a new issue is posted.

Investigating Astronomy: Developed by TERC in partnership with NOAO and the ASP, this modular high school curriculum integrates real life, data driven applications into the astronomical and physical science content of the activities.

AstroShop: Education Products Online: The web-based AstroShop features ASP publications and products available to help K-14 teachers and astronomers who work with them, college educators, families, and amateur astronomers doing outreach.

Acknowledgments.   Founded in 1889 in San Francisco, the ASP is long devoted to improving people's understanding and enjoyment of astronomy and space. The ASP's education programs are funded by NASA, the National Science Foundation, corporations, private foundations, and its own members.

EPO and a Changing World
ASP Conference Series, Vol. 389, © *2008*
C. Garmany, M. Gibbs, and J. W. Moody

Developing the "Multiwavelength Astronomy: Galaxies in a Different Light" Activity

Mary Kay Hemenway, Shardha Jogee, Kyle Fricke, and Randi Worhatch

University of Texas, Dept. of Astronomy, 1 University Station C1400, Austin, TX 78712, USA

Laurie Ruberg

Wheeling Jesuit University, Center for Educational Technologies, 316 Washington Avenue, Wheeling, WV 26003, USA

Abstract. "Multiwavelength Astronomy" is designed to lead high school students to understand astronomers' use of different wavelengths in studying the nature of galaxies. When developing the activity we followed the NASA-funded Virtual Design Center guidelines. With the project rationale and standards-alignment analysis completed, we surveyed high school students from several classes about their knowledge and interest in topics related to galaxy research. Their responses, and later pilot tests with secondary teachers and students, informed the development team's efforts. Topics included are the electromagnetic spectrum, false-color imaging, image resolution, Wien's law, and galaxy morphology. These were chosen to serve as prerequisites for future computer-intensive activities, which would involve students with data sets from the HST GEMS survey, one of the widest-area galaxy surveys conducted in two filters to date. Our description of the development process illustrates how we integrated topics of student interest into the activity while adhering to the design goal of incrementally augmenting student conceptual learning through a series of successive activities. Products for this activity include student and teacher guides, series of galaxy images in different wavelengths, a PowerPoint presentation, and sample materials for student assessment and evaluation of the activities.

1. Goals and Procedures

The goal of this project was to produce a series of activities on research of galaxy evolution for students at several levels and varying abilities. Five consecutive activities are planned, including an initial activity to sort galaxies using visual images (for example, CERES[1]) followed by this activity on multi-wavelength inspection of galaxies. The third activity covers stellar color and evolution - key concepts for understanding galactic evolution. The two final activities will use the *Galaxies and Cosmos Explorer Tool* (GCET[2]), which uses an Internet interface, to examine very distant galaxies and how they differ with redshift. After receiving EPO awards (PI: Jogee) to develop these activities, the education

---

[1] http://btc.montana.edu/CERES/html/Galaxy/gal1.html, accessed 20Sept2006

[2] http://www.as.utexas.edu/gcet/, accessed 1Aug2007

team at Texas began to work with the NASA Virtual Design Center (VDC[3]) created by the Classroom of the Future program of the Center for Educational Technologies at Wheeling Jesuit University. The VDC process is to identify the areas of greatest need and how these align with project goals, identify education standards, focus on the investigative question and activity structure that engages students, and develop a product using best practices in science education, including assessment and uses of learning technologies. As part of this process, we surveyed high school classes in September 2006 with questions designed to probe their knowledge and interest in areas related to galaxy research. The results showed high student interest in multi-wavelength observations, which drove the team to create this activity to engage and prepare students for activities using GCET.

2.   The Activity and Evaluation

The multi-wavelength activity includes a teacher guide, a set of student worksheets, a PowerPoint presentation, an exercise in false colors/resolution, and a set of galaxy images in visible, ultraviolet, and radio wavelengths (from the Cool Cosmos web-site[4]). Important concepts covered in this unit address radiation, resolution, and abilities of telescopes/instruments to receive different wavelengths.

At various stages of development, the activity was pilot-tested with groups of teachers or classes of students (grades 9-12). Interactions with the VDC took place through conference calls, a videoconference, and at least two face-to-face meetings. The VDC led the team to consider enhancing the students' problem solving skills while piquing their curiosity. This prompted improvements in the activity such as requiring students to justify their solutions (i.e., writing explanations they could defend in their teams), and providing information about the telescopes used to gather the images. VDC advice helped the development team focus on increased student learning and objectives, which changed the development process by initiating a procedure to test and refine the investigation question before writing the activity.

In the evaluation, student responses were reviewed to see if the activity prompted scientific thinking and retention of important concepts. In general, the higher grade-level students were applying critical thinking and problem solving skills, whereas the grade 9 students were not. However, a vast majority of the students recognized the important concepts. Evaluation and development for further activities is continuing.

The VDC interactions and pilot testing resulted in an educationally well-structured activity that met most of the VDC goals and the team's educational goals.

The authors wish to thank Manetta Calinger and Sandra Preston for their help with this project. Support from NASA grants NAG5-13063 and NNG-06GB99G and NSF grant AST-0607748 is gratefully acknowledged.

---

[3]http://vdc.cet.edu, accessed 25Sept2006

[4]http://coolcosmos.ipac.caltech.edu, accessed 30Sept2006

EPO and a Changing World
ASP Conference Series, Vol. 389, © *2008*
C. Garmany, M. Gibbs, and J. W. Moody

Smart Images in a Web 2.0 World: The Virtual Astronomy Multimedia Project (VAMP)

Robert L. Hurt

Spitzer Science Center, MS 220-6, Pasadena, CA 91125

Lars Lindberg Christensen

ESA, Karl-Schwarzschild-Strasse 2, D-85748 Garching bei München, Germany

Adrienne Gauthier

Steward Observatory, 933 N. Cherry Ave., Tucson, AZ 85721

Ryan Wyatt

California Academy of Sciences, 875 Howard St., San Francisco, CA 94103

Abstract. High quality astronomical images, accompanied by rich caption and background information, abound on the web and yet are notoriously difficult to locate efficiently using common search engines. "Flat" searches can return dozens of hits for a single popular image but miss equally important related images from other observatories. The Virtual Astronomy Multimedia Project (VAMP) is developing the architecture for an online index of astronomical imagery and video that will simplify access and provide a service around which innovative applications can be developed (e.g. digital planetariums) Current progress includes design prototyping around existing Astronomy Visualization Metadata (AVM) standards. Growing VAMP partnerships include a cross-section of observatories, data centers, and planetariums.

1. Problems with Web Images: Search and Context

While we rely on the web as a source for multimedia imagery in astronomy, there are two key problems that arise: finding what you want, and identifying what you have.

While everyone uses Google and similar search engines to locate multimedia resources, the "flat search" technology is very limited, even with search engines that allow for image-specific searching. For instance, searching for the "M16" nebula will likely turn up more hits on rifles than astronomical objects. Changing the search to "Eagle Nebula" does produce more astronomy images, but the results are mixed.

Typically one must sort through pages of thumbnails before finding something suitable. Problems include: numerous unrelated results; sensitivity to exact search terms; repetitions of same image duplicated on many sites, also making it hard to find the source; highest quality/resolution usually missing; relevant results may be buried on later pages.

Even once a desired image is on hand it can be difficult or impossible to identify the content of the image. This is especially true if one does not know the originating website of an image file! What object is pictured? What telescope made the observation? How should the colors be interpreted? Where on the sky does it fall?

2.   Metadata is the Solution; VAMP Provides the Standard

Metadata is a set of data that describes and characterizes another set of data, for instance and image. Such a set of descriptors forms the basis for any structured method for cataloging content in a database.

The Virtual Astronomy Multimedia Project (VAMP) has at its core the Astronomical Visualization Metadata (AVM) standard. This comprises a set of tags to fully describe astronomical imagery, particularly the wealth of high-end image products intended for the non-technical user. The scope includes telescopic observations, photography (e.g. of telescopes), illustrations/diagrams, and data visualizations. Eventually it will include tags for video and multimedia.

The AVM uses the XMP standard from Adobe Systems, a variation of XML. This is the same technique your digital camera uses to record time, date, and expo-sure information in your photographs. AVM builds on the IPTC metadata standards that are widely used in image software and in the publishing industry. The more general tags under Content and Creator will be available in many existing image management programs (e.g. iPhoto). The astronomy-specific tags are defined as XMP extensions which may be accessed using custom panels in Adobe Photoshop and Bridge. Custom software can easily access the embedded metadata as well.

3.   VAMP Server for Smart Searches

The other aspect of VAMP is to provide a database search system to allow for intelligent searching of multimedia images utilizing the full contextual information captured within the metadata. A more powerful function for the VAMP server is to sup-ply image references and contextual information to web and desktop applications searching for astronomy visual resources. A prototype system is in development at the Infrared Science Archive (IRSA) at Caltech.

The AVM/VAMP Server model will allow dramatic new ways to utilize imagery in innovative applications. For instance, images tagged with sky coordinates could be input directly into desktop or planetarium sky dome software and placed accurately in context. Custom web or museum kiosk applications could employ dynamically-updating content based on queries to the VAMP server, drawing on new images as quickly as they are released to the web.

4.   Using VAMP Now!

The architecture for AVM is in place and tools now exist for tagging image libraries. Anyone interested in increasing the flexibility of their image archives is encouraged to start tagging their images now and contact the VAMP team for ongoing collaborative efforts. For more information about VAMP and to download the Astronomy Visualization Metadata standard visit our website at: http://www.virtualastronomy.org

EPO and a Changing World
ASP Conference Series, Vol. 389, © *2008*
C. Garmany, M. Gibbs, and J. W. Moody

A Farewell to S2N2

Julie Lutz

Department of Astronomy, University of Washington, Box 351580, Seattle, WA 98195-1580

Abstract. Space Science Network Northwest (S2N2) was funded by NASA to be a Science Mission Directorate (SMD) Support Network Education Broker/Facilitator from January 2001 through June 2007. The intent of this poster is to describe some of the characteristics of S2N2, to discuss some of the advantages and disadvantages associated with the organizational structure, to enumerate some of the accomplishments of S2N2 and some of the lessons we learned during the organization's life-time.

1. S2N2 Organizational Structure

Space Science Network Northwest (S2N2) was one of seven NASA Science Mission Directorate (SMD) Education Broker/Facilitators that were funded from January 2001 through June 2007. S2N2 was headquartered in the Washington NASA Space Grant office at the University of Washington in Seattle. S2N2 contracted for services in each of the seven states in its territory (AK, HI, ID, MT, OR, WA, WY) via the NASA Space Grant consortia in each of those states. Thus, S2N2 had a "distributed" organizational model that was unique to the SMD broker/facilitator network. The purpose of this poster is to reflect upon the advantages and disadvantages of this distributed structure in carrying out S2N2's mission of brokering and facilitating relationships between NASA space scientists and missions and other constituencies (formal and informal educators, students, general public).

2. Advantages and Disadvantages of the S2N2 Distributed Structure

The "state representatives" model allows for adaptation of the SMD education materials and programs to specific state needs and circumstances. For example, the S2N2 Alaska representative was able to take space science materials to remote communities for schools and public events in areas that were served only by small airplanes. The Wyoming S2N2 representative devised a small exhibit on meteorites that could be mailed between small libraries in the state.

Because the S2N2 state representatives were local, they had easier access to (and knowledge of where to find) scientists, educators and institutions in their state. Thus, the possibilities for authentic networking possibilities were enhanced. S2N2 was able to work with local and state Boys and Girls Clubs, 4-H, amateur astronomy clubs, state science teachers associations, after-school programs and many other organizations that might not have been reached by a more centralized organizational model.

A disadvantage of the distributed organization was that each representative was just on a small part-time appointment for S2N2, and thus, we had to plan carefully with regard to group communications, reporting to NASA and other organizational matters. Communications were a challenge. It was hard to find times when all the representatives could attend phone calls and group meetings.

3.   Accomplishments of S2N2

S2N2 brought greatly increased awareness of and participation in NASA SMD education programs on the part of scientists, educators and the general public in our region. The S2N2 region does not have and NASA centers and very few of the NASA mission principal investigators happen to live in our states. We provided opportunities for other parts of the SMD Support Network (forums and missions) to do things in our region. We are particularly proud of the high-quality professional development workshops that we were able to offer for K-12 educators and of the programs we facilitated with out-of-school time groups such as 4-H, Boys and Girls Clubs, Girl Scouts, School's Out Washington and others.

4.   Lessons Learned

One of the major things we learned during the five-plus years of S2N2 operations, was that NASA benefits from a state-based presence. This is because people in our largely rural region perceive NASA as a remote and inaccessible program. However, if there is a program locally (a robotics program, astronomy camp, teacher professional development workshop, etc.), the participants see themselves connected to NASA and are likely to continue and enhance the connection. Another lesson we learned was that we had to be very proactive in reaching out to various constituencies. The attitude of "I'll help if you come to me and ask" didn't produce results. We had to contact people and organizations multiple times and sometimes had to wait until the time was right for the group or individual to be interested in NASA space science.

Acknowledgments. Text of acknowledgements runs on after this command. Everybody in S2N2 is most grateful to NASA SMD for funding us under grant.NCC5-605. We also thank all the space scientists, educators and others who participated in our programs.

EPO and a Changing World
ASP Conference Series, Vol. 389, © *2008*
C. Garmany, M. Gibbs, and J. W. Moody

The Global Telescope Network

Kevin McLin,[1] Gordon Spear,[2] and Lynn Cominsky[3]

Sonoma State University, Dept. of Physics and Astronomy, 1801 E. Cotati Avenue, Rohnert Park, CA 94928

Abstract. The Global Telescope Network is an informal association of scientists, students, individuals and observatories interested in supporting the NASA Gamma-ray Large Area Space Telescope (GLAST), Swift and XMM-Newton missions by obtaining and reducing ground based observations for objects related to the primary science goals for these missions.

1. Introduction

The GTN was initiated in 2003 in an effort both to support the scientific programs of high energy Earth-orbiting observatories and to provide opportunities for amateur astronomers, K-12 students and teachers as well as under-graduates to contribute to projects of astrophysical importance. Since its inception, more than twenty observatories around the world have joined the network, making their telescopes available for observations. An additional number of people have volunteered to make observations on network telescopes or to reduce observations.

Typical of GTN member telescopes is the one we have built at Sonoma State. This telescope, the GLAST Optical Robotic Telescope (GORT) is located on the Pepperwood Nature Preserve, approximately ten miles northeast of Santa Rosa, and not far from the town of Calistoga. GORT is a Celestron 14-inch reflector mounted on a Paramount ME and housed in a Technical Innovations dome. It has been used by SSU students and by high school and Junior High School students to make various observations. Because GORT can be operated via the Internet, our observers can be located anywhere in the world with high speed web access.

Since early 2006 we have partnered with the PROMPT collaboration run from the University of North Carolina. They maintain a system called SkyNet by which telescopes can be shared over the Internet. SkyNet enables the automatic scheduling, performing, archiving and retrieval of astronomical observations. It is mainly through the SkyNet system that teachers and K-12 stu-dents have carried out observations. In addition, SkyNet enables non-GTN members to schedule observations on telescopes connected to SkyNet, and for GTN mem-

---

[1]mclin@universe.sonoma.edu

[2]gordon.spear.sonoma.edu

[3]lynnc@universe.sonoma.edu

bers to make observations on any SkyNet telescopes, assuming that they are themselves on SkyNet.

With the launch of GLAST scheduled for early 2008, the network has already begun operations. It has been part of multiwavelength campaigns in conjunction with Swift and XXM-Newton and with radio telescopes on the ground.

2. Observing Projects

The primary observing projects for the GTN involve support observations for GLAST, Swift and XMM-Newton. Such observations include monitoring a set of Active Galactic Nuclei (AGN) and polars (strongly magnetized white dwarf stars). These long-term monitoring activities are critical if we are to understand the underlying processes in active galaxies. Additionally, GTN instruments undertake coordinated observations of interesting objects from time to time. These include intensive monitoring of AGN or other x-ray and gamma ray sources during outburst, as well as transients such as supernovae and gamma ray bursts (GRB).

3. GTN Membership

Membership in the GTN is open to any interested parties. It is not necessary for members to have their own observing facilities. Individuals or groups who would like to contribute to the project by reducing images are encouraged to do so. Such individuals are also invited to make their own observations on network telescopes where this is practicable.

For more information visit http://gtn.sonoma.edu

EPO and a Changing World
ASP Conference Series, Vol. 389, © 2008
C. Garmany, M. Gibbs, and J. W. Moody

CI-Team: Introducing Quasar Research to High School Science Teachers using the Cyberinfrastructure

Karen E. Carney, Lucy F. Fortson, and Michelle M. Nichols

The Adler Planetarium, 1300 S. Lake Shore Dr., Chicago, IL 60605, USA

Abstract. This is an exciting time for astronomy research. Never before has so much astronomy data been so easily available to the general public. But a difficulty has been making it accessible to and usable by multiple audiences. Our team, led by the Adler Planetarium, has designed a teacher professional development and student research program to allow participants to actively participate in quasar research using tools developed for the cyberinfrastructure (SCI-0537460). This allows students to learn about science through meaningful science research.

1. Project Goal

This multi-partner endeavor was built on a prior project funded through NSF: the Strategic Technology Astronomy Research Team (START) Collaboratory (STI 0334168). The START Collaboratory program sought to create online tools to allow users to gather and manipulate data and information from external astronomy database websites, while housing student work in an electronic collaborative environment. The goal of our current demonstration project is to bring 21st century science research techniques into high school classrooms using large internet-accessible astronomy databases, remote-request telescopes, web visualization, and other online tools. The primary research activity supported is the visible light variability of active galaxies, or especially quasars.

2. Project Design

During the first phase of the research scenario, high school teachers and students learn background information about quasars. While stepping through a series of specific activities, participants become skilled at operating the online tools in the activities, select a quasar to study from the Sloan Digital Sky Survey (SDSS) online data-base, develop a research plan, request images of the selected quasar from a remotely-accessible telescope, construct a quasar light curve using multiple images of the quasar, and mathematically determine the probability of light output variability. Along the way, astronomer- and teacher-mentors provide assistance "at-a-distance" through email and web tools.

The partners involved in the development, implementation, and evaluation of this program include several institutions that specialize in formal and informal education and electronic environment design. The Adler Planetarium leads the project, and is responsible for teacher training and support, research scenario design, participant mentoring, and project evaluation. The Collaboratory Project staff at Northwestern University work with other partners to incorporate external tools and resources into the Collaboratory environment. A partnership with the Sloan Digital Sky Survey allows for development of tools for accessing the SDSS astronomical database through the Collaboratory. The Hands-On Universe Project at the University of California-Berkeley provides remote access to the Perth Observatory telescope through the Collaboratory. Western Kentucky University assists with project design, participant mentorship, and tools development to access the Bell Observatory telescope through the Collaboratory.

3. Project Results to Date

Evaluation during the demonstration project was intended to assess implementability of the design in the high school classroom. To determine this, project designers had to ascertain whether and how teachers would implement the active galaxy/quasar research scenario, if there were specific roadblocks to implementation, and how to improve the resources for potential new teachers. The key categories of anticipated difficulty were use and navigation of the Collaboratory, using specific data collection tools, software and hardware robustness and availability in the classroom, implementation time, student motivation, and conceptual understand- ing/science content.

Preliminary indications are that for the most part, the predictions of the first twelve teachers were borne out by technological difficulties while implementing. The one exception was that teachers had less difficulty teaching the content than they anticipated. Because so many teachers indicated that time would be a challenge, the completeness of the implementation was also tracked. Several groups of students were able to successfully complete all of the project tasks, and these are currently housed in the Collaboratory.

Year one evaluation data was used in a formative way. In the second year of the grant, these data were used to inform a fuller redesign of the VQRS. A new group of thirteen teachers was trained on the VQRS in the summer of 2007. Survey results saw increased confidence and decreased perception of difficulties or roadblocks in this group of teachers. Unresolved issues for the teachers include the time necessary to complete the scenario and some initial discomfort with using the Collaboratory.

4. Still to Come

Evaluation is ongoing with the current teacher and student participants through the 2007-8 school year. So far, we feel that the analysis of project results to date stands us in good stead to continue with development of further implementation projects, as well as move into the next phase of work: adaptation. Having identified and studied issues related to implementation and the use of the VQRS and the implementation itself for two sets of high school teachers, the team is now in position to work with new groups of implementers in new contexts.

Acknowledgments.   This paper is written on behalf of the members of the Adler Planetarium Cyberinfrastructure Team, including David Barnaby (Western Kentucky University), Gary Greenberg (The Collaboratory Project, Northwestern University), Carl Pennypacker (Hands-On Universe, University of California at Berkeley), and Jordan Raddick (Sloan Digital Sky Survey).

EPO and a Changing World
ASP Conference Series, Vol. 389, © *2008*
C. Garmany, M. Gibbs, and J. W. Moody

Ten Ways to Engage High School Students With Innovative Technology

Brenden Noon

Argo Community High School , 7329 W. 63rd Street, Summit, IL 60501

Abstract. I present ten ways, learned from experience in Chicago, to use innovative technology to inspire students and teachers alike.

1. General Introduction

As a high school science teacher I have been very fortunate to be able to develop educational outreach material for both Chicago's Field Museum and the Fermi National Accelerator Laboratory. I believe the internet can be used not only to inspire students and educators alike, but, properly developed, can also save millions of desperately needed dollars to help improve the national standard of science education in America. Here are ten ways I use innovative technology to inspire students and teachers alike:

1. The E-learning Environment: Advances in information technology and new developments in learning science provide opportunities to create well-designed, learner-centered, engaging, interactive, affordable, efficient, easily accessible, flexible, meaningful, distributed, and facilitated e-learning environments. A successful e-learning environment can extend the classroom experience beyond the limited time period available at most schools.

2. Animated Presentations: PowerPoint presentations have been instrumental in focusing key concepts with visualizations, but when placed on the internet their blunt points can become meaningless. Animated tutorials are an excellent method of captivating the student's interest while conveying the under-lying principles established in traditional textbooks.

3. Streaming Video Podcasts: The most powerful and easiest method of developing online content is the streaming video presentation. With relatively cheap digital technology a video presentation can be recorded and quickly uploaded to a variety of free host sites like Google, Yahoo, and the infamous YouTube. In the high school setting, streaming video presentations not only gives students 24 hour access to relevant content, but also allow parents to get more involved in the educational process.

4. Wikis: A Wiki is essentially a combination of a Web site and a Word document. At its simplest it can be read like any other web site, with no access privileges necessary. Its power is in allowing groups to work collaboratively on the content of the site using only a standard web browser.

5. Online Assessment Modules: The definition of interactivity has changed over the years, but the goal has always been to create interactivity in

the mind beyond just clicks with a mouse. Interactive quizzes are an ideal method for improving reading comprehension skills since students can proceed at their own pace and receive instant feedback after each problem. Students who recognize that they are doing poorly are often motivated to improve their score.

6. Interactive Science Simulations: The inquiry-based approach to laboratory investigations is arduous when students have no clue what they should expect. When using simple simulations, students can learn by correlating correct behaviors with positive outcomes. Pre-inquiry based investigations familiarize students with physical phenomenon so they know how to recognize success in a lab. Simulations are an ideal environment in which students can examine one variable at time and learn its role in a system.

7. Remote Access Assessment: Technology offers a variety of engaging environments to both individuals and groups. The Classroom Performance System (clickers) allows teachers to collect self-graded responses from an entire class instantly. The ability to review and interpret student understanding of key concepts in an effective manner while keeping them engaged is invaluable. Combining clicker technology with "America's Favorite Game Show", Jeopardy creates a competitive environment that is a great way to review material for an upcoming examination.

8. Video Conferencing: Having guest speakers visit a school can be burdensome and unpredictable. Live web conferencing is an opportunity for scientists all over the world to give guest presentations without leaving their office. I hope to continue developing collaborations with scientific institutions so that my students will gain better insight into actual research.

9. Sim-Teach Second Life: Computers provides a unique and flexible environment for educators interested in distance learning, cooperative work, simulation, new media studies, and corporate training. Second Life provides an opportunity to use simulation in a safe environment to enhance experiential learning, allowing individuals to practice skills, try new ideas, and learn from their mistakes. The ability to prepare for similar real-world experiences by using Second Life as a simulation has unlimited potential! Students and educators can work together in Second Life from anywhere in the world as part of a globally networked virtual classroom environment.

10. Mobile Technology: Computers are often a difficult commodity for public school teachers to gain access to. Recent advances in cell phone and gaming markets have created a new generation of compact and affordable internet accessibility. The Sony Play Station Portable contains full wireless internet access with hi resolution video capability for a price of approximately $169.

Early in my career I was introduced to an Integrated Science program developed by the University of Alabama and adopted by public schools schools state wide. It incorporated video presentations with hands on inquiry allowing students to participate in a diverse range of activities. It is my goal to create my own online version of this program with additional interactive laboratory simulations and self-grading computer-based learning modules.

EPO and a Changing World
ASP Conference Series, Vol. 389, © *2008*
C. Garmany, M. Gibbs, and J. W. Moody

Designing an Open House for a Rural Community

Sandra Preston, F. Cianciolo, D. Wallace, R. Johnson, and N. Davis

The University of Texas at Austin, One University Station 2100, Austin TX 78712

Abstract. What do people who work at an observatory do? How do we communicate what we do to a rural community? McDonald Observatory is located in a rural part of West Texas, in one of the least populated areas of the state. Our Open House model offers a wide range of activities for people to learn about what we do, how we do it, and learn a little astronomy too.

1. Introduction

The Open House model we will provide offers free admission to guests from 10 a.m. to 11:30 p.m. on the day of the event. It invites people from a 100-mile radius and beyond. Open House daytime events include showing off a bright orange fire truck, serving hot dogs for lunch, participating in a family educational activity, staff and astronomers demonstrating the telescopes, astronomers talking about their research, viewing the moon and Venus, and taking a 4-wheel vehicle tour into a unique ecosystem of the Davis Mountains. Evening events start out with live music at the Star-Date café and move on to a Twilight program, Constellation Tour, and viewing through telescopes at the Visitors Center. Media are also invited to attend.

Our model includes planning tools for inviting and informing the media, advertising the event to the community, involving and communicating with staff working on the event, inviting staff and their families, as well as invitations to other constituents.

We will report on the results of the Open House and make recommendations from lessons learned.

2. Advertising Tools Used

The advertising tools used were press advisory, press release, newspaper ads, radio ads, and Web ads. Special invitations were issued to VIPs.

Lessons learned. There was a bond election on the same day as the event and most members of the press were covering that event. It was also Mother's Day weekend and the Texas Star Party was starting on the following day. We learned to take the time to carefully research what is going on in the area before choosing a date.

3. Program Admission

Program admission was free and the Open House program was completely different from the regular public program. While we were trying to let our neighbors see the members of their community at work, most of these staff members are not accustomed to doing public programs.

Lessons learned: We need a system in place to track how many people attend, how many were from the local area, and how many were regular. We might want to train the staff and astronomers who are unaccustomed to doing public programs or use our regular public program people.

4. Communication

There were two key audiences: 1.) Staff working the event and 2.) Guests attending the event. We used two communication tools, one for each audience.

5. Budget

The Director, who requested the event, paid for it from his discretionary funds. The total cost of the event was about $10,000.

6. Evaluation

We created two evaluation tools: one for the staff working the event and the other for the visitors attending. We received 19 evaluations from the staff and 19 from the visitors.

7. Results

Guest results: 90 percent of the guests completing the survey agreed that their understanding of what research is done and what staff and astronomers do at McDonald Observatory was deepened by attending the Open House. The same percentage also indicated their interest in science was stimulated and their motivation to learn more about astronomy was increased.

When asked for recommendations on how to improve, one guest said to advertise more and another suggested tours of the 107-inch and 82-inch telescopes.

Staff results: Most staff agreed that the Open House was an effective way for making our West Texas neighbors aware of what we do. Most staff felt that their role in the Open House was clearly explained to them and that the overall communication about the event was adequate. Most staff also agreed that the timing of the event was adequate.

When asked to recommend how the event could be improved, staff recommendations included choosing a better day, starting later in the day, offering more activities for children, having astronomers practice their talks, and providing some special recognition for the staff working the event.

8. Summary

We believe that the Open House model works for making the community of aware of what we do. We want to be very clear about our target audience and research the best dates for future events. The jury is still out on how often we want to do an event like this. For more information, contact Sandra Preston, Assistant Director, Education and Outreach, sandi@stardate.org, 512 475 6765.

EPO and a Changing World
ASP Conference Series, Vol. 389, © *2008*
C. Garmany, M. Gibbs, and J. W. Moody

Las Cumbres Observatory Global Telescope Network: Keeping Education in the Dark

Rachel J. Ross, Jessica A. Barton, and Wayne E. Rosing

Las Cumbres Observatory Global Telescope Network, 6740 Cortona Dr Suite 102, Goleta, CA 93117

Abstract. The Las Cumbres Observatory Global Telescope Network is a privately- funded, non-profit organization that is creating a global network of telescopes ranging in size from 0.4 meter to 2 meters for educational and scientific uses. All will be equipped with high quality CCD imagers with the larger ones with spectrographs. An online interface will be used for observing both in real time and in a queue. Any registered school or group will have the capability to remotely observe using a telescope that is currently in the dark from the comfort of their classroom or science center, half a world away. Accompanying the online telescope-control interface will be a library of resources and activities that will be available in the formal classroom setting, informal groups and clubs, and for public outreach in the community for all age groups and levels of science. Using the LCOGT network as a tool to enjoy real astronomical research will not only create a new awareness and excitement towards science and technology, it will also make visible connections between science and humanities.

1. Introduction

Las Cumbres Observatory Global Telescope Network (LCOGTN) will provide tools and resources to inspire educators and learners to participate in real scientific research. This, in turn, will motivate learners to pursue and interest in science, technology, engineering, and math (STEM).

The tools that will be offered will be access to the global network of telescopes. These telescopes will be completely controllable through the internet through both a real-time and queued-based observing modes. All the data will be stored in a freely accessible data archive. Online data processing tools will be available to do all processing on the LCOGTN servers to avoid issues with both installing and running soft-ware and bandwidth on local computers.

The website will be very interactive and will allow educators and learners to find everything they will need to learn background science to how to use a robotic telescope and observing to participating in several research projects. LCOGTN will share resources with other organizations to create a rich library of information and activities.

LCOGTN will work cooperatively with groups already doing exciting things in education and outreach. These partnerships will allow the sharing of a cast amount of experience, knowledge, resources, and tools.

2.   The Telescope Network

Two 2.0m telescopes (Faulkes Telescope North on Maui and Faulkes Telescope South at Siding Spring Observatory). These two telescopes will eventually be a part of the science network, but currently being used by primarily United Kingdom (UK) schools as a part of the Faulkes Telescope Project (FTP). The education network will consist of approximately twenty eight 0.4m telescopes that will be clustered in four in seven sites around the globe for complete sky coverage in both the Northern and Southern hemispheres. This network is currently being designed and prototyped with the first group to be deployed mid-2008 in the Santa Ynez Valley, CA.

3.   The Education Network

The education of LCOGTN currently is based in Santa Barbara, CA with another team in Cardiff, Wales. Working with affiliates at the University of Hawaii, the Australian National University, as well as several other US and international organizations, the previously known FTP, now LCOGTN, is spreading from the UK to the US, Australia, and several countries in Europe. Several schools are already participating in science, including searching for open clusters and supernovae follow- up. Other projects will involve NEO search and follow-up, hunting for extrasolar planets, studying variable stars, and more.

     To help in spreading LCOGTN to the US from the UK, a program is being put in place that will pair a US school with a UK (later other international locations) school on a research project. Not only will the schools be using the LCOGTN tools and resources, they will be learning different cultures (and eventually language) and making international friends.

EPO and a Changing World
ASP Conference Series, Vol. 389, © *2008*
C. Garmany, M. Gibbs, and J. W. Moody

Efforts of Space Science EPO Professionals to Meet the Needs of Pre-Service Students and Faculty: Analysis of Results

Laurie Ruberg,[1] Denise Smith,[2] Stephanie Shipp,[3] Christine Shupla,[3] and Jennifer Grier[4]

Abstract.   We report on the activities of the NASA Science Mission Directorate Education Support Network Pre-Service Education Working Group.

To forge relationships with those charged with preparing tomorrow's teachers, NASA's Science Mission Directorate Education Support Network formed the Pre-Service Education Working Group in 2004. Made up of scientists and educators from across the United States, the Working Group seeks to better prepare teachers in core science concepts and pedagogy while bringing the excitement of space science directly into the classroom. It facilitates partnerships and coordinates efforts to:

- Develop a deeper understanding of pre-service programs and needs.

- Identify diverse ways to meet those needs in space science education.

Gleaned from the Working Group's needs assessments, partnerships, survey findings, and corporate lessons learned, this presentation highlights five key guidelines for working with the pre-service education community.

1. Seek partnerships and lessons learned from these and other organizations already involved in pre-service education reform. o The Association of Teacher Educators collects data about educator needs.

    - NASA Langley Research Center's Pre-Service Teacher Program provides a venue for faculty and pre-service student professional development that is especially targeted to colleges and universities serving minority and underserved populations.

    - The National Association of Research in Science Teaching shares similar goals and collaborates on professional development programs.

    - Community colleges, four-year, and graduate postsecondary institutions have been good venues for long-term, regional pre-service science education reform activities. They also facilitate access to space science resources.

[1] Center for Educational Technologies, Wheeling Jesuit University, 316 Washington Ave., Wheeling, WV 26030-6243

[2] Space Telescope Science Institute, 3700 San Martin Dr., Baltimore, MD 21218

[3] Lunar and Planetary Institute, 3600 Bay Area Blvd., Houston, TX 77058

[4] Planetary Science Institute, 620 N. Sixth, Tucson, AZ 85705

- The National Science Teachers Association, American Association for the Advancement of Science, and the National Science Foundation have chartered goals and opportunities to improve the quality of pre-service teacher science education.

2. Begin program planning with assessment of audience needs and identification of strategic partners.

   - Help pre-service educators access NASA's authentic science materials and expertise to expand K-12 academic capacities.
   - Work with pre-service education faculty to improve academic resources (content and performance) that a student brings from secondary school into higher education.
   - Give special consideration in pre-service teacher training initiatives to performance disparities in mathematics and science documented among underserved populations.

3. Assess current involvement of space scientists and the education community in pre-service education.

   - Investigate ways space scientists are already involved in assisting pre-service educators and faculty before launching a new program.
   - Identify where sufficient curriculum resources exist and can be leveraged as well as noting where there are gaps and missing materials.
   - Include a review of how existing resources align with formal education standards and what resources address specific audience needs as part of program planning.

4. Communicate and coordinate professional development needs, recommendations, and opportunities to the NASA community.

   - Keep the NASA science and education communities informed of pre-service education activities and concerns through the Working Group's listserv, telecoms, and quarterly working group presentations.
   - Advocate science, technology, engineering, and math content and process skills training, rather than NASA mission-specific messages.
   - Consider state-based policies to promote teacher professional development that impact teacher preparation programs.

5. Recognize that Teachers and Future Teachers are central to any science education reform effort and must share in shaping reform activities.

   - Help teachers in their efforts to get administrative and public support to incorporate space science initiatives.
   - Encourage academic colleagues in space science and other relevant subject matter areas like child development, learning, and the potential of educational technology tools to support efforts to improve pre-service teacher education.

Further information on the Pre-Service Education Working Group is at: http://www.lpi.usra.edu/education/score/pre_service.shtml.

EPO and a Changing World
ASP Conference Series, Vol. 389, © *2008*
C. Garmany, M. Gibbs, and J. W. Moody

Tormenta Espacial: Engaging Spanish Speakers in the Planetarium and K-12 Classroom

Francisco Salas, Doug Duncan, and Suzanne Traub-Metlay

Fiske Planetarium-408 UCB-Boulder. CO 80309

Abstract. Reaching out to Spanish speakers is increasingly vital to workforce development and public support of space science projects. Building on a successful partnership with NASA's TIMED mission, LASP and Space Science Institute, Fiske Planetarium has translated its original planetarium show - "Space Storm" - into "Tormenta Espacial."

1. Introduction

This show explores the Sun-Earth connection and explains how solar activity affects technology and life on Earth. Solar scientists from NOAA's Space Environment Center and the University of Colorado at Boulder contributed to provide scientific accuracy.

Show content and accompanying educational materials are aligned with state and national science standards. While designed for students in grades 6-8, this show has been positively evaluated by students from grades 4-10 and shown to the general public with favorable responses. Curricular materials extend the planetarium experience into the K-12 classroom so that students inspired and engaged by the show continue to see real-life applications and workplace opportunities.

Fiske Planetarium offers both "Space Storm" and "Tormenta Espacial" to other planetariums at a minimal rate, including technical support for the life of the show. Thanks to a request from a planetarium in Belgium, a version of "Space Storm" is available with no spoken dialogue so that languages other than English or Spanish may be accommodated.

Collaborative projects among planetariums, NASA missions (planned as well as active), research scientists and other parties keep EPO activities healthy and well-funded. Fiske Planetarium staff strive to develop and maintain partnerships through-out the EPO and informal education communities.

Your URL for More Information: http://fiske.colorado.edu.

EPO and a Changing World
ASP Conference Series, Vol. 389, © 2008
C. Garmany, M. Gibbs, and J. W. Moody

Adaptive Optics Educational Outreach and the Giant Segmented Mirror Telescope

Robert T. Sparks, Stephen M. Pompea, and Constance E. Walker

National Optical Astronomy Observatory, 950 N. Cherry Ave., Tucson, AZ 85719, USA

Abstract. One of the limiting factors in telescope performance is atmospheric seeing. Atmospheric seeing limits the resolution of ground based optical telescopes. Even telescopes in good locations on top of mountains cannot achieve diffraction-limited resolution. Until recently, the only way to overcome this limitation was to use space-based telescopes. Adaptive Optics (AO) is a collection of technologies that measure the turbulence of Earth's atmosphere and compensate for the turbulence, resulting in high-resolution images without the expense and complexity of space based telescopes. Our Hands-On Optics program has developed activities that teach students how telescopes form images and make observations about the resolution of a telescope. We are developing materials for high school students to use in the study of adaptive optics. These activities include various ways to illustrate atmospheric distortion by using everyday materials such as bubble wrap and mineral oil. We will also illustrate how to demonstrate the workings of a Shack-Hartman sensor to measure atmospheric distortion through the use of a unique model. We will also show activities illustrating two techniques astronomers use to improve the image: tip-tilt mirrors and deformable mirrors. We are developing an activity where students learn how to use a tip-tilt mirror to keep an image focused at one point on a screen. The culminating activity has students learn to use a deformable mirror to correct a distorted wavefront. These activities are being developed in conjunction with the Education program for the Giant Segmented Mirror Telescope (GSMT).

1. Atmospheric Seeing

The Hands-On Optics program developed a series of six modules focusing on different areas of optics education. Module 3 was designed to specifically deal with refraction, lenses, telescopes and resolution.

Students learn how lenses form an image in refracting telescope. They build a small refractor and measure the resolution of the telescope using a resolution chart. After students learn about resolution, we introduce the concept of atmospheric seeing. Seeing refers to the blurring and twinkling of astronomical objects due to turbulence in Earth's atmosphere.

Our early experiments with illustrating atmospheric turbulence have involved using a laser to simulate a star and bubble wrap to simulate a "turbulent" atmosphere. Without bubble wrap in its path, a laser will make a fine point on a screen. The bubble wrap will cause the point to become smeared out over a larger area, much like out atmosphere does to star light. We are also experimenting with using moving water to illustrate seeing.

2.   A Model Shack-Hartmann Sensor

Measuring the distortion caused by the atmosphere is the first step to improving the image. A Shack-Hartmann sensor is employed in many adaptive optics systems. A Shack-Hartmann sensor is an array of small lenses (called lenslets all with the same focal length. The lenslets focus incoming light on a CCD detector. If the wavefront from the star is not distorted, the images on the sensor will form a perfect array. If the wavefront is distorted, the images will move to slightly different locations, By measuring the locations of these images, we can measure the amount of atmospheric distortion.

We are designing educational activities around a model of a Shack-Hartmann sensor. We mount an array of equal focal length lenses on a heavy cardboard holder and use the model to focus light on a screen. Introducing a clear container of water into the light path will simulate the distortion caused by Earth's atmosphere.

3.   Correcting the Image

After measuring the distortion of a wavefront, a deformable mirror is used to correct the image. Based on the measurements carried out by the Shack-Hartmann sensor, a mirror is bent to remove the effects of the atmosphere. The mirror can be bent into new shapes over 100 times a second to compensate for the constantly changing atmosphere.

We are exploring different ways for students to experiment with Mylar and other deformable mirrors. Multiple laser pointers can be used to simulate light rays passing through different parts of the atmosphere. We are exploring different techniques for students to deform a flexible mirror to correct for the atmospheric distortion. This work is ongoing as we have not arrived at an easy to implement solution at this time.

Acknowledgments.   NOAO is operated by the Association of Universities for Research in Astronomy (AURA), Inc. under cooperative agreement with the NSF. Funding for the Adaptive Optics Activities comes from the Giant Segmented Mirror Telescope (GSMT).

EPO and a Changing World
ASP Conference Series, Vol. 389, © *2008*
C. Garmany, M. Gibbs, and J. W. Moody

Inspiring 1000 Middle School Students at Princeton University's Materials Science and Engineering Expo

Daniel Steinberg and Shannon Swilley

Princeton University, PRISM/PCCM, 317 Bowen Hall, 70 Prospect Ave Princeton, NJ 08540

Abstract.   The Princeton Center for Complex Materials Education outreach program in partnership with other outreach programs in molecular biology, chemistry and physics, created the Science and Engineering Expo at Princeton University (SEE Princeton) in 2004. SEE has given Princeton University engineering and science faculty an opportunity to share their enthusiasm for science with 1,000s of middle school students.

1.   The Princeton Science and Engineering Expo

The Princeton Center for Complex Materials (PCCM) Education outreach program, in partnership with other outreach programs in molecular biology, chemistry and physics, created the Science and Engineering Expo at Princeton University (SEE Princeton) in 2004. Each year we create an opportunity for Princeton University scientists and engineers to re-energize middle school students' excitement for science and engineering. Middle school is a stage when many students lose their interest in science. We hope to inspire these students by introducing them to our scientists and engineers in the most entertaining yet educational manner possible. The key is carefully considered and designed table activities arranged thoughtfully in four venues: Materials Science and Engineering Physics, Molecular Biology and Chemistry.

SEE Princeton has grown so large that we hold the Materials Science and Engineering venue in the Dillon Gymnasium which spans 4 basketball courts (over 10,000 sq ft) turning the gym into a hands-on "science center" for the day. The Expo allows students to interact with real scientists from every point along a scientist's career path including undergraduate students, graduate students, post-docs, research scientists and professors. Graduates of our other K-12 outreach programs also participate. In addition, high school science and engineering students who have participated in a materials science outreach program (PUMA) share their enthusiasm for science and engineering.

On March 22, 2007, over 100 volunteers participated in the 4th (PCCM)-run engineering venue. Partnership was one of the big themes. Partners included Stevens Institute of Technology's Engineering Our Future program, Goodrich Corp. and Sensors Unlimited, National Oceanic & Atmospheric Administration, and the US-Africa Materials Institute. Astronomy had its biggest showing at the Expo yet in 2007. SEE 2007 included demonstrations of 3D Mars Rover images by Amateur Astronomers Association of Princeton and "Edible Astronomy" from Hofstra University and Hubble Space Telescope EPO materials from STScI Office of Public Outreach.

Figure 1.   Each year over 100 Princeton University volunteers participate in the Princeton Center for Complex Materials (PCCM)-run Materials science and engineering venue to re-energize students' excitement for science and engineering.

Figure 2.   Electrical Engineering Professor Mansour Shayegan of PCCM reveals the inner working of solar energy power production.

EPO and a Changing World
ASP Conference Series, Vol. 389, © 2008
C. Garmany, M. Gibbs, and J. W. Moody

An Innovative Field Trip Experience for Ohio Middle School Students and Teachers

Donald M. Terndrup

Department of Astronomy, The Ohio State University, 140 West 18th Ave., Columbus OH 43210

Mary Ann Wojton, Leonard Sparks, and Robin Dungan

COSI Columbus, 333 West Broad Street, Columbus, OH 43215

Abstract. As part of a new collaboration between astronomers and educators at a major science center, we have created a program which combines a field trip experience for middle school students with professional development opportunities for their teachers. The program consists of interactive lectures by astronomers, teacher workshops on space science ideas, and inquiry-based student workshops on fundamental (astro)physical concepts. We conducted a pilot program in 2007 consisting of four schools with different student demographics. Initial results show significant improvement between pre- and post-workshop testing in several areas. Several logistical problems remain to be worked out, especially in the operation of the teacher workshops.

1. Program Design

OSU Astronomy and COSI Columbus are operating a new program which combines a school field trip experience with a professional development session for teachers. Here we summarize the program as implemented in its pilot phase.

The principal objectives of the project are (1) to provide teachers and students with current science content closely linked to Ohio's state standards; (2) to involve teachers in inquiry-based lessons that can be replicated in their classrooms; and (3) to encourage student interest in astronomy as a potential career.

Middle school teachers bring their classes to COSI for a three-hour learning experience. During the first hour, teachers and students meet with an OSU scientist who presents her/his current research in ways intended to be understandable, engaging, interactive, and relevant. Following this, students attend a student workshop in small groups for one hour, and then explore the science museum for one hour, completing experiences that complement the research presentation.

At the same time, teachers take part in a two hour professional development seminar, during which they participate in inquiry-based lessons that parallel the activities of the students and build on the information presented by the OSU scientist. Teachers receive in-depth content and also experience inquiry-based lessons through modeling, followed by a discussion on the basics of inquiry-based science. Teachers leave the session with all the materials needed to bring these lessons to their classrooms in the weeks following their visit to COSI.

Teacher and student sessions are conducted by COSI teaching faculty and OSU faculty, postdocs, and graduate students in Astronomy. The content of the workshops center on astrophysical concepts included in the science education standards of the state of Ohio.

2.   Results of the Pilot Program

We conducted three workshops during the spring of 2007. Four schools were selected to bring students from a variety of backgrounds. The student participants were from a private academy, a large suburban school district, a small religious school, and a large urban school district. A total of 13 teachers and 196 students participated.

Students were given pre- and post-workshop tests of fundamental concepts involved in astronomy and physics. The largest samples were from the private academy in Columbus (school #1), and a large, suburban public school (#2). The number of students in the full sample is too small to draw any general conclusions about students from different backgrounds. The results from school #1 showed a statistically significant improvement in seven of the nine questions, while the results from school #2 were generally unchanged from the pre-workshop survey.

Selection effects undoubtedly play a role in the outcomes. Interviews with the teachers revealed that the students from school #2 were selected in favor of top performers or students with good scientific knowledge. The selection from school #1 was, by comparison, less biased with respect to the general student population.

The most significant challenge was with teacher professional development. The implementation of the concurrent (but separate) student and teacher workshops was ineffective for several reasons. Some teachers wanted to observe their students during the hands-on portion of the workshop. Other teachers felt uncomfortable leaving their students with COSI staff because they did not have many chaperones. Finally, some teachers wanted a longer and deeper exposure to inquiry-based lessons than was available during the few hours of the workshops.

3.   Changes for 2007–8

During the upcoming academic year, we will expand from three workshops to at least fifteen, increasing the number of students served from 196 to potentially 2250. To insure teachers are able to participate in the professional development portion of this plan, we are exploring options to recruit and train college students and other adults to serve as chaperones. Finally, we are revising our professional development portion to meet the needs of the teachers served during the limited amount of time available. We also will provide teachers with more materials and lesson plans.

Acknowledgments.   The work reported here was partially supported by a grant from the Smithsonian Astrophysical Observatory, Chandra EPO program.

EPO and a Changing World
ASP Conference Series, Vol. 389, © 2008
C. Garmany, M. Gibbs, and J. W. Moody

Selene: A Videogame for Learning about the Moon

Charles A. Wood and Debbie Denise Reese

Center for Educational Technologies, NASA-sponsored Classroom of the Future, Wheeling Jesuit University, Wheeling, West Virginia 26003, USA

Abstract. The Selene game-based, metaphor-enhanced (GaME) learning object prepares players with concrete knowledge of basic lunar geology processes. Selene is embedded within an online research environment studying learning and assessment within videogames.

1. Making Hard Science Intuitive

National education agencies are desperate to find effective ways to engage kids in science, technology, engineering, and mathematics (STEM) learning (Commission on 21st Century Education in Science Technology Engineering and Mathematics 2007). One new attempt is based upon the consuming interest youth have in videogames. It is well documented that kids will play videogames for 10s to 100s of hours, building many valuable skills such as planning, interpreting, collaborating and decision-making (Federation of American Scientists 2006). We propose that the players can also learn actual concepts and relations between them when that information is necessary for game success. We do not propose that instructional games should take the place of formal instruction. Rather, we are studying how instructional games can prepare learners for learning STEM concepts, and how to use gameplay performance to track (assess) growth in conceptual knowledge and self-perceptions of skill and challenge (flow). Selene is a research videogame that we have developed to provide learning experiences to players in forming Earth's Moon through accretion and differentiation, and modifying it by volcanism and impact cratering. Through Selene gameplay, the learner constructs an intuitive understanding of the mechanics of these physical processes. By intuitive, we mean that the game helps learners construct requisite knowledge necessary for domain- specific concept learning. This knowledge is pre-conceptual. Apt prior knowledge prepares the student to construct normative, robust, and coherent knowledge of the targeted complex concepts during subsequent formal instruction.

2. Theory-based Design of Game-based, Metaphor-enhanced (GaME) Learning Objects

Applying videogame design theory (Fullerton, Swain, & Hoffman 2004), Selene involves the learner in authentic gameplay in which player actions work toward a game goal. Successful games provoke flow experiences. Flow is an intrinsically rewarding (pleasure) state of intense focus and productivity accompanied by a perception of control (Csikszentmihalyi 1990). Successful instructional STEM games engineer flow to make learners learn and apply STEM content.

GaME design applies cognitive science metaphor theory, developing game systems analogous to targeted conceptual domains. Conceptual domains are composed of concepts, their properties, and the relations that connect them (Gentner 1983; Gentner & Kurtz 2006). Much of the higher-order thinking required for learning and conducting scientific enterprise involves ubiquitous application of analogical reasoning (Hummel & Holyoak 1997). GaME-based design requires complete specification of a targeted learning domain, followed by specification of a game world, game system, gameplay mechanic, and game goal isomorphic (in one-to-one correspondence) with the target domain. In the case of Selene, a content expert (Wood) and GaME-design expert (Reese) specified the relational structure connecting 101 accretion, differentiation, volcanism, and impact cratering concepts and subconcepts. This was followed by col- laboration with a game design team to develop a game concept within a game world isomorphic to the target domain specification. The result is Selene.

GaMEs are computer-mediated learning objects: self-contained modules for use within most curricula, and supporting most pedagogical paradigms. People require apt prior knowledge to construct new knowledge (Bransford, Brown, & Cocking 2000). When learners do not have viable and relevant prior experience, the learning environment must provide experiences for learner construction of viable pre-conceptual knowledge (Merrill 2002). This readies the learner to profit from the formal instruction (Schwartz, Bransford, & Sears 2005). When real-life experience is insufficient, GaMEs provide embodied transactions with targeted STEM concepts.

Acknowledgments.   This research was supported by NASA-sponsored Classroom of the Future grant NNX06AB09G.

References

Bransford, J. D., Brown, A. L., and Cocking, R. R., *How People Learn: Brain, Mind, Experience, and School* (National Academy Press, Washingotn D.C., 2000)

Commission on 21st Century Education in Science Technology Engineering and Mathematics, *A National Action Plan for Addressing the Critical Needs of the U.S. Science, Technology, Engineering, and Mathematics Education System: Draft for Comment* (Arlington, VA: National Science Foundation, Arlington, VA, 2007)

Csikszentmihalyi, M., *Flow: The Psychology of Optimal Experience* (Harper & Row, New York, 1990)

Federation of American Scientists, *Summit on Educational Games: Harnessing the Power of Videogames for Learning* (Author, Washington D.C., 2006)

Fullerton, T., Swain, C., and Hoffman, S., *Game Design Workshop: Designing, Prototyping, and Playtesting Games* (CMP Books, San Francisco, CA, 2004)

Gentner, D., Cognitive Science, **7**, 155 (1983)

Gentner, D. and Kurtz, K. J., Cognitive Science, **30**, 609 (2006)

Hummel, J. E. and Holyoak, K. J., Psychological Review, **104**, 427 (1997)

Merrill, M. D., Educational Technology Research and Development, **50**, 43 (2002)

Schwartz, D. L., Bransford, J. D., and Sears, D. in *Transfer of Learning from a Modern Multidisciplinary Perspective*, edited by J. P. Mestre (Information Age, Greenwich, CT, 2005), p. 1

EPO and a Changing World
ASP Conference Series, Vol. 389, © 2008
C. Garmany, M. Gibbs, and J. W. Moody

The Sky is the Limit!: The Benefits from Partnering with the Project ASTRO National Network

Daniel Zevin,[1] Constance Walker,[2] Robert Wilson,[2] Wil van der Veen,[3] Theresa Roelofsen Moody,[3] Andrew Fraknoi,[1,4] Suzanne Gurton,[1] Vivian White,[1] Janice Harvey,[5] Larry Cooper,[6] Dean Regas,[7] Paul Guttman,[8] and Richard Smith[8]

Abstract. Project ASTRO is a national program that partners professional and amateur astronomers with local educators at regional sites around the country. Developed by the Astronomical Society of the Pacific, Project ASTRO provides training for astronomer-educator partnerships in hands-on, inquiry-based science activities while emphasizing the importance of student preconceptions as a starting point for learning. During an intensive two-day training workshop, a partnership is forged that blends the teacher's knowledge of instructional methods and classroom management with the astronomer's knowledge of and passion for science and astronomy. The regional sites' directors and coordinators are part of a "National Network" whose aims are to foster communication and cooperation among its members and with other science education and research communities. Nationwide, over 500 active astronomer-educator partnerships bring the excitement of astronomy to over 20,000 students annually.

1. Background

Project ASTRO is a national program that partners professional and amateur astronomers with local educators at regional sites around the country. Developed by the Astronomical Society of the Pacific, Project ASTRO provides training for astronomer-educator partnerships in hands-on, inquiry-based science activities while emphasizing the importance of student preconceptions as a starting point for learning. During an intensive two-day training workshop, a partnership is forged that blends the teacher's knowledge of instructional methods and classroom management with the astronomer's knowledge of and passion for sci-

[1]Astronomical Society of the Pacific, 390 Ashton Ave., San Francisco, CA 94112

[2]National Optical Astronomy Observatory, 950 N. Cherry Ave., Tucson, AZ 85719

[3]NJACE Teaching Institute, Raritan Valley Community College, P.O. Box 3300, Somerville, NJ 08876

[4]Foothill College, 12345 El Monte Road, Los Altos Hills, CA 94022

[5]Gemini Observatory, 670 A'ohoku Place, Hilo, HI 96720

[6]NASA Headquarters, Office of Space Science, Washington, DC 20546

[7]Cincinnati Observatory Center, 3489 Observatory Place, Cincinnati, OH 45208

[8]Space Science for Schools, 930 Tahoe Blvd., #802-520, Incline Village, NV 89451

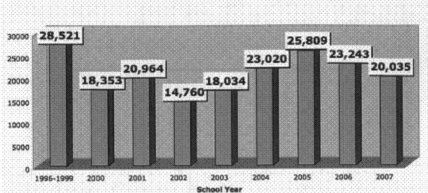

Figure 1.   On average, the Project ASTRO National Network has reached over 20,000 students annually since 2000.

ence and astronomy. The regional sites' directors and coordinators are part of a "National Network" whose aims are to foster communication and cooperation among its members and with other science education and research communities. Nationwide, over 500 active astronomer-educator partnerships bring the excitement of astronomy to over 20,000 students annually.

All Project ASTRO sites follow the same model for partnership training and support and meet annually to consider the year's accomplishments, discuss common strategies, and share new ideas. Many sites also target families/communities through the Family ASTRO sister program. Each site (there are 13 total in the Network) is managed by a Lead Institution supported by a Local Coalition of scientific and educational organizations who help with recruiting of new participants, programming, and fund-raising.

2.   Main Benefits of Partnering with the National Network on EPO

2.1.   Access

As a partner for EPO programs, the Project ASTRO National Network offers access to hundreds of trained educators and astronomer-educator partnerships across the country. This makes the Network extremely suitable for dissemination and/or testing of new science education products, in particular those that benefit from support by scientists and/or (through Family ASTRO) those that target families/communities.

2.2.   Brokers

As a national program that partners scientists with educators, the Network essentially serves as a natural broker between the scientific and education communities, and understands the needs of both.

2.3.　Collaboration/National Dissemination

Continuous information exchange, a consistent training model, and annual teacher workshops makes the Network an attractive EPO partner.

2.4.　Experience

Many of the Network's self-sufficient regional sites have partnered with members of the scientific community in the past as a means of increasing their funding options. Some 20 EPO proposals have in some way leveraged Project/Family ASTRO thus far. For example, the Network (through NASA funding) is currently being tapped to create and disseminate nationally new hands-on classroom activities on solar physics.

3.　How to Begin

Partnering with the Project ASTRO National Network on an EPO program is a fairly simple process. We are ready to work with you throughout the year to adapt your research and EPO ideas to best suite a variety of target audiences. Even if you don't have an EPO program already in mind, Network representatives can consult with you free of charge on a partnership idea that will meet the requirements of your funding agency, or one that will be highly competitive for both national and regional grant opportunities.

　　For more information on the various ways you or your institution can partner with the Project ASTRO National Network, please contact Suzy Gurton with the Astronomical Society of the Pacific at sgurton@astrosociety.org.

Keynote Speaker, George Nelson

Martin Harwit - Catherine Bruce Gold Medal Winner

Part II

Broadening the Audience

EPO and a Changing World
ASP Conference Series, Vol. 389, © *2008*
C. Garmany, M. Gibbs, and J. W. Moody

Partnerships with Planetariums to Broaden the Audience and Communicate Advances in Astronomy

Jeanne Bishop

Westlake Schools Planetarium, Parkside Middle School, 24525 Hilliard Road, Westlake, Ohio 44145-3518

Larry Cuipik

Adler Planetarium and Astronomy Museum, 1300 S. Lake Shore Drive, Chicago, Illinois 60605-2403

Jon Elvert

Pennington Planetarium, Louisiana Arts and Science Museum, 100 South River Road, Baton Rouge, Louisiana 70802

Wayne James

Illinois State Board of Education Consultant, ROE Schoolworks, 200 S. Fredrick Street, Rantoul, Illinois 61866

James Kaler

University of Illinois, 103 Astronomy Bldg., 1002 W. Green St., Urbana, Illinois 61801

Rob Landis

NASA Johnson Space Center, International Liaison Office, 2101 NASA Parkway, Houston, Texas 77058

Abstract. This workshop consisted of panel presentations by six people. Bishop, Cuipik, Elvert, and James all are active in the planetarium community. Kaler and Landis work closely with planetarium professionals to communicate advances in astronomy. Bishop outlined the history of planetarium communication. Members of the panel discussed ideas for communication and recent collaborative projects for communicating astronomy to more people in creative ways. After the panel presentations, participants broke into three groups to discuss possible future collaborations involving planetariums that would expand astronomy learning.

1. Jeanne Bishop: A Brief History of the Planetarium and Its Use for Education

After Walther Bauersfeld initiated the concept of the optical-mechanical planetarium in 1919, the first Zeiss planetarium was installed beneath a 30-foot dome in the Munich Museum in 1923. The number of planetariums grew very slowly until 1959, with the Adler Planetarium in Chicago being one of the first in the U.S. An exponential rise occurred between 1961 and 1970 with the advent of the Space Age, and there has been continued slower growth in the U.S. and the world thereafter.

In the U.S. planetariums had an important effect in erasing astronomical ignorance. Some years ago I uncovered what I perceive to be a relationship between a large decline in astronomy education in public schools in the first half of the twentieth century and decisions made by a so-called Committee of Ten that met in 1898. Prior to 1898, astronomy was a major subject in secondary schools, but my study revealed a distinct drop-off after the committee decided that astronomy no longer was required for college entrance. Other societal issues may also have influenced the disappearance of astronomy from schools. By the time of Sputnik, very little astronomy could be found at any level in public schools. In the U.S., as politicians and educators called for reforms in math and science, small planetariums were installed by the hundreds in almost all states. This was a pivotal time in the history of both astronomy education and planetarium development.

In 1958 and 1960 about 100 people attended the first national planetarium education conferences. The International Society for Planetarium Education, later changed to the International Planetarium Society began in 1970 and six U.S. regional planetarium groups exist as well. All are committed to improving astronomy education.

Today we find portable planetariums, as well as small Spitz, Nova, Goto, and even home-built planetariums used in public schools, colleges and universities, museums and science centers, and elsewhere.

The original planetarium program typically was a lecture, sometimes with slides. Today many technological innovations have been added in some planetariums, including whole-dome video. Evans and Sutherland and other companies, who produce for small as well as large domes, allow audiences to roam the solar system or be transported to locations billions of light-years distant. Procedures in line with current educational thinking often are utilized, and small planetariums have taken a lead in their use: inquiry, hands-on interaction, audience feedback, and attention to misconceptions. Many have written on the purposes of the planetarium. I believe that the planetarium is a remarkable tool that, in the hands of capable planners and presenters, can transcend compartmentalism into education on one hand and education on the other. It can create holistically more than the sum of its parts-knowledge and inspiration.

An activity that has benefited a lot, both in training and testing, is the astronomy portion of all levels of Science Olympiad, usually elected by bright students interested in science. For many years I have helped elementary, middle school, and high school students prepare for tests, and I have designed the regional and state tests. Thousands of bright students learn astronomy by identifying stars and constellations, understand right ascension and declination, locate positions of deep-sky objects, and find planets in planetariums.

2. Larry Cuipik

In early 2000, Paul Knappenberger, President of the Adler Planetarium and Astronomy Museum, received a phone call from the Vice President of Sesame Workshop, asking his help to develop a planetarium program. After about six years of planning, Sesame Workshop, Adler Planetarium, the Beijing Planetarium, and the Liberty Science Center have partnered to produce a planetarium program, ancillary materials, and an outreach program for pre-school children and their caregivers in China and the U.S. The goals of this informal science education project are: to provide young Chinese and U.S. children an age-appropriate introduction to astronomy, to promote positive attitudes toward science among young children in both countries, to foster understanding of one another among children in China and the U.S., and to establish a successful an lasting bi-national collaboration among informal science educators and institutions in China and the U.S.

The planetarium show and other project materials will appear in three linguistic versions: English and Spanish for the U.S. and Mandarin for China. Each version of the program will feature characters from *Sesame Street*, Sesame Workshop's long-running educational television series, and from *Zhima Jie*, the Chinese adaptation of *Sesame Street*.

The program is expected to premier in Beijing, Chicago, and Jersey City in late 2008. Conservatively, the program life span of 5 years or more will reach more than 1 million pre-school children in the U.S. and a similar number in China. An outreach program based on portable planetarium technology ill take the program to many children who lack access to fixed planetariums. Summative research will assess the educational effectiveness of the program and the results of our bi-national collaboration.

The basis for this collaboration lies in the global relevance of the night-time sky, both as a starting point for early science education and as a bridge between Chinese and U.S. children. Early childhood experiences of observing the Moon, stars, and planets can be important first steps in intellectual and emotional science understanding. The observations, reflected in astronomy-rich stories, folklore, and traditions from both countries also afford a novel context in which Chinese and U.S. children can begin to learn about one another and their respective countries and cultures.

Regrettably, a meaningful view of the night sky is a rare occasion in many urban and suburban settings. Also, caregivers rarely have the background to support children interest in the sky. Few present planetarium programs have satisfied the need to give very young children an introduction to the sky, although this is a time when child interest in science is great and should have support. In effect, pre-school children constitute a large under-served population for planetariums both in China and the U.S.

There will be three versions of the program in each country, one for a planetarium with full dome video technology, one for those using a traditional star projector, and one for a portable planetarium. Producers, 3-D modelers, and artists from Adler Planer and Beijing Planetarium jointly are producing the programs. Live-action video of the Muppet characters is integrated with various show elements: full-dome backgrounds, animations, and special effects. Close collaboration between the planetarium staffs is critical during all planning and production stages. Although much of this interaction is being accomplished through mail, E-mail, and phone conferences, on-site collaboration has been extremely valuable.

As this program is in the final stages of pre-production, the Adler Planetarium has been working actively with other partners to evaluate and explore other pre-school programs such as "The Zula Patrol."

3.   Jon Elvert

Planetariums often are considered informal learning centers for effectively teaching basic principles of astronomy while sharing the latest discoveries of our known universe. However, one of planetarium's most overlooked assets is using their uniqueness with their communities to leverage partnerships. Planetariums attract different audiences, and each audience may need to be targeted differently. Collaboration is an effective marketing strategy, largely underestimated by many planetarians (those who work in planetariums). I'll describe my experience with some successful collaborations.

Immersive Earth Consortium: Originally a NASA funded collaboration of five planetariums, three vendors, and a university, the idea was to create an inexpensive portable planetarium with a single fish-eye lens to project full-dome, immersive digital programs which also were created by the consortium. These inflatable portable domes then would be available to planetariums and museums worldwide, at a cost. The project would create a high-tech, relatively inexpensive way to spread astronomy education.

Previous research indicated that students are more engaged and more likely to master complex concepts after an interactive program using full-dome projections, whether in a fixed or a portable dome. Since its inception, the collaboration between Rice University, NASA, the Houston Museum of Natural History, vendors, and the talent of people from five planetariums, this product, now called the e-Planetarium, has reached over 50,000 school children. The consortium now has over twenty participants using this system.

Red Stick Animation Festival: In 2004 our planetarium combined resources with the Louisiana State University's Center for Computation and Technology and the Shaw Center of the Arts to provide a forum to link and showcase artistic creativity and technology. The project provided a venue for animators, students, artists, writers, scientists, and educators to share their collective knowledge and skills to promote animation. Our planetarium's collaborative role was working with physics students to created computer visualization of black holes and double star dynamics and utilizing the planetarium's full dome digital display as an immersive environment for showcasing many animation products.

M.A.R.S. van (Mobile Astronomy Resource System): To celebrate National Astronomy Day two years ago, our planetarium teamed up with the Baton Rouge Recreation Observatory (with a 24" Cassegrain), the university's Cain Center, and the Louisiana Space Consortium to deliver astronomy activities and demonstrations a 1600 cubic foot truck, the M.A.R.S. van. Funds for the van and astronomy outreach contents came from a grant from the Space Telescope Science Institute's IDEAS program. Its primary mission is to coordinate astronomy education outreach to rural schools and communities, with demonstrations specifically related to the Earth-Sun-Moon system. The van includes a portable planetarium, computer-controlled telescopes, and laptop workstations. Current events such as the Transit of Venus, lunar eclipses, meteor showers, and planetary conjunctions are promoted.

School Districts; and IDEAS Grant Project: The most fundamental type of collaboration a planetarium can foster, if the planetarium is not a part of the district already, is one with the local school district. It is important for planetariums to learn and follow the state and Federal astronomy education standards, which the school is required to follow.

Three years ago we started a conversation with our school district's curriculum trainers, people responsible for teacher training. We discovered that our trainers desperately were in need of ways to give their teachers more effective methods to teach astronomy. An agreement resulted for planetarium staff to give credited teacher astronomy workshops, both at the planetarium and district offices. For their participation, teachers were offered funding for their classes to attend our large planetarium or to have our portable planetarium be brought to their school. This fourth successful collaboration has resulted in increased planetarium attendance and better teaching and learning in the district classrooms.

4. Wayne James

My work involves teaching astronomy with a portable planetarium. I have traveled throughout nine counties in East Central Illinois for 17 years with a STAR-LAB, manufactured by Learning Technologies. I work through the Regional Office of Education, located in Rantoul, Illinois, Champaign County, where the University of Illinois is located. I also teach beneath the "real sky." I live on a family farm 25 miles west of Champaign-Urbana, where it is relatively dark. Students enrolled in Astronomy 101 and 102 at parkland Jr. College are sent to me for a telescope lab, which is focused on the experience of getting the eye to the eyepiece instead of seeing computer-generated animations. This means that on some days I teach students that range from pre-school to college age, beneath the artificial sky of the planetarium and/or the real sky.

I have taught several workshops for teachers focusing on easy hands-on lessons for different grade levels. I initiated a concept of using paper plates to help students learn by doing, often in close connection with planetarium programs. Chuck Bueter and others have taken up this idea. You can find a number of my ideas on Chuck Bueter's paper plate web site. (Search for "paper plate astronomy.")

I want to share some things I've gleaned from using a portable planetarium. One can take the STARLAB to so many places/ I have set up the STARLAB in an airport hanger for a workshop with the AIR Force. This summer I had it in the lobby of the Krannert Center for Performing Arts at the University of Illinois in connection with a summer solstice celebration. I have taken the STARLAB to libraries focusing on summer reading programs. The Illinois Migrant Council sponsored me to travel throughout Illinois to places where children of migrant families had come to special summer school programs.

Some of the unique characteristics of teaching with a STARLAB portable planetarium (and I don't sell them) are as follows. First, the STARLAB system is very flexible. I can switch from the sky as you see it (STARLAB uses a "photo" created sky, so it is very accurate) to a sky with H. A. Rey asterism, to different skies of artistic mythology characters-Greek/Roman, Native American, Chinese, Egyptian. In 1 second I can change latitude. In 5 seconds I can change starfield cylinders and take the audience to the Southern Hemisphere. In about 15 seconds I can change to 12 different moon phases. This flexibility allows me to respond to teacher or student questions or comments. I can help every student "own" the lesson.

Second, the STARLAB is relatively inexpensive, costing under $15,000 for a complete basic system. And third, the small space allows me to sit in the middle of the group. This facilitates interactive lessons. Teacher and student questions are natural. I know if students are interested or not by whether or not I hear movement. Sounds in a STARLAB are amplified.

It's not a perfect world. I've experienced some problems: First there has to be a place to store the STARLAB and a place to set it up at each place where you teach. I am not a big hit with gym and some other teachers, as I frequently use their space. I have put the STARLAB in a gyms, classrooms, cafeterias, music rooms, weight rooms, Vocational AG rooms (once next to a big fish tank), and libraries. The STARLAB won't work well outside-where some people say they want it. Second is a problem of time. You may not plan correctly for distance to a location, or you may have car trouble. STARLAB producers advertise set-up as taking 10 minutes, but this does not allow for everything. Third are communication problems. The school may forget things-to tell the gym or other room teacher, or simply forget they scheduled you to come. And I always ask if I will be working with substitute teachers and I want to know if I have to move for lunch.

To give you an idea of what is possible with a portable planetarium: In a 180-day school year, I have worked as many as 150 days, gone to about 60 different schools, and presented 700 lessons to over 900 teachers and 14,000 students.

5.   James Kaler

I am an astronomer. Astronomers, indeed all scientists, especially those operating with public funds, have the obligation to return fruits of their investigations back to the public. This is not only for appreciation of what the science has wrought, but also to spark enthusiasm in footing the bill to keep backing the work. Public support includes not just direct grants from Federal sources, but also employment at both public and private universities and colleges.

There are many ways for astronomers to communicate. There are the standard media-newspapers, magazines, and an astronomy web site (which I have maintained for a long time). But one mode of communication of great personal importance to me is the planetarium. Even though I have been a research professional for decades, I have been engaged with planetariums since I built my first one when I was 13. Over the years, and into my transition of activity to public astronomy outreach, I maintained my fascination with the power of planetariums in getting people to understand the beauty, meaning, and science of the sky. To me, planetariums-large and small, museum and school-represent one of the great interfaces between the professional astronomer and people of all ages. That is because planetariums and planeta-rians have the ability to engage those who initially are not interested in astronomy and science; they bring people into the astronomy fold.

But planetarians need help. My personal contribution, which I invite others to follow (indeed, lead), has been three-fold. In 1989 I was invited to present a lecture on "what's new in astronomy over the past year" at the annual meeting of the Great Lakes Planetarium Association (GLPA) being held in my home town of Champaign, Illinois. I said, "Sure; easy," and then. Immediately afterward, "What have I done?!" The effort was far more than I expected, but the results were welcomed-not just by the GLPA group, but by me personally because of what I learned in preparation. That type of talk must have been what the audience wanted and needed, because I am still at it. This fall I'll be giving the "18th annual Astronomy Update" at the Triple Conjunction meeting of GLPA, the Southeast Planetarium Association, and the Middle Atlantic Planetarium Society. All of the Updates, representing almost 20 years of progress in astronomy, have been published; and they are available online.

The Update lectures led to an invitation to give GLPA's Armand Spitz lecture in 1999. And this led to a video production, designed expressly for the planetarium. It is a sort-of bio, titled "The Stargazer." Its prime purposes have been to teach stellar astronomy and to explore the personal excitement of the science through the life of an astronomer. Although conceived, written, and produced by Bob Bonadurer and David DeRemer, I was allowed full access to the script and production. Parts of it were video-recorded, showing the nature of my work, and it was completely tape-recorded. Through the medium of the planetarium, we were then able to reach far more people than through live lectures given one at a time. The program was purchased by over 80 planetariums, both large and small.

We all have our own ways of reaching the public. Mine has been through writing, lecturing, and especially by sharing what I have learned as an astronomer with the planetarium community. I urge other science professionals to think similarly, and a prime way is through your local planetarium.

6. Rob Landis

Collaborations between large planetarium and organizations like NASA can be fraught with bureaucratic inertia, political agendas, and misunderstanding. The "misunderstanding" aspect is perhaps most significant.

Planetarium programs produced under the auspices of collaborating with NASA often are not well received by most audiences. Many times this is the result of those of both sides of the collaboration barrier not understanding the culture and philosophies of each other's institutions. Healthy personal relationships between/among individuals at institutions sharing needs and goals can alleviate some of the confusion. However, usually NASA education/public outreach personnel do not understand the venue and environment of the planetarium realm. Conversely, planetarium people often do not comprehend the constraints under which NASA must operation. Both sides need to compromise and have a commitment to persevere.

In my career with NASA there have been some productions that have turned out very well. I want to share these as examples of what can and should be. All involve enormously successful space science missions: the Hubble Space Telescope, the Cassini-Huygens mission to Saturn and Titan, and the intrepid Mars Exploration Rovers Spirit and Opportunity.

Through the Eyes of Hubble opened on the Ides of March, 1995 at the Henry Buhl, Jr. Planetarium, Carnegie Science Center, in Pittsburgh, Pennsylvania. Initial discussions for this program idea began about a year earlier at the Mid-Atlantic Planetarium Society (MAPS) conference in Portland, Maine, between me and Martin Ratcliffe, Buhl Planetarium Director. NASA had just completed the first service mission of Endeavor (STS-61) to the Hubble Space Telescope (HST), fully obviating the effects of spherical aberration of the primary mirror; the Space Telescope Science Institute (STScI) had finalized plans to observe Comet Shoemaker-Levy 9's collision with Jupiter; and one impressive science result after another continued to stream out of STScI. The time seemed ripe for a NASA facility to team up with a world-class planetarium and its staff to produce a program about HST and its story. Further informal discussion continued at the International Planetarium Society (IPS) meeting in Cocoa Beach, Florida, and shortly thereafter a memorandum of understanding was drafted.

The synergy between STScI and the Buhl Planetarium resulted in a quality program, *Through the Eyes of Hubble.* That was distributed around the world and translated into Chinese, Japanese, Spanish, Dutch, French, German, and Russian. *Through the Eyes of Hubble* underscored the universality of appeal of wonders of astronomy and some aspect of what we do at NASA. This planetarium program also demonstrated what is needed to produce good planetarium-NASA collaboration.

Another excellent example of a planetarium program showcasing NASA results is part of a live program devised by Carter Emmart at the Hayden Planetarium, Rose Center, New York City. To explain and illustrate the nature of the Cassini-Huygens mission, employing a virtual model of the Cassini spacecraft along with the heliocentric and Saturnocentric orbital elements of the vehicle, Emmart demonstrated the do-si-do path of Cassini-Huygens to the outer solar system. Arriving at Saturn Emmart took advantage of the immersive planetarium environment to point out where within the flower-petal-shaped orbits Cassini currently was located. He went even further to present the view of Saturn, its rings, or a moon, as seen from the spacecraft. In order for Emmart to develop this flowing, articulate, easy-to-follow presentation, connections had to be made between the Jet Propulsion Laboratory (JPL) and the Hayden Planetarium, so that both sides understood needs and capabilities.

A third successful set of visualizations of a NASA mission, seen on PBS's NOVA, the Discovery Channel, the History Channel, NASA TV, and the Disney IMAX movie *Roving Mars* is the work of Dan Maas for the Mars Exploration Rover (MER) program. None of us on the team anticipated such a long-lived mission, having Spirit and Opportunity last so far beyond their warranties. The keys to Maas' success are a deep-rooted commitment to excellence and personal contact on different aspects of the MER project.

Planetariums are cathedrals of inspiration. NASA needs the planetarium in order to communicate its findings and goals to a broad public, especially as we embark on a new phase of human exploration to the Moon and beyond. How well we communicate the goal of the Constellation Program to get humans back out on the frontier depends on both professional and personal connections made between NASA and planetariums.

7. Small Group Brainstorming Discussions

Three groups generated ideas for expanding creative projects with planetariums. The direction was to think of possibilities that will improve astronomy education within classrooms (all levels), expand extra curricular school experiences, reach more people in the general public of all ages, and serve those in specialized groups. Ideas about particular groups or people to be involved, additional technology or materials to incorporate as collaborations between groups all are of interest. Further, questions are welcome.

Group A Ideas: 1) Before going to a full-blown elaborate planetarium program, large planetariums might try a "kios" experience to learn if it will be successful. Preferences for different visualizations, descriptions, and /or music could be compared. Simple test questions could also determine which visualization or wording is better for learning. 2) In large planetariums make better use of multi-channel speakers. For space missions can data be turned into sounds?

Group B Ideas: 1) Involve college students and astronomy clubs in planetarium use. 2) Have an Evening Night for local businesses, with catchy titles of things done, like "a black-hole drink." 3) Fixed planetariums might incorporate a day-of-the-week theme, such as "Far Out Fridays." This could increase interest in planetarium attendance and awareness of what is happening there. 4) Partner with TV stations. A particular person at the planetarium should know a particular person at a station, probably on the weather or news teams. The relationship could lead to better TV coverage of astronomy events, publicity for the planetarium, and collaborations for projects, such as fairs or telescope nights. 5) Host more teacher workshops to increase teacher interest in bringing students to the planetarium. 6) Have local people who circulate in the community serve as planetarium ambassadors. 7) Have drawings by teachers for free educational materials from vendors. The vendors who donate materials get publicity. 8) Have as a goal in both planetarium programs and outreach activities the individual "personal ownership of the program."

Group C Ideas: 1) Let kids create their own planetarium shows using current digital planetarium software. Have many do this in classrooms. When done, good show files are taken to a dome (large or small planetarium) to view there. 2) Have after-school programs for students to develop programs. When finished student-made programs can be advertised and shown to classes, parents, special groups.

Kenneth Zeigler - Thomas J. Brennan Award Winner

Jeanne Bishop and May Kay Hemenway

EPO and a Changing World
ASP Conference Series, Vol. 389, © 2008
C. Garmany, M. Gibbs, and J. W. Moody

Your Face(book) and MySpace: Let's Hook Up

Pamela L. Gay[1,2] and Thomas Foster[2]

Abstract. In the public social network venues of MySpace and Facebook, individuals of all ages and nationalities look for like-minded online denizens with whom they can build relationships. Through social networking sites, it is possible for EPO programs to bring together diverse individuals to laugh, learn, and socialize around pet projects and favorite topics. Astronomy is popular among these people, with over 5000 members of the MySpace community listing "astronomy" as an interest. By building interesting MySpace and Facebook profiles for your programs, you can plug into the intellectual and social hunger of these individuals.

In this workshop, we will discuss the tricks for creating an interesting profile, how to hide such weirdnesses as age and zodiacal sign, and the proper netiquette for nurturing large friends lists and building large communities. Specific emphasis will be given to using Facebook to build one-on-one relationships with program volunteers and students, and how to use MySpace as a way to distribute program announcements to large populations. We will also address the issues of contacting minors, and coping with stalkers and crazies. Come learn how to reach people who already want to learn and love the cosmos, and are just waiting to hear what you have to share.

1. MySpace vs. Facebook

The world of online social networking is, like the real-world social scene, constantly leaping from one hot trend to another. In the ebb and flow of what's hot and what's not, different people lead and lag and even follow different waves. Today, the online scene has people floating away from Friendster to join MySpace and Facebook. MySpace currently boasts the over 200 million members on their website (http://www.myspace.com). Facebook's site cites over 55 million users (http://www.facebook.com).

There are socio-economic differences between the populations on both sites. This is in part due to their histories. Facebook started as a digital version of the classic campus facebook at Harvard University in February 2004. Over the course of that year it expanded to additional colleges, and by 2005 it had become a home for students from universities all around the world. In September 2006 they opened their online doors to allow anyone to join. Today, the members of Facebook tend to be better educated than MySpace members, or to be the children of better educated parents. (Hargittai 2007).

---

[1] Astronomy Cast, http://www.astronomycast.com

[2] Southern Illinois University Edwardsville, Department of Physics, Campus Box 1654, Edwardsville, IL, 62026-1654

These sites offer different features that allow them to be utilized by EPO activities in different ways. MySpace accounts can be set up for any email address, and have features to support non-profits (listed under "Impact"), and to create and join groups. Users can write blogs, maintain calendars of events, and participate in chat rooms and forums. This is an excellent way to blast "Friends" with information on upcoming events and distribute announcements. MySpace also makes it relatively easy to create fictional profiles for organizations or programs. Today, several NASA missions, including GLAST and Swift, have their own MySpace profiles.

Facebook accounts can be set up for people, bands, or businesses. It is a bit harder to set up profiles for programs, as Facebook works hard to prevent fictional profiles, but it is easy to setup fan clubs and groups. Space related groups in Facebook are quite popular, with the group "When I was you age, Pluto was a planet" having over 1.1 million members. Groups have built in discussion areas, news feeds, photo albums, and allow for "officers" to be named.

2.   Producing Profiles with Personality

In creating online profiles for EPO programs it is important to consider the cynicism of online audiences. Many of the people visiting social networking sites are looking for reasons to be turned off by individual profiles. In building your own profile, it is good strategy is to view it from the perspective of a middle school student looking to make fun of something (channel you inner evil 12 year old). For instance, empty calendars will be seen as someone not doing anything. A picture of an activity site that doesn't show people will be seen as some place no one ever goes. Decide who you want your program to be online and craft your content to create that personality.

Discussion: During the session we setup an unofficial Facebook fan club for the Astronomical Society of the Pacific using input from the audience. This group was given the name "ASP Rocks Astronomy" and the description, "It's more than the west coast. The Astronomical Society of the Pacific is an international constellation of astronomy educators." Under recent news, "Recent studies have confirmed that only experts should stargaze while hopping on one foot. We are those experts" was posted. This group had nearly 50 members before the end of the meeting weekend.

3.   Making "Friends"

When doing online outreach it is always important to consider privacy issues and the potential to interact with minors in unsupervised arenas. With social networking this is more difficult than in real world interactions because it is impossible to know if the 24 year old female you exchange messages with is really that person or a 52 year old male or a precocious 12 year old. Beyond the normal care that should be taken to keep posted content clean and innuendo free, it is also important to moderate the content of those who your profile is connected to and to keep copies of all communications.

Part of the dynamic of social networking sites is the process of making "Friends." On both Facebook and MySpace, friends are people who have (unless otherwise specified) greater access to your profile, are publicly listed for anyone to see, and can leave public messages on profiles. Every person has the option to accept or reject friendship requests and to extend friendship requests. The MySpace profile of the International Year of Astronomy has primarily had normal people who are honest space enthusiasts request "Friend" status. Mixed in with these people, however, have been individuals with fictional profiles designed to sell items or solicit attention for services. It is important to review each friend request and check the profile of the requester to make sure you aren't linking to people who are clearly going to associate you with things your program doesn't wish to be associated with. This can be a tricky matter as a real astronomy enthusiast may have a semi-pornographic profile or worse. The author has dealt with these friendship requests with brief profile-to-profile messages thanking the person for their friendship request and apologizing that their profile is one that can't be linked to for an honest stated reason. This has consistently been met with a positive response conveying understanding. One netiquette nicety is to respond to every friendship request that is accepted with a thank you post on the requesters public message roll.

Discussion: Several attendees raised questions related to concerns about dealing with fictional people and profiles. On MySpace it is not uncommon to come across profiles that are fan profiles of individuals ranging from Albert Einstein to Luke Skywalker. In some cases, such as a fan profile of Neil Tyson, fan sites dedicated to living astronomers can be easily mistaken for the actual profiles of real people. In deciding if you want to be a friend to these fan profiles, it is important to ask what spirit have they been created in? Many fan profiles are created as tributes and as such are positive to link with as they promote astronomy and astronomers.

Discussion: The question of who to friend to was also raised. A good starting point is to friend people you know, to other EPO professionals and programs, and sites clearly identifying themselves with astronomy. Examples include Phil Plait (aka The Bad Astronomer), GLAST (a NASA mission), the authors of this paper, and tribute sites to the planets and other astronomical objects. If a profile takes off, it will spread virally. This means that when you friend one person, their friends will see you and friend you, and then their friends will follow suite, allowing explosive spreading of content.

Discussion: Several people expressed concern over how MySpace and Facebook profiles and groups would be professionally perceived. This question offers a possible line for future research.

Discussion: The question, "Should we friend our students?" was asked. As instructors it is probably inappropriate for us to solicit our students as "Friends" within Facebook or MySpace. At the same time, however, it may be appropriate to tell students in real life that they are welcome to friend us and remind them of profile privacy controls that allow individuals to hide or reveal as much as they want. Being friends with students is beneficial to students who may seek recommendation letters several years after a class has been completed.

References

Hargittai, E., Journal of Computer-Mediated Communication, **13**(1) article 14. (2007) http://jcmc.indiana.edu/vol13/issue1/hargittai.html

EPO and a Changing World
ASP Conference Series, Vol. 389, © 2008
C. Garmany, M. Gibbs, and J. W. Moody

The Living Astronomy and People of the Mayan World Today: Engaging Hispanic Populations in Science

Isabel Hawkins

UC Berkeley Space Sciences Laboratory, 7 Gauss Way, Berkeley, CA 94720-7450, USA

Felipe Tapia

Orgullo Yucateco, 120 Park St., San Rafael, CA 94901, USA

Abstract.   From long ago, the Maya civilizations of Mesoamerica have been keenly attuned to the cycles of nature. The Maya have always been careful observers, and more than a thousand years ago, they recorded the motion of the planets, the Sun, and the Moon, and predicted eclipses. These observations were used to create a complex calendar to organize the events of their world. The Maya built great cities containing buildings aligned with the Sun, Moon, and the stars to mark important times of the year. Many astronomical traditions are still practiced today by the Maya of the Yucatán peninsula, Southern states in México, and other areas in Mesoamerica. Traditional farming communities time the cultivation of corn by observing the sky. The living culture of the Mayan people in the Yucatan integrates science and astronomy with every other aspect of their culture. Yucatec Maya, the language spoken by more than 1 million people in the Yucatán today, still carries through oral histories the ancient knowledge of nature. Our hope is that you'll increase your interest and knowledge of the Mayan people and of the enduring wisdom reflected in the daily lives of Mayan families. We present the results of education and public outreach efforts that position astronomy within its cultural context as an effective means of capturing the interest and enabling authentic participation of under-represented populations in science.

1.   Introduction

Humans across all cultures have venerated, observed, and studied the Sun, the Moon, the planets and the stars for thousands of years. The Maya developed astronomical tracking systems and detailed calendars spanning many generations. Astronomical knowledge is reflected in the architecture of ancient buildings in thousand-year-old archeological sites and monuments in México, Guatemala, Honduras, and other areas of Mesoamerica. In addition to amassing a great body of astronomical knowledge, the Maya developed a complex system of mathematics that used the concept of zero. They recorded their knowledge in bark accordion-like books or codices using a writing system of glyphs. They observed the motions of celestial bodies in the sky for the purpose of planning and celebrating key dates in their ritual calendar including for purposes of agriculture. Many of these astronomical traditions are still practiced today by traditional farming communities that time the cultivation of corn and other crops by observing the movements of the Sun and the stars.

The strong and rich astronomical traditions that still thrive in the Mayan community throughout the world can provide a framework for Hispanic communities in the United States to integrate contemporary astronomical knowledge with worldviews that are grounded in thousands of years of tradition. For example, in the San Francisco Bay Area, there are more than 30,000 Yucatec Mayan immigrants who are keenly interested in participating in science and technology but have not found an easy entry point. Among the most under-represented groups in science are Hispanic-Americans. Of all working scientists and engineers, less than 4% are Hispanic (AIP 2005). Disconnection from scientific fields, both in terms of access to concepts and knowledge, and opportunities in education and research, are important factors that contribute to the low numbers of Hispanic-Americans in scientific and technical careers. Hispanic youth in particular fare poorly in math and science achievement, even though large numbers of the US Hispanic population come from a rich indigenous heritage that includes a wealth of knowledge about botany, astronomy, mathematics, engineering, ecology, etc. (Fixico 2000; Snively & Corsiglia 2001). By highlighting the astronomical legacy and current astronomical practices of the Mayan culture in the Yucatan, we have been able to collaborate with community based groups of Mayan immigrants in California to attract and engage youth and their families in contemporary astronomy and science.

2.   Science Festivals with and for the Mayan Community in California

Working with the Mayan community leadership in California, we have implemented implement six community and family science festivals since 2005. The one-day, week-end events are free of charge to the general public, and attract on the order of 500 people. The festival includes: talks by NASA and other scientists, educators, and native and non-native experts on the astronomies and mathematics of indigenous cultures; presentations by members of the Hispanic community especially elders and others who can share oral traditions; science activities for families mainly focused on the Sun since the festivals take place during the day; solar telescope viewing; hands-on activities related to solar energy; cultural demonstrations such as traditional dances, arts and crafts; and traditional food. Mayan community leaders partner with UC Berkeley to plan and coordinate the festivals, and receive support in the form of seed funding and access to NASA materials and content expertise. Community participation is keenly dependent on their established relationships with community leaders, thus the recruitment of participants is led by the Mayan community groups. Community leaders tap existing infrastructure for dissemination such as Mayan language radio, flyers and Internet communication in Yucatec Maya and Spanish, and by word of mouth. UC Berkeley provides follow-up support through ongoing communication and sharing of appropriate resources and science opportunities for families in their neighborhoods.

3.   ASP Conference Session

To best demonstrate the spirit and characteristics of the community science festivals, our presentation at the ASP involved 10 members of the Mayan community in San Rafael, California, who have been instrumental in the planning and implementation of the program. The participants included the group's Grand-mother, Doña María Oliva Díaz, who began the presentation speaking in her native Yucatec Mayan language, introducing her family and the two authors of this paper (Felipe Tapia and Isabel Hawkins). Subsequently, the authors gave a brief presentation of Mayan astronomy and summarized the community events in California. A Q&A session focused on the living knowledge of astronomy in the Mayan community today. To demonstrate the activities during the events, the Diiaz family facilitated small groups in the audience who participated in demonstrations of the types of astronomy hands-on activities done at the festi-vals (e.g. construct a solar clock; experiment with UV detecting beads; discuss Mayan language and astronomy using a print resource; explore the magnetic nature of the Sun using a magnetism kit; participate in a demonstration of the Sun-Earth size and distance scale model; and play with solar energy toy cars, etc.). The session ended with a traditional *Jarana* dance demonstration by Fe-lipe Tapia and three of the Díaz children, who were dressed in their elegant *huipiles*. The presentation highlighted program characteristics that were identi-fied as important elements of our collaboration by the Mayan community leaders themselves:

- The program enables the Mayan community to take initiative and become self-motivated to learn about our own scientific and cultural legacy.

- The program disseminates Mayan knowledge of astronomy and science to our own Mayan community and to the world, in a way that assures authenticity, integrity, and accuracy.

- The festivals serve as an example to other indigenous groups so they can also research and learn about their own astronomical legacy, for example, Zapotec and Mixtec immigrants in California who came from Oaxaca, México.

- Astronomy makes science in general more accessible to our children.

- Our project takes into account the daily activities and cultural expressions of our community to attract their participation.

- The program talks and activities include many themes related to the Sun and astronomy that highlight science in general, making connections to the living knowledge of the environment and the sky by Mayan people today.

4. Program Evaluation

The program's ability to attract and engage Hispanic communities of Mayan heritage in astronomy and science has been evaluated by *Contemporánea*, an independent marketing and evaluation firm in San Francisco. Results indicate that the program is being received extremely well by the Mayan community in California, and that the program succeeds in providing access to science and astronomy in a cultural context that resonates with indigenous people of Mayan descent. Specific results include:

- Children and adult festival participants agree that they are **highly interested in learning more about astronomy**. Children were highly interested in attending the program in the future and asked that it contain even more activities.

- These events were successful at **linking new concepts to participants' existing knowledge base**. These participants, many of whom were Maya, had fundamental knowledge of science, astronomy and the accomplishments of the ancient Maya; however all agree that these programs added new layers of information and new scientific concepts to this foundation.

- **Perceptions of personal Maya heritage were strong** among attendees. In describing the contribution of their ancestors, many participants spoke with pride, using the collective "we" and "our." Many feel that much of today's Maya culture and everyday life continues to reflect this rich heritage. Respondents say they use this knowledge, even today, for agriculture and to check the time or weather.

- The program was particularly effective at boosting **perceptions of access**. Attending the festival events generated excitement and awareness that there are avenues to astronomy and scientific content.

By providing opportunities for the Mayan community in California to increase their knowledge and appreciation of their culture's scientific legacy and their current astronomical practices, our community events are increasing and facilitating access to science, mathematics, and technology for Hispanic children, youth, and families.

References

AIP – American Institute of Physics *American Institute of Physics Education and Career Statistics for US Population* (2005) (http://www.aip.org/statistics)

Fixico, D. *The Urban Indian Experience in America* (University of New Mexico Press, Albuquerque, NM, 2000) .

Snively, G. and J. Corsiglia, "Discovering Indigenous Science: Implications for Science Education", Science Education **85** 6-34, 2001
http://www.d.umn.edu/b̃munson/Courses/EdSe4255/Snively-IndigenousScience.pdf#search='indigenous%20science%20knowledge%20base

EPO and a Changing World
ASP Conference Series, Vol. 389, © *2008*
C. Garmany, M. Gibbs, and J. W. Moody

When Everybody Wins: Strategies for Diverse EPO Partnerships

Sanlyn R. Buxner, Carla Bitter, and Andrew J. Shaner

Phoenix Mars Lander, Lunar and Planetary Lab, University of Arizona, 1415 N. 6th Ave, Tucson, AZ 85705, USA

Abstract.   We present issues to consider when expanding EPO partnerships beyond traditional partners. Working with non-traditional partners has both risks and benefits. We share a series of case studies drawn from the experiences of the Phoenix Scout Mission EPO team and include feedback from the session for a list of collective lessons learned.

1.   Introduction

In this session we presented critical issues to consider and strategies that the Phoenix Mars Scout Mission used in the past year as we diversified our Education and Public Outreach partnerships. We presented key questions to consider when thinking about target audiences and have included the session participants' responses to these questions. Additionally we presented a series of case studies illustrating some challenging situations the Phoenix EPO team encountered in the past year, our solutions to each situation, and feedback on each situation from the session participants. We end with a set of collected lessons learned from our session as well as potential benefits to expanding EPO partners beyond current partners.

2.   Defining Your Audience

One of the first questions you should ask yourself and your institution when beginning the path to diversify your EPO partnerships are:

What does diverse mean in regards to our audience?

What does underserved mean in regards to our audience?

What does underrepresented mean in regards to our audience?

Despite formal definitions used by NASA, NSF, and other organizations, it is important that you and your institution decide on a set of working definitions. These definitions may or may not match those set forth by other organizations. As these definitions change from organization to organization it is important to realize that the term "traditionally underserved" means many things to different people. To answer the question: Who are part of an underserved population? There are many possible answers that include:

Females

Rural participants

Hispanic, African American, Native American participants

Economically disadvantaged (low SES) participants

Scientifically illiterate participants

Anti-evolution participants

Hearing impaired participants

Visually impaired participants

Adult learners

The answers to this question provided by participants in this session included:

People we are not currently reaching

Those with a psychological barrier to coming to our institution

Those with transportation problems that prevent them from visiting our institution

Teenage youth with no access to science programs

3. Being Strategic About Your Target Audience

3.1. Decide Who Your Target Audience Is

Once you have decided on your definitions about diverse, underserved, and underrepresented you must decide which of those audiences you want to serve. In the world of shortages in staff, money, and time it is usually not possible to serve every audience you may want to - despite the fact that we want to serve "everyone". The question that may help you narrow your focus down is exploring the reason you have for targeting a diverse or underserved audience. Your possible answers may include:

It is the law

It is a requirement of your funding agency

You have a desire to help others

It is part of you mission statement

You want to capitalize on new funding opportunities and others.

Having a clear and public answer to why you are serving a specific audience will help you focus on serving the new audience and meet their needs appropriately. Your answer may also determine new staffing decisions, funding allocations, and future collaborations.

3.2.   Target Your Audience

Before you start any programming for a new audience you should do s ome research. The first assumption that must be made is that this is a group of people that would like your information/service/product. Be careful, not everyone is interested in what you have to share even if you consider it to be important, if it is a free service for them, or they seem to have a need such as low standardized test scores. What you may see as a benefit may not be interpreted as such by certain groups. The only way to make a partnership is when both sides are invested. The first piece of information you should find out is if there is a need for what you have to share that is felt by the community you are going to target. The best way to determine this is to talk to community members that are well vested in the community and are already filling roles of serving the community such as teachers, school administrators, religious leaders, elders, or social workers. You want to be careful to communicate with someone inside of the community and not only other outside organizations that work in the community. In this way you can benefit from insider information about the need, norms, and your new role in the community.

Once you have determined that there is a need a positive partnership can be made. Several points that need to be investigated: For an effective partnership you need to find out the needs, goals, and limitations of the audience. Do they need content information, role models, teacher training, standards based curriculum, after school programming etc? Do they have money, space, transportation, or other barriers that will make it difficult to participate in your programs? Would it be better for them to come to your institution or for you to come to their community? Will evening or Saturday programs work for this audience? Be sure to consider many extraneous factors may impact participation beyond their interest in your program. These extra factors may include taking care of family, religious considerations, work schedules, etc.

What they need may or may not match what you had intended to share. For example, you may have a formal curriculum ready to share but they are only looking for summer camp programs. In this instance you need to decide if you can help because sharing what you have ready will most likely have no impact as it will not be used by the community. In our partnership with the Louisiana Children's Museum, the Phoenix EPO staff transformed a formal curriculum into camp activities and provided staff training in both content and enactment to museum staff and volunteers so that they could provide summer programming in their community. Additionally we provided money for lunches for all children and for scholarships so that more kids could attend camp. In this case, providing only the activities would have fallen short of the need, goals, and limitations of the program they wanted to run.

4.   Case Studies to Explore Potential Issue in Practice.

In this session we discussed several real-life situations that occurred during the past year as the Phoenix EPO staff worked with new partners. Participants in this session were asked to consider the following questions:

What would you do in that situation?

How could you better prepare for that situation in the future?

Below we present the case studies, the solution that the Phoenix EPO staff used, and session participants' feedback on the situation and how to avoid similar situation in the future.

4.1. Last Minute Inflation

You have planned a special event for a local school district for 300 students as a reward for completion of an academic program. Your facility is most likely the only field trip the students will get to attend this year. One day before the event, the coordinator informs you that they are confirming for 800 students. Your facility cannot accommodate 800 students and you do not have the staff to complete the program.

When faced with this situation for their own institution, session participants suggested contacting other institutions for help or attempting to work out a rotating schedule to accommodate all if the students on that day. The Phoenix Mission was not able to accommodate all of the students for the program. The mission is housed in a working science building in which accommodating more than 300 students was out of the question as it would have caused conflict with science and engineering teams. This made extended programming on that day out of the question. We were able to refer back to a letter of understanding signed with the district to stick to the original number of students and then helped direct them to other places on campus. In this case we were confined by the limitations of our institution and could not meet the needs of this audience at the last minute. The key to avoiding the situation would be good communication with the key contact so that expectations are clear for both sides and last minute emergencies can be avoided.

4.2. Under-Attended Party

You have planned a Saturday event to host 300 students and their families for a special event. You have paid for and provided lunch and staff for the event. Only 20 students and their families show up for a total of 50 people.

When faced with this situation for their own institutions, session participants suggested having someone call each of the families to remind them of the event, send out flyers, and identify and lower hurdles that led to the low attendance. A key piece is to realize that their lives may be very different than your own. You may need to pay for a bus, try a different time due to parents' schedules, or take your program to their community. The key is to understand the community needs and incentives to understand how to improve the experience for the next time. Be sure to talk with the group leader in advance to work out these types of issues so that you work together to increase attendance. The Phoenix EPO staff ran the event with those that attended. We then worked with another group at our institution who regularly works with this community to help improve future events. With this population we need to pay for travel for participants, pay for food for events and work with our partners to increase attendance. We rely heavily on our partners for advertising because we do not have the staff available to call and write family members. By leveraging on another organization with good community ties we were able to have other successfully and well attended events.

4.3. Calculus for Third Grade Reading

You are part of a special outreach program to do classroom outreach in an urban school district. The school is in desperate need of math and science resources for their students. You show up with plans to do a well aligned hands-on minds-on standards-based activity. The students do not seem engaged ... you come to realize that the students cannot read the activity you had planned. Some do not read at grade level and some do not read English.

When faced with situation for their own institutions, session participants suggested having students work in mixed ability groups to get through the activity, having literate or English speakers explain the activity to other students and to check if there is a bilingual educator available to help with the activities. Additionally understanding the needs of the classroom prior to coming to the class would be very beneficial; talking to the teacher might help you understand the realities of the class. If you are unable to get good information about the class or if the teacher misrepresents the abilities of the students, having a full bag of tricks is important. This may include possible demonstrations that can engage many levels of students. In this situation the Phoenix staff did not have access to the teacher before the program which was conducted out of state on behalf of another organization. Once the mismatch between the intended activity and level of the students was realized, the staff member transitioned to an activity usually used with younger students which included a version in Spanish. In this case it was essential to have the backup materials available even though they were not intended to be used.

4.4. What is the Phoenix Mission?

You have financially supported a full summer camp for underserved (low socioeconomic status) students in a high need area run by an independent group of educators. All reports from parents and campers indicate that the camp was successful. During the informal wrap-up with the independent group they tell you "we would have loved to have mentioned your program/mission/topic but we just didn't get to it, hopefully next time."

When faced with situation for their own institutions, session participants suggested calling the local press to highlight your institution's contribution to the program to satisfy institutional recognition needs, making t-shirts for students bearing your logo and stipulating that next year they will cover your program. The Phoenix EPO team was thrilled that we had supported such a successful program even without formal recognition during the camp. We are making activities to highlight our mission that will better fit into this camp next year based on feedback we received this year.

4.5. Lonely Saturday Professional Development

You provide a Saturday morning professional development workshop to support a program that will serve a high need population. You have received commitments from the coordinator that at least 10 people that will attend. You have gathered staff and consumable materials for the event. No one shows up.

When faced with situation for their own institutions, session participants suggested re-evaluating the audience to determine their investment and interest in the material being presented. Make sure that the program has arisen out of community need and is accessible to the intended audience. The Phoenix EPO staff relied again on our mutual letter of understanding with the group and put together a monetary value of the event including staff and consumable costs. A new commitment was established with the group and the program was successfully implemented a month later. In this case communication with the group contact was essential to communicating mutual expectations and finding a good time and location for a successful event.

4.6.   Who cares about Mars?

You are invited to give a presentation at a local school. You come to the classroom well prepared with an engaging talk and activities. You are a very engaging speaker and have had great reception at other venues such as the university and public programs. You are now faced with a room that include: teenage pregnant mothers, students kept in school by law but not by interest, students that are falling asleep, students doing other things, disruptive non-attentive students. Needless to say, things are not going as you had planned.

When faced with situation for their own institutions, session participants suggested being willing to throw away the intended presentation and talk to students about issues important in their own life. Again, it is important to know your audience in advance before you prepare your talk. If you cannot get to know the audience ahead of time, start by surveying them and find out what they may be interested in. The Phoenix staff member scrapped the intended lesson on Phoenix and began a conversation about space policy and local politics to engage students in a relevant conversation that still bordered on the intended topic. In this situation flexibility is the key to making the most of the situation.

5.   Conclusions

There are potential issues when working with non-traditional partners which may include a mismatch between the number of participants that you expect and get, needing to provide basics for the field trip that you have not provided to other groups such as food and transportation etc. Understanding your partners' needs, goals and limitations will help you plan and have more successful programs that meet the goals of both your institution and your partner.

5.1.   Lessons Learned

Letters of Understanding were key to successful partnerships for the Phoenix EPO staff. These letters were documents signed in good faith by both our EPO team and the group that we partnered with. In the letter we laid out what each group would provide in terms of resources, staff, and what was expected by each group. For example if we supported a camp we laid out all the materials that were to be given, loaned for return and what things money could be used for (for example scholarships and lunches but not staff salary).

Quite often providing lunch and transportation helped many of our local partners overcome barriers to visiting our facility. This was an issue also raised by many session participants. It is very important to find out what will make participation possible for different audiences. In situations of staff shortages, leveraging on other organizations, especially volunteer organization such as Americorps and high school clubs, can make programs much more successful.

We found that being upfront about the dollar cost of our "no cost" programs helped communicate the value about the service we were providing and increased buy in from partners into working with us to make a program successful.

In an attempt to expand partnerships to other states we looked for ways to keep live connections part of the partnership. MacBooks and iChat are an inexpensive alternative to video conferencing ($\sim$\$700 per unit) and allowed us to do live chats with audiences from all over the country. We provided the MacBooks on loan and helped partners find projectors, speakers etc. One issue continues to be consistent internet in some parts of the country, even in major cities and is an issue that must be worked out before your program, as with all technology.

Overall we found that we had to reality check our goals that we started with and adapt our programs to meet the needs of our partners. We found that our traditional products such as formal curricula were not useful without adaptation with our new partners and flexibility was the key to adapting to meet varying needs.

5.2. Grow the Partnerships

As with many programs supported on soft money, the Phoenix Mission is creating many partnerships that will not be able to be continued after the mission, and money, is over. To continue the benefit of our partnerships we are careful to support work with other institutions so that programs do not end with your program that may not always be there. After working hard to make connections and providing a service, make sure there will be a good transition to other resources so that the service you provide to the community goes beyond the initial partnership.

5.3. Benefits Realized through Phoenix Mission Partnerships as Example

In the past year the Phoenix Mission partnered with new partners: Arizona Gear Up program Louisiana Children's Museum, Wildcat Charter school (Tucson, AZ), Chabot Space and Science Center, urban and rural classrooms in AK, FL, Chicago, WA, RI, NY, through our teacher partners, Exploration Place (Wichita, KS), and Imagine Mars (NASA ongoing program).

In response to our partnerships our formal curriculum was adopted by St. Bernard Parish school district in Louisiana, we made connections between local schools and the local University College of Science for future collaborations, we were able to provide summer camp programs at no cost to 100 kids that could never have afforded it at 5 institutions and a better experience for all campers for around \$10,000 infused into those organizations. In addition to students and instructors, we reached countless adult, high school and middle school volunteers through support of programming and were able to reach families of students who attended non-traditional programming.

In the end it is important to remember that positive outcomes often occur when there is careful planning and flexibility, helping an at-risk population is more powerful if it goes beyond your institution, you are there to support and not "improve" necessarily, and look for other ways to help such as increasing the number of books in the library. Look beyond the traditional ways of helping to expand the impact you can have on new partners.

EPO and a Changing World
ASP Conference Series, Vol. 389, © *2008*
C. Garmany, M. Gibbs, and J. W. Moody

Touching the Moon and the Stars: Astronomy for the Visually Impaired

José L. Alonso

Arecibo Observatory[1] / NAIC , HC03 Box 53995 Arecibo, Puerto Rico 00612

Carmen A. Pantoja, Gloria M. Isidro and Paul Bartus

University of Puerto Rico Department of Physics PO Box 23343 San Juan, Puerto Rico 00931-3343

Abstract. Astronomy provides a content that is normally communicated through images and physical models. In order to present science concepts to a visually impaired public requires special adaptation of images, graphs, and diagrams. In this workshop participants will learn to use tactile materials that are available to teach basic astronomy to visually impaired public. These materials can be adapted to be used in both classroom and museum settings. The first part of the workshop introduces participants to various examples of tactile materials, and applies them to describe the phases of the Moon. Participants will then explore (blindfolded) the surface of the Moon and will learn to identify its characteristics. These will include craters, valleys, and mountain ridges. On another activity participants will construct a tactile model for a constellation.

1. Introduction

The goal of this workshop is to present some education tools and strategies that can help students or people with visual impairments to understand some basic concepts of astronomy. Students or people with special needs may have learning disabilities, difficulties with mobility, hearing or visual impairments among others. The best way to help these students is to include them in the activities in which the rest of the class is participating (Bartus *et al.* 2007). Reasonable accommodations are practices and procedures in the areas of presentation, response, environment, and time that allow equal access to education and evaluation for the individuals with disabilities.

This workshop has been developed in a cooperative effort between the Arecibo Observatory Ángel Ramos Foundation Visitor Center and the Department of Physics at University of Puerto Rico. Our intention is to develop and have readily available materials that will enhance the public understanding in science for the general population, teachers and students in Puerto Rico. All materials are developed in Spanish and English.

---

[1]The Arecibo Observatory is part of the National Astronomy and Ionosphere Center (NAIC) a national research center operated by Cornell University under a cooperative agreement with the National Science Foundation (NSF).

The strategy used to present this workshop was to prepare three activities and set up three tables with the materials needed for each activity. The workshop participants were organized in three groups. As each group completes an activity they move to the next table. A detailed description of the materials used and Braille files of the instructions for the activities can be found at the following link: http://ltp.upr.clu.edu/astrolab/ASP_119th.html

2.   Phases of the Moon

2.1.   Goal

That the participants are able to associate the phase of the Moon with its revolution around the Earth and the Sun, Earth and Moon positions.

2.2.   Materials

- 3-dimensional model of the Sun-Earth-Moon system.

- Cardboard cards with the phases of the Moon

- Movable card illustrating the phases of the Moon

- Wire circle with bead model

2.3.   Background Information

The Moon revolves around the Earth once each month (27.3 days). The Moon's orbit forms a 5°angle with the ecliptic plane. The Moon rotates on its axis at the same rate as it revolves around the Earth. It maintains the same side facing the Earth (synchronous rotation).

We see the Moon because of sunlight reflected from its surface. The Moon's hemisphere that faces the Sun is always illuminated but the illuminated side does not always face the Earth. The change in position of the Moon with respect to the Sun gives place to the phases of the Moon. As the Moon rotates around the Earth, the amount of the lunar sphere that is illuminated by the Sun and that we are able to see changes. Those changes are called phases and they are repeated each month in a specific cycle. This is called the synodic period (29.5 days).

The four most important phases are: New Moon, First Quarter, Full Moon, Third Quarter and New Moon. These correspond to the configurations in which the Earth-Moon-Sun form an angle of 0°, 90°, 180°and 270°respectively.

New Moon: The angle between the Earth-Moon direction and Earth-Sun direction is 0°. The Sun and the Moon rise, cross the local meridian and set at the same time and for this reason we do not seehyperref the Moon.

First Quarter: The angle between the Earth-Moon direction and the Earth-Sun direction is 90°. The Moon is in quadrature and half of the disk is illuminated. The Moon rises when the Sun is in transit and it sets at midnight.

Full Moon: The angle between the Earth-Moon direction and the Earth-Sun direction is 180°. The Moon is in opposition. The entire disk that is visible form Earth is illuminated. The Moon rises when the Sun sets and is visible during the entire night.

Third Quarter: The angle between the Earth-Moon direction and the Earth-Sun direction is 270°. The Moon is in quadrature and half of the Moon's disk is illuminated. The Sun rises when the Moon is in transit, and it is visible during the morning towards the west. Each phase occurs approximately a week after the previous one.

Points to Stress:

- The amount of the Moon's disk that is illuminated changes gradually during the week that it takes to go from one phase to the next. The Moon does not change instantly from one phase to the next.

- The Moon is not limited to the night sky. It is possible to see the Moon during the day near to First and Third Quarter.

- The phases of the Moon are due to the change in the fraction of the illuminated lunar surface that is pointed towards us as the Moon rotates around the Earth.

2.4. Procedure

1. Familiarization with the material.

   (a) Facilitator will present the concepts of rotation and revolution of the Earth and Moon kinesthetically. Rotate with your body and guide the revolution with a piece of string.

   (b) Facilitator stresses concepts of revolution with the wire circles model.

   (c) Facilitator presents the 3-dim model of the Sun-Earth-Moon geometry. Spheres have a dark and illuminated hemisphere. We will consider the hemisphere with the beads to be the dark side of the Moon.

   (d) Facilitator will present the set of phases of the Moon on cardboard. The dark side of the Moon is represented by the felt material. Facilitator presents embossed material (Grice 1998, 2005).

   (e) Facilitator presents the sliding cardboard model that stresses the gradual changes of the Moon phases.

2. If all the participants are sighted, decide if some would try the material and activity with a blindfold.

3. As a group assemble the 3-dim model that represents the Sun-Earth-Moon geometry and be able to explain its parts and what it represents.

4. From the Sun-Earth-Moon configuration selest the card with the corresponding moon phase.

5. Indicate the Sun-Earth-Moon configuration for the card provided by the facilitator.

6. How many days have passed since the New Moon phase for the phase indicated in the provided cards?

7. As a group discuss the experience in terms of:

   (a) usefulness of the models

   (b) variations to the models

   (c) difficulties in presentations and alternative strategies

   (d) other comments. Write a summary of the most important points

2.5.   Useful Links

- http://aa.usno.navy.mil/data/docs/RS_OneDay.html: This gives the sunrise, sunset, moonrise and moonset data for a specific day and location.

- http://www.spacescience.org/education/instructional_materials.html: This is the Kinesthetic Astronomy resource by Cherilynn Morrow and Michael Zawaski.

- http://analyzer.depaul.edu/SEE_Project/: This contains adapted materials on astronomy designed for reproduction with a thermal expansion machine or braille embosser. It contains an activity by Noreen Grice on the phases of the Moon.

- http://www.yale.edu/ynhti/curriculum/guides/1998/6/98.06.06.x.html: This is a curriculum adapted for use with blind and visually impaired students by Joanne Pompano entitled "Exploring the Moon."

- http://www.tsgc.utexas.edu/space_vision/ This has diverse activities adapted for the blind and visually impaired and includes an activity on lunar phases. The program contact is Dr. Judit Györgyey.

3.   Constellations

3.1.   Goal

Become familiar with the positions of the stars of the constellations Leo and Hercules. Build tactile materials for a constellation. Identify the motions of the Moon with respect to the stars.

3.2.   Materials

- Graphs of the constellations Leo and Hercules

- Transparency sheets

- Tracing wheel

- Adhesive gems

- Paper

- Markers

3.3. Background Information

A constellation is a pattern in the sky made with the stars. There are 88 constellations defined on the celestial sphere. The stars in the pattern are not necessarily at the same distance. An asterism is a pattern of stars within the constellation. An example of an asterism is the Big Dipper in Ursa Major.

At night you can see about 3000 stars and they appear with different brightness and different colors. During the night the Moon and the stars move from East to West with respect to the horizon. When you observe the Moon with respect to the stars it moves from West to East. It moves at a rate of about 0.5°per hour.

3.4. Procedure

1. Facilitator will present the materials.

2. If all the participants are sighted, decide if some wish to use a blindfold for the activity.

3. Each participant will design a constellation with a given group of stars.

4. The facilitator will provide the constellation of Leo. For this constellation the participants will identify the pattern, the stars, and the relative brightness (indicated by size). Sighted students may help in the description of the lion pattern in Leo.

5. The participants will identify the asterism in Leo (Sickle pattern).

6. The participants will prepare a tactile constellation with the materials provided by the facilitator.

7. As a group discuss the experience in terms of:
   (a) usefulness of the models
   (b) variations to the models
   (c) difficulties in presentations and alternative strategies
   (d) other comments. Write a summary of the most important points

3.5. Useful Links

- http://stardate.org/nightsky/constellations/(English) or http://radiouniverso.org/maestros/ (Spanish). This link will give you a guide to the constellations with interesting audio information about astronomy.

4. Geology of the Moon

4.1. Goal

Recognize different geological features on the surface of the Moon.

4.2.   Materials

- Tactile model of the Moon

- Earth+ sonification program

4.3.   Background Information

When you look at the Moon at night you can notice it has dark areas and light areas on its surface. With binoculars you can observe that the light areas have many craters, while the dark areas are relatively smoother.

The dark areas on the surface of the Moon are called "maria", from the Latin word "mare" that means oceans. The astronauts described these regions as smooth, and are thought to have formed early in the formation of the Moon from the flow of lava. The maria have few craters and are covered by a type of rock called basalts that are similar to the rocks formed by lava here on Earth. These rocks are estimated to be 3.1 to 3.8 billion years old. Another type of rock brought to Earth by the astronauts was the breccia. This type of rock was collected near the rims of craters in the maria. They are produced by impacts and are estimated to be 4 billion years old.

The light areas have mountains and many craters. These are called the terrae or highlands (because they are higher than the maria). The color of these areas is lighter because of a type of light colored rock called anorthosite. This type of rock is found on Earth only in the oldest mountains (see Mottana *et al.* 1978). These Moon rocks are more than 4 billion years old.

The Moon's soil is called regolith and is composed of particles of different sizes. Its detailed composition and texture varies with location but it is thought to be created by meteor impacts.

When observing the Moon with binoculars or a small telescope you will notice that there are many craters, with different sizes and shapes, but usually they are round. From some of these craters you will see bright rays surrounding them giving the impression of a big blast. Craters are formed by impacts from objects from space. Large craters are named after scientists, scholars and artists. Small craters have common first names.

In addition to optical images of the Moon, astronomers can make radar observations of the Moon. In this activity we will use the Earth+ software developed by NASA in collaboration with the Filius Institute at the University of Puerto Rico. This software allows the student to explore jpeg format images using sound cues about the features in the image. The program is still in a beta version. In the activity the participants will explore an image of the South pole of the Moon taken using Arecibo Observatory and Greenbank radio telescopes. The image is about 250 km by 100 km. This region is difficult to observe optically.

4.4.   Procedure

1. The facilitator will present the tactile Moon and the program Earth+.

2. If all the participants are sighted, decide if some wish to use a blindfold for the activity.

3. Explore the tactile map. Identify the different textures and different craters like Tycho, Clavius, Copernicus, Aristarchus and Langrenus and the different maria like Mare Serenitatis and Mare Tranquilitatis. You might want to use Earth+ to identify these particular features or have a Moon map from an atlas (e.g., Ridpath 2004). Describe the surface features you find most interesting.

4. As a group describe the craters and how they formed.

5. The facilitator will locate a radar image of the Moon that can be explored with Earth+. This image was obtained by transmitting at 13 cm wavelength from Arecibo Observatory and receiving the radar echo at the Greenbank radio telescope (Courtesy Cornell University/Smithsonian Institution). It is an image of the South Pole of the Moon. The rotational axis of the Moon lies near Shackleton crater. This crater is 19 km in diameter.

6. As a group discuss the experience in terms of:

   (a) usefulness of the models

   (b) variations to the models

   (c) difficulties in presentations and alternative strategies

   (d) other comments. Write a summary of the most important points

4.5. Useful Links

- http://www.adlerplanetarium.org/cyberspace/moon/: This link provides more details of the geology of the Moon.

- http://www.nasm.si.edu/exhibitions/attm/enter.html: This link has more details on the Apollo mission from the exhibit at the National Air and Space Musueum.

- http://www.aaccoreconcepts.com/: To order the Tactile Moon maps go to this link or contact Robin Hurd at hurd4kids@aol.com.

- http://www.nasm.si.edu/research/ceps/research/moon/radar_south_images. cfm: Visit this site for examples of radar images of the Moon.

- http://prime.jsc.nasa.gov/earthplus/: This is the site from which a person can download the Earth+ software.

- http://www.manolo.net/nasa1.htm: This gives a description in Spanish of the Earth+ project.

- http://www.freedomscientific.com/fs_downloads/jaws.asp: Download a demo of jaws screen reader software from this location.

- http://www.touchgraphics.com: This link contains information on the "Talking Tactile tablet" suggested by Noreen Grice.

5. Discussion

This workshop demonstrated materials that can be used to present some basic concepts in astronomy relying more on the sense of touch and sound. Alternative demonstrations and activities help in creating a more inclusive setting for students and people with different capacities or abilities.

Several comments were made about the models and how to improve or modify them. Noreen Grice demonstrated a kinesthetic approach to present the concept of the phases of the Moon. In this method two participants, represent the Earth-Moon system, hold each other as if dancing. A third participant will stand at some distance from the two, representing the position of the Sun, indicating their position by the sound of a bell. The sliding model for the phases was not accurate but it was suggested that it could be used to present the concept of a solar eclipse. The observation was made that the tactile maps of the Moon were not uniform and it is important that all the maps be the same so the Moon is accurately represented. It was suggested to combine the tactile maps of the Moon with the sonification by using a "Talking Tactile Tablet." This has been considered by the Earth+ project. The activity of the constellations was well received because it was easily incorporated in a classroom setting.

Modifying the traditional presentation of astronomy concepts requires preliminary preparation. But this investment will result in a better understanding of the concepts.

Acknowledgments. We would like to thank Mr. José Alvarez for demonstrating the use of the program Earth+. Mr. Alvarez is the Coordinator in the area of electronic accessibility at the Filius Institute at the UPR. He is blind and also helped us evaluating the workshop material. We would like to thank Mr. Luis Pérez, an undergraduate student at the UPR who is blind and helped us evaluating the material and with the Braille printing of the activities. We would like to acknowledge Dr. Don Campbell for the radar images of the Moon used for the sonification program. The image used was a courtesy of Cornell University/Smithsonian Institution.

References

Bartus, P., Isidro, G. M., La Rosa, C., and Pantoja, C.A., AER, **6**, 1 (2007)

Grice, N., *Touch the Stars*, 3rd ed. (Museum of Science and Charles Hayden Planetarium, Boston, 1998)

Grice, N., *El Pequeño Libro de las Fases de la Luna* (Ozone Publishing Corp., Puerto Rico, 2005)

Grice, N., AER, **5**, 1 (2006)

Mottana, A., Crespi, R., and Liborio, G. *Simon & Schuster's Guide to Rocks and Minerals* (Simon and Schuster Inc. 1978)

Norton's Star Atlas and Reference Handbook 2004, edited by I. Ridpath (Pi Press, New York, 2004)

EPO and a Changing World
ASP Conference Series, Vol. 389, © 2008
C. Garmany, M. Gibbs, and J. W. Moody

Multicultural Astronomy Learning Using Sunrise and Sunset Phenomena

Taha Massalha[1]

*The Academic Arab College for Education in Israel, Hahashmal St. 22,
Haifa, Israel 33145*

Abstract.   Effective learning mixed with enjoyable activities needs a suitable
environment different from the normal curriculum that we (the teachers) and the
students are familiar with. On this note, Astronomy activities are attractive and
involving. We believe that there is always room to propose educational projects
that are implemented outside the classroom walls. In this conference, we will
give practical examples of Astronomy Peace Projects that were implemented in
middle schools (for Jews, Christians, Moslems and Druzes) in Israel, during the
2002-2007 school years.

1.   Introduction

Measurement of time according to the sun's position in the sky is mentioned in
the Old Testament, the New Testament and the Koran. Moslem prayer time
is determined by the location of the sun in the sky. The Hebrew and Moslem
months depend upon the presence of the moon in the sky, while the Christian
months depend on the presence of the sun.

   "Astronomy with a Stick" is a program of nine activities, written by Sylvia
K. Shugrue, for upper elementary and middle school students. It was created in
order to enable the students to study astronomy during school hours on school
grounds (Shugrue 2001). Shugrue's activities are applicable without conflict to
the three dominant religions in the Holy Land. All three religions in Israel are
dependent upon the changes in the location of the sun in the day or the moon
at night. People in India and China share this dependence too.

   Middle school students in Israel are sitting in the middle of a dilemma,
exactly between the relaxed environment of elementary school and the increasing
pressures of the high school curricula. Generally, the top students in middle
school are not required to take advantage of their own potential for critical
thinking, or for the acquisition of skills and methods of investigation or further
exploration (Abadi & Massalha 2006). We believe that there is always room to
propose educational projects, particularly scientific ones, for upper elementary
and middle school students. These projects help increase and deepen science
teaching in general and physics education in particular, thus maximizing the
advantages of the hidden potentials of students.

   Teaching by using guided investigation and exploration in performing astronomical projects is one amongst many methods of teaching (Grossman, Shapiro

---

[1]tahamas@gmail.com

and Ward 2000). The uniqueness of this method is in its level of function in critical thinking and its authenticity and intellectual gratification to both students and teachers (Gardner 1984). This is specifically accurate in the integration of art, mathematics, computer science, and the natural science phenomenon. It fosters rich experiences and enhanced critical thinking by personal observation, thus deepening the process of analyzing a phenomena and building a scientific model for the theories which evolve (Gardner 2006). While students are building hypotheses and making conclusions, an educational environment is created that enhances students' group work, at the same time encouraging individual free thought and the development of the desire to widen knowledge.

In this conference, we give practical examples of two projects that were implemented in middle schools in the Galilee, Israel, during the 2002-2007 school years. These examples can be divided into two scientific subjects:

2. The Rising/Setting Sun

This part of our study, describes an interdisciplinary teaching approach that integrates both science and art. The objective is to help students understand a daily astronomical phenomenon by observing it and learning to represent it through sketching and analyzing pictures. This study focuses on the teaching and learning process (Perkins 2004), of the "Sunrise Sunset" phenomenon (Massalha & Shugrue 2003). Furthermore, this study was created in order to change previous misconceptions in regards to phenomena that we face in our daily lives, particularly misconceptions about the sunrise and sunset phenomena. These phenomena include the recurrence phenomenon, the yearly recurrence of sunrise and sunset at a specific time and location, as well as the recurrence of the time interval between sunrise and sunset.

The examined parameters are:

1. Changes in the location of the rising/setting sun during the year.

2. Changes in the time of the rising/setting sun during the year.

With the collection of measurements, we question whether these recurrences depend on the geographic location and if there is any natural law applicable to these recurrences. Conversely, we question if it is possible to determine the geographic location on Earth of the sunrise/ sunset, based on knowledge about the locations characteristics. Our goal is to stimulate scientific thought and to strengthen the student's knowledge about astronomy phenomenon, through observation over a long period of time.

The study began with multiple assignments for the students, revolving around the rising and setting of the sun. The students were asked to:

- Observe the sun rise and set once a week and record their observations.

- Carefully sketch the eastern horizon according to its appearance from their location, marking the position and time of sunrise.

- Carefully sketch the western horizon according to its appearance from their location; marking the position and time of sunset.

Figure 1.   Sunset (location and time) as measured by one of the students from Nazareth. The "yellow sun" represents measurements from 12.9.2003 to 21.12.2003 (the sun appears to be moving south), the "red sun" represents measurements from 17.1.2004 to 17.6.2004 (the sun appears to be moving north).

- Construct a table stating the date and time of sunrise and sunset.

In the beginning of the study, the students found these tasks to be silly and arduous and did not think there was anything to learn about the sunrise and sunset that they did not already know. As the study progressed, the students spent more time observing the properties of the recurrence of the sunset, and came to recognize this previously unfamiliar phenomenon. This realization motivated and increased curiosity about the revolution of the earth around the sun amongst the students.

An example of the sketches (the art and the measurement results) that the students made during one academic period is found in Figure 1. Through their sketches, the students found that the apparent location of the sun in the horizon during sunrise/ sunset moves throughout the year.

This finding is exemplified in Figure 2. The graph is a compilation of the findings of the students in regards to the location of the sunset in the horizon over an extended period of time.

For the location of sunset, which was measured over a year, we arrived at a graph (Figure 2) that clearly demonstrates the sunrise locations in arbitrary units, relative to the location of sunset on Sep. 21st (or on Mar. 21st), in a yearly cycle.

We see that the sun rises/sets at different locations throughout the year. Additionally, the daily movement of the sun will always be from the east to the west. Tanking this into account, our observations must always take place from the same place; otherwise there is no relevance to these measurements. From here we can see that there is more than one direction for "east", and more than one direction for "west". Now if this is so, where is the actual east, and where is the west? What we learn is that west is the direction of the sunset from the observer on the 21st of March, or 21st of September of every year, and east is the direction of the sunrise from the observer on these same dates.

The participants' observations of sunrise and sunset over two years yielded results that clearly demonstrate the "recurrence" phenomenon and "recurrence of the hour of sunrise/ sunset". When comparing the graphs of the time of

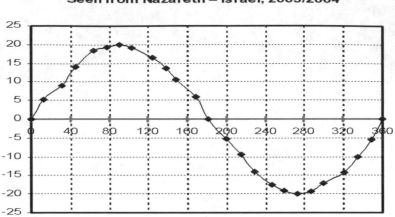

Figure 2.   The relative location of sunset in the region of Nazareth during the 2003/4 academic year. The location of sunset on 21.9.2003 was selected as point zero.

sunrise and sunset, we came to an interesting observation, an earlier sunrise, does not denote an earlier setting of the sun, and a later sunrise does not denote a later sunset. The results showed the flip side to be true, the days of early sunrise were also the days of late sunset, and the days of late sunrise were the days of early sunset. Although the recurrence of sunrise and sunset are interdependent, we did come to the conclusion that there is a recurrence of the change in the number of daylight/night hours (Gilbert & Ireton 2003).

Daily phenomena related to astronomy are complicated to observe, nevertheless, they are significant to the students understanding of their environment (Heyden 1975). Misconceptions about sunrise and sunset were found among all groups of participants: middle and high school students and teaching trainees majoring in physics, science and other similar subjects, and science teachers too (Abadi & Massalha 2006). The students come to class with "some" knowledge about the world which contrasts scientific reality. Pre-existing knowledge affects the way they explain and comprehend new information. It is possible to deal with this issue through several strategies: different disciplinary perspectives, different teaching methods, or through a variety of teaching materials. This study describes a procedure of operational perception of teaching and learning through an experiential and active process carried out diligently by the students. The participants developed thinking habits relevant to research learned in an active manner; and made connections between the learning material and the daily phenomenon (Perkins 1992, 2004).

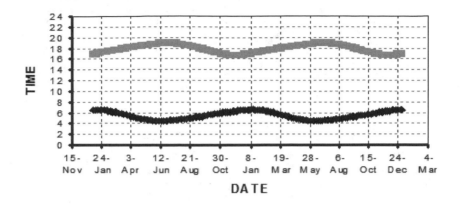

Figure 3.   Sunrise and sunset hours and the number of daylight hours based on measurements in Nazareth during the years 2003-4 according to the local wintertime.

3.   Observing Changes in the Length of Shadows

In this part of our study, we investigate how shadows change in direction and length throughout the day (Grossman, Shapiro, & Ward 2000). Additionally, we focus our measurements on learning more about the shortest shadow of the day, and its direction.

Questions were raised in the classroom, for student contemplation, in order to engage them in the topic. These questions mainly revolved around the size of shadows, be they large or small, and asked the student to recall previous shadows that they had seen. Before beginning the activity, we asked the students to sketch their predictions about the changes occurring in the length of the shortest shadow, during the year. We can see samples of the student's predictions of the shortest shadow length during the year in Figure 4.

After the student's made their predictions about the shortest shadow during the year, they began observing and measuring:

- The changes in the length of shadows during the day, and the changes in the direction of the shadows.

- The length of the shortest shadow and its direction.

- The changes in the length and direction of the shortest shadows.

Through the use of various materials, including a flagpole, a meter stick, and a wristwatch, the students were able to observe, and learn about changes in shadows throughout the day, through firsthand experience.

The goal in this activity is to observe, measure, and "try" to understand, how shadows change in direction and length throughout the day. The activity

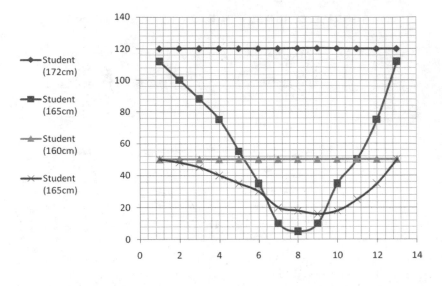

Figure 4.   The variation of student values with respect to student 172.

began early in a holiday, while the sun was still shining brightly in the sky. The students were directed to find the shadow of a flagpole and to observe its changes throughout the hours of day light. Measurements of the length of the shadow, taken from the base of the object, till the end of the shadow, were taken as precisely as possible. Standing at the base of the flagpole, and using a magnetic compass, students found the direction of the shadow. The students recorded these measurements in a notebook, noting the time of day, the length of the shadow, and it's direction, including the measurement of the shortest shadow. These measurements were repeated every hour, with the exception of noon, when they were repeated every five minutes. Diagram of these shadows, and their measurements, were drawn by the students (Figure 5).

While measuring the length and direction of shadows, the students observed changes that occur throughout the day. As the day progresses from morning to noon and the sun gets "higher" in the sky, the length of the shadows shorten and the direction of the shadow begins to face north. Conversely, as the day proceeds on from noon to evening and the sun begins to set, the shadows get longer and the direction of the shadows moves toward the east.

4.   Conclusions

These studies were implemented in order to increase and deepen science teaching in general and physics/astronomy education in particular, thus maximizing the advantages of the hidden potentials of students. Teaching by using guided dynamic investigation and exploration in performing, projects is one among many methods of teaching. The uniqueness of this method is its level of the function in leading critical thinking, and its authenticity and intellectual gratification to

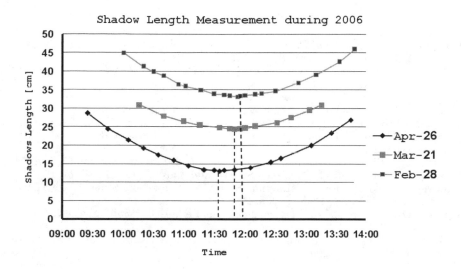

Figure 5.   Three Days Shadow Length Measurements', we find the shortest of shadow length in each day – the dash lines. In the early morning, the shadows face the west. As we get closer to noon, these shadows shorten, and begin to face the north. At solar noon, the length of the shadow is the shortest and its direction is to the north in the northern hemisphere and to the south in the southern hemisphere. At this time, solar noon, Muslims pray their noon prayer. As noon passes, and the sun begins its decent in the afternoon, the shadows begin to face east, and grow in length in this direction till the setting of the sun.

both students and teachers, especially in a multicultural environment. Throughout the study, the students slowly realized that subjects that they had previously found dry and boring were actually interesting and fun. They found that there was much more to learn about the apparent movement of the sun and its cycles. By being an active participant in their own education, the students were not only able to learn more about astronomy, but to enjoy the learning experience as well.

References

Abadi, R. and Massalha, T., "Critical and Creative Thinking in Science Education: An Active Model for Teaching/Learning Comprehensive Understanding". Proceeding of International Science Conference (NSSE Community, Singapore, 2006)

Gardner, H., *Art, Mind and Brain: A Cognitive Approach to Creativity*, (Basic Books – A Subsidiary of Peruses Books, L.L.C., 1984)

Gardner, H., *Five Minds for the Future* (Harvard Business School Press, 2006)

Gilbert, S. W. and Ireton, S. W., *Understanding Models in Earth and Space Science* (NSTA Press, Arlington, Virginia, 2003)

Grossman, M. C. Shapiro, I. I. and Ward, R. B., "Exploring the Earth in Motion: Daylight, Sun, and Shadow Patterns", in Science Journal and Teacher Manual (Astronomy-Based Physical Science, Harvard-Smithsonian Center for Astrophysics, 2000)

Heyden, F. J. "The Complete Astronomer", (Ateneo De Manila, Quezon City, 1975)

Massalha, T. and Abadi, R., "Between Sunrise and Sunset," Tehuda (2) 25, 17 (2005)

Massalha, T. and Shugrue, S., "Daytime Study for High School Students", NSTA National Convention, Philadelphia, PA. (2003)

Perkins, D., "Understanding Performances," in Perkins D. *Smart Schools*, The Free Press, 75-79 (1992)

Perkins, D., "What is Understanding", in Wiske, M. S. *Teaching for Understanding* (Jossey-Bass Inc., 2004)

EPO and a Changing World
ASP Conference Series, Vol. 389, © 2008
C. Garmany, M. Gibbs, and J. W. Moody

When Everybody Wins: EPO and Underserved Communities

Carla Bitter, Sanlyn R. Buxner, and Andy Shaner

Phoenix Mars Mission, Lunar and Planetary Lab, The University of Arizona, 1415 N. 6th Ave, Tucson, AZ 85705

Abstract.   We present our recent summer programs implemented by the Phoenix Mars Scout Mission that took a traditional Mars curriculum and utilized it in summer camps serving scientifically underserved communities.

1.   Phoenix Mars Scout Mission EPO Opportunities With Underserved Communities

1.1.   Overview

The Phoenix Mars Scout Mission's EPO team had a unique opportunity to expand beyond the realm of traditional curriculum development and dissemination and take a new set of Mars activities directly to underserved science communities. By creating working partnerships with The Louisiana Children's Museum in New Orleans, LA, Exploration Place in Wichita, KS, The Wildcat School in Tucson, AZ and Chabot Space & Science Center in Oakland, CA, Phoenix's EPO program funded MarsBots summer camp experiences for nearly 300 children in grades 1-6. EPO staff provided partners with hands-on staff training, curriculum, supplies, and student scholarships, as well as live, interactive updates from Cape Canaveral during Phoenix's launch week in August 2007. Working with diverse communities across America presented some challenges, but ultimately many rewards for all of the participants.

1.2.   Workshops

Mission staff conducted one and two day workshops for museum staff and volunteers highlighting science content, inquiry pedagogy, and implementation plans. Dozens of new learner/teachers were created to oversee the summer programs.

1.3.   Summer Camps

Museum staff, student and local volunteers led the week-long MarsBots camps for need-based local elementary school children. Mission staff organized a daily live "Ask an Expert" video chat from Kennedy Space Center using loaned Mac-Books.

1.4.   Lessons Learned

We found that the staff training was beneficial for centers to adapt the activities for use in their own settings. The trainings allowed us to provide Mars content for the summer camps to staff that were not well informed about current Mars science and allowed time for troubleshooting their specific implementation plan and technical issues. Loaning summer camp sites MacBooks for the summer helped facilitate many of the non-traditional camp activities such as showing animations, the launch event, and doing live videoconferencing. Each MacBook was pre-loaded with all presentations, animations, lesson plans, and needed software. This helped eliminate barriers that sites may have had with slow internet connects and helped reduce hard-ware and software problems.

Using iChat was an inexpensive way to allow the camps to interact with mission personnel as none of the sites were equipped with videoconferencing equipment. Campers were able to see and hear mission personnel during launch week events each day live from Kennedy Space Center. We found that having all sites on a chat at once, while more efficient for the expert, was not effective for the kids at each site since they were not engaged when they were not the target audience for answering questions. Rather we found by the end of the week that doing shorter segments with each site improved the experience for campers at each site. Additionally, using iChat was an effective way for students to present their projects to mission personnel as a culminating event for their camp.

Overall, using loaned MacBooks was an easy, inexpensive way to bring the sights and sounds of launch week for the Phoenix Mission to our underserved audiences all over the county.

EPO and a Changing World
ASP Conference Series, Vol. 389, © 2008
C. Garmany, M. Gibbs, and J. W. Moody

University Astronomy: Instructional Strategies for the Visually Impaired

Dennis W. Dawson

Department of Physics, Astronomy & Meteorology, Western Connecticut State University, Danbury, Connecticut 06810, USA

Abstract. While teaching a spring laboratory course in general university astronomy, I agreed to provide instruction to a student who had been advised against laboratory work in chemistry and biology because of her significant visual impairment. This poster describes our mutual learning experience as we developed tactile concept demonstrations and laboratory exercises. Progress assessment issues and gaps in educational resources will also be discussed.

1. Introduction

In the spring of 2007, I was asked to accommodate Ashley C., who is severely visually impaired, with a cataract in one eye and very low vision in the other, in my general astronomy class. She had been advised not to take chemistry or biology laboratory science courses because of the potential for injury from the equipment and be-cause laboratory experiments normally require close visual work.

General Astronomy is also a laboratory course. How was I to present materials and activities in astronomy, which is in general a hugely visual science, in ways which were at a level equivalent to knowledge gained by sighted students?

2. Methodology

Ashley had difficulty using a standard astronomy textbook with two columns of text per page and numerous figures and images; her scanner could not properly translate the multimedia format. Not all publishers have Braille equivalents of the recent editions of their textbooks or access to online text which can be read through JAWS or similar software. Organizations like the National Printing House for the Blind have a modest selection of textbooks, but they are often several years out of date.

Dawson and Grice (2005) developed tactile versions of celestial objects to assess their learning enhancement potential on sighted people during planetarium shows and sky viewing sessions at the WCSU 20-inch telescope as part of the NASA SEE Project (http://analyzer.depaul.edu/SEE_Project).

I created tactile concept diagrams and lab exercises by photocopying pages onto sheets of thermal expansion paper and running them through a ZY-Fuse Heater thermal machine (Zychem Ltd.; http://www.zychem-ltd.co.uk/).

I adapted six laboratory exercises to tactile format: (1) the Moon's sidereal period; (2) determination of the Moon's mass; (3) spectral classification; (4) the

Sun's rotation; (5) lunar cratering; and (6) the spiral structure of our galaxy. The first two exercises were modified from visual versions in Hoff and Wilkerson (2006), the manual used by the class. Solar full-disk images for the fourth exercise were downloaded from the Project SEE website. The lunar cratering exercise was based on one that I had developed for a planetary science course. The visual version of the spiral structure exercise is in my own lab manual (Dawson 2002).

2.1. Discussion

Ashley and I found that tactile exercises were most comprehensible when the units of information (e.g., data points, graph subdivisions, line and area textures) were kept to limited but appropriate amounts. The solar rotation and lunar cratering exercises were least well negotiated because of information crowding on the tactiles. Compromises had to be made between an accurate portrayal of the physical situation and an intelligible rendition of the concept.

To deal with mathematical manipulations beyond basic operations requires that instructor and student be familiar with Nemeth code or a similar markup language. That was beyond the scope of the current work because of time constraints.

3. Conclusions

I plan to develop other lab exercises as well as a tactile set of fundamental concepts figures for use with blind or visually impaired students who may attend my other classes. Tactile images of many celestial objects are also available (e.g. Grice 2002).

Improvements in assistive technology have made the sciences ever more accessible to people with disabilities, especially when there are creative ways to address them. It is only in failing to try that we make progress impossible. The mind's eye is never blind.

Acknowledgments.   I thank Noreen Grice, and the WCSU Office of Disability Services, in particular its director Jack Sikora, for constructive consultations during the work.

References

Dawson, D.W., *Out of the Classroom: Observations & Investigations in Astronomy* (Brooks/Cole, Pacific Grove, 2002)

Dawson, D.W. and Grice, N.A., "Using Tactile Images to Enhance Learning at Astronomy Public Nights", (poster; 118th Annual A.S.P. Meeting, Engaging the EPO Community: Best Practices, New Approaches, Baltimore, 2005)

Grice, N.A., *Touch the Universe: A NASA Braille Book of Astronomy* (Joseph Henry Press, Washington D.C., 2002)

Hoff, D.B. and Wilkerson, J.A., *Contemporary Activities in Astronomy: A Process Approach*, 3rd Edition (Kendall/Hunt, Dubuque, 2006)

EPO and a Changing World
ASP Conference Series, Vol. 389, © 2008
C. Garmany, M. Gibbs, and J. W. Moody

Gemini Observatory Outreach and Educational Programming in Chile

Ma. Antonieta Garcia Ureta

Gemini Observatory, Colina El Pino s/n, La Serena, Chile

Abstract. I discuss how Gemini is reaching out to the local residents of Chile and Hawaii.

1. General Introduction

A core element in the Gemini Observatory's Public Information and Out-reach effort has been to address the needs of our two local host communities in Chile and Hawaii. This has resulted in a significant increase in awareness of the benefits that the state-of-the-art observatory brings to our local communities. In addition to the obvious economic and career opportunities, the Gemini host communities have benefited by educational programming for students, teachers and the public. In return we have been able to disseminate key messages such as the importance of dark skies to preserve the sky for future research and conserve our planet's natural resources.

A key advantage that Gemini has in implementing education and outreach programming is that there are two telescopes, each separated by the earth's equator. This provides a programmatic synergy that is exemplified by joint programs like the StarTeachers teacher exchange that involved interactions between Chilean and Hawaii teachers. Other parallel programs include adaptations of the ASP's FamilyAstro program and a Chilean AstroDay that is modeled on the success of the AstroDay program in East Hawaii.

In 2007, Gemini began raising the level of career awareness and how the observatory can provide new opportunities for youth in our host communities. Bilingual educational products are being developed that address questions like: What are the jobs that are available to Chileans at an astronomical observatory? What training and education is necessary to participate in this work? What can students do now to prepare for the type of work at an institution like Gemini?

Engaging an observatory's host community(s) is/are a critical part of any observatory's operation and crucial to the long-term sustainability of an institution. The benefits to both the observatory and community(s) can be profound if efforts are sustained, consistent and well-executed.

Personal discussions at the posters were common

Teaching special-needs children in unique ways

EPO and a Changing World
ASP Conference Series, Vol. 389, © 2008
C. Garmany, M. Gibbs, and J. W. Moody

Teaching Astronomy 101 at a Native American Community College

Catharine D. Garmany

National Optical Astronomy Observatory, 950 N. Cherry Ave, Tucson AZ 85719

Damascus Francisco

Member, Tohono O'odham Nation

Abstract. We discuss the challenges and experience of teaching introductory astronomy to Native Americans on an Indian reservation

1. Introduction

What is it like to teach in a community college on an Indian reservation, 60 miles from Tucson? After years teaching introductory astronomy in various large research universities, the first author has been offering astronomy 101/102 at Tohono O'odham Community College (TOCC) in Sells, AZ and the second author has taken two classes with her.

The Tohono O'odham reservation, about the size of Connecticut, is home to about 14,000 of the 24,000 tribal members. Like many Indian reservations, there are severe social problems. The high school graduation rate is about 60%. Sitting along some 60 miles of the US border with Mexico, there is a growing problem with Illegal immigration. Gangs are acknowledged to be an issue, and the homicide rate is twice that of other Indian reservations. Over 50% of the people suffer from type 2 diabetes. (http://www.tocaonline.org)

What is unusual is the presence, on their reservation, of a major observatory, Kitt Peak National Observatory. The lease setting up this agreement is now 50 years old, but only recently has serious collaborative outreach begun. As part of this efforrt NOAO offers an astronomy instructor to TOCC which is a two year institution with a student population of about 200 founded in 1998 . They maintain a website at http://www.tocc.cc.az.us

2. Garmany's Viewpoint:

In many respects, teaching at TOCC is no different from any community college. My students are older than typical college students. They have jobs, children and many demands on their time, and they frequently come to class unprepared. Their background, especially in math, is very weak. So much of the astronomy material is new so that it is hard for them to absorb it all.

The college is committed to incorporating their himdag (culture) in all courses. But how could I make the connection between the sky as seen by European astronomers and the traditions of my students? First, I tried to learn all I could about Tohono O'odham star stories. There is little material published, and even Elders that I talked with do not remember stories told by their grandparents. Is it even appropriate for me to talk about these? For example, these stories are traditionally told only during the winter months (when the snakes sleep). Damascus advises me that it is okay to talk about these stories in the context of "this is what I've read." There will be variations in legends even within a tribe. Be aware that published legends purporting to be Native American may be an amalgam from many tribes, hence indigenous to none.

Your student's vocabulary may not include words that you take for granted. These include not just scientific vocabulary, but other words as well. For example, words such as "companion", "horizon", "submerge" are not readily understood by some of my students. However, most of my student did not grow up speaking their native language, and this seems to hold for other Native American tribes as well. Do not make any assumptions about this: it will depend on the tribe and the student's background.

NOAO hosts a website with links to useful sites concerning science education and Native American nations. This was developed by Garmany in preparation for teaching at TOCC, but may be of use to to others. See the website http://www.noao.edu/education/native/

Francisco's Viewpoint:

I was always been interested in astronomy, so I signed up for this course at Tohono O'odham Community college. The sequence of classes fulfilled my science requirement. My educational goal is to complete a business degree, which I plan to earn after transferring to the U of Arizona in fall 2007 with my TOCC Associate's degree.

Here are some cultural things that instructors should be aware of.

My Grandmother told me, "We don't listen with our eyes, we listen with our ears". This is something to keep in mind if your students do not look you in the face.

Your students may not have the educational background you expect. But saying to them "You should know this" won't help, and will only make them feel uncomfortable.

Each Native American tribe is unique. And even what you learn about a particular tribe only represents someone's opinion. For example, legends will be told in different ways by different people. Many Tohono O'odham words for different stars and constellations reflect the Spanish influence of the 16th century, and cannot be considered as traditional.

Your students may have conflicts that you aren't aware of. They may have family obligations and ceremonies, which conflict with classes and assignments. Going to school will be harder for more traditional students. There may be issues with transportation, with care of elderly family members, and with other family issues. These will take precedence over school.

Acknowledgments.   NOAO acknowledges the Tohono O'odham Nation for leasing land for the national observatory. NOAO is operated by the Association of Universities for Research in Astronomy (AURA), Inc. under cooperative agreement with the NSF.

EPO and a Changing World
ASP Conference Series, Vol. 389, © 2008
C. Garmany, M. Gibbs, and J. W. Moody

Touch the Invisible Sky: A Multi-Wavelength Braille Book Featuring Tactile NASA Images

Noreen Grice

You Can Do Astronomy LLC, 125 Jones Drive, New Britain, CT 06053

Simon Steel

Harvard-Smithsonian Center for Astrophysics, 60 Garden St, Cambridge, MA 02138

Doris Daou

NASA Headquarters, 300 E. Street SW Washington, DC 20546

Abstract. According to the American Foundation for the Blind and the National Federation of the Blind, there are approximately 10 million blind and visually impaired people in the United States. Because astronomy is often visually based, many people assume that it cannot be made accessible. A new astronomy book, *Touch the Invisible Sky*, makes wavelengths not visible to human eyes, accessible to all audiences through text in print and Braille and with pictures that are touchable and in color.

1. Touch the Invisible Sky

Multi-wavelength astronomy - the study of the universe beyond visible light, has revolutionized our understanding and appreciation of the cosmos. Hubble, Chandra, and Spitzer are examples of powerful, space-based telescopes that complement each other in their observations spanning the electromagnetic spectrum.

Why create a tactile book on wavelengths that are not accessible to human eyes? Tactile images of a universe that until recently had been invisible to human eyes is an important learning message on how science and technology broadens our senses and our understanding of the natural world.

Touch the Invisible Sky not only displays tactile images of previously unseen celestial objects, but also presents them in a "family" album style. Each celestial object is shown as a set of four multi-wavelength views so the reader can directly compare and explore distinctive features.

The book includes a foreword by professional mountain climber Erik Weihenmayer, who describes his sense of discovery as the world's first blind person to climb Mt. Everest. Erik's frontier widens as he climbs to new heights, just as our understanding of the universe widens through previously unseen views.

The main body of the text begins with an introduction to wavelength and the electromagnetic spectrum. Tactile views and descriptions of Hubble, Spitzer, Chandra and an antenna from the Very Large Array radio telescope introduce some of the equipment and techniques used to reveal new views of the cosmos.

The featured astronomical objects were chosen to give a flavor of the diverse nature of the universe, from our own Sun to distant galaxies and the extreme universe of supernovae and pulsars. The features revealed by the different wavelength observations show how multi-wavelength observations can be synthesized to attain a deep understanding of the structure of astronomical objects and mechanisms that shape them.

Noreen Grice designed the tactile images and teacher Ben Wentworth and students at the Colorado School for the Blind evaluated the prototype tactile images.

The text pages have both print and Braille. The tactile images are in color with Techno Braille (acrylic) overlay by Ozone Publishing, San Juan, Puerto Rico.

2.   Funding

The prototype of this book was funded by a peer-reviewed Cycle 5 education and public outreach grant from the Chandra X-ray Center to Dr. Mark Lacy of the Spitzer Science Center.

The Space Telescope Science Institute, the Chandra X-ray Center, the Spitzer Science Center and NASA's Origins and Universe Forums contributed funds for publication.

References

American Foundation for the Blind, Blindness Statistics, http://www.afb.org
National Federation of the Blind, Astronomy Resources Web Portal,
        http://www.blindscience.org
Ozone Publishing Co., http://www.ozonepublishing.net
You Can Do Astronomy LLC http://www.youcandoastronomy.com

EPO and a Changing World
ASP Conference Series, Vol. 389, © 2008
C. Garmany, M. Gibbs, and J. W. Moody

What Can Science Do for Me? Engaging Urban Teens in the Chandra Astrophysics Institute

Mark Hartman, Irene Porro and Fred Baganoff

MIT Kavli Institute for Astrophysics and Space Research, 77 Massachusetts Ave-nue, NE80-6095, Cambridge, MA 02139

Abstract.   We present three years of longitudinal data showing how we can engage underrepresented high-school youth in out-of-school time research science. Over three years our participant population has evolved to be more reflective of the Boston student population as a result of changes in our recruitment strategy. In addition, changes in 4 major program areas helped all participant populations move toward our intended outcome of better understanding of the process of research science.

The goal of the CAI is to provide an opportunity for students underrepresented in STEM to build the background skills and knowledge necessary to understand how research science is done, by actually doing it. Students practice these abilities during a 5-week summer session at MIT. They then apply these skills to undertake year-long investigative projects involving Chandra data from x-ray targets proposed by MKI Chandra researchers. Students develop their own questions based on their summer experience and preliminary investigation of patterns in their data, and MKI researchers mentor the developing projects with guidance on how to possibly answer those questions. In this poster, we examine data from 3 cycles of the CAI (2005-2006, 2006-2007, and 2007-2008, cohorts of 15 students each year) to answer the following question: Do participants understand the process of research science? In other words, do they understand the nature of research science as question-driven, evidence-based, predictive, and a collaborative effort that requires clear communication?

EBAPS (http://www2.physics.umd.edu/~elby/EBAPS/home.htm) was administered several times to evaluate changes in participants' views of the way science is done and learned. Overall average score did not change significantly (paired t-test for mean) for either Cycle 2 or 3. However, compared to a group of 11th grade honors chemistry students, our participants came in with significantly higher scores on sub-scales indicating that science is more than just disconnected facts, that a constructivist approach is necessary for effective learning, and knowledge is not absolute but still relies on strong evidence.

A lack of strong changes on EBAPS performance leads us to examine incoming group characteristics. Demographics of students who completed the summer session show that over the three cycles, we see a shift to a younger, more diverse group, with less formal physics training. Over the three cycles, we also see higher recruitment and retention rate, moving from 25year) to 94

On discriminating statements as observations versus models, cycle 2 / 3 have statistically significant ($P¡0.05$) higher mean than cycle 1 at the end of the summer session, regardless of the stronger science background of cycle 2 participants. Ability to distinguish observations from models is a prerequisite for understanding how research science is done. When asked what participants value most about CAI, over the course of the program, we see a shift away from science content knowledge and to-ward transferable science research skills like communication, collaboration and confidence.

Strategies in 4 areas have guided program changes we feel have helped the CAI obtain its outcome of retaining students so they can develop a working understanding of how research science is done. (1) Recruitment effort: Spend more direct contact time with students, after gaining educator input and buy-in. Work directly with as many schools as possible: district-level interaction gives poor results. (2) Opportunities for participant independence: Shift toward more time spent on students' own projects, developing their own questions. (3) Repeated practice of skills: Shift away from basic facts toward utilitarian knowledge. (I.e. limit the concepts to that which you actually measure: linear size, distance, motion, luminosity, spectra). Cast investigations to be more like research projects with respect to data examined and interactions with group: oral/written communication, use of collaboration tools/wikis. (4) Scientist mentor involvement: Students should work with real adults from the scientific community, and develop a relationship with them. Provide effective scaffolding for the goal setting and clear communication necessary for steady progress on school-year research project. Students should have their own in-sights/ideas to bring to the table to discuss with mentors, to make the most of limited interaction time.

EPO and a Changing World
ASP Conference Series, Vol. 389, © 2008
C. Garmany, M. Gibbs, and J. W. Moody

Expanding the Partnership of Researchers, Teachers and Parents Through Science Museum Activities

Kaoru Kimura

Japan Science Foundation Science Museum, Tokyo, 2-1 Kitanomaru-Koen, Chi-yoda-ku, Tokyo, 102-0091, JAPAN

Vivian Hoette

University of Chicago, Yerkes Observatory, 373 West Geneva Street, Williams

Abstract. The Science Museum of Tokyo brings science and the general public together through an international collaboration of institutes, universities, and K-12 projects. These include the live science show "UNIVERSE", a "live observing" program with Hands-On Universe (HOU), Internet telescopes and the constellation cameras i-CAN. We are expanding these activities into formal education in an after-school program. We model partnerships between educators, researchers, university students, teachers and parents to create informal and formal education programs.

1. Partnerships

1.1. Connecting Researchers and the Public with "UNIVERSE"

The live science show "UNIVERSE" initiated in 1996 with RIKEN, involves researchers and university students in Science Museum activities. "UNIVERSE" provides state-of-the-art simulations to help its audience understand recent scientific discoveries. Perhaps its most important component is where real scientists explain contemporary astronomy/science face-to-face. In addition to educating the public, the show acts as a training facility for researchers to improve their communication skills. University students form a team "Chi-mons" and assist the live show.

1.2. Internet Telescopes and Camera Networks

The KITANOMARU Internet Telescope (KIT) and the Yerkes Rooftop Telescopes (YRTs) are examples of successful educational robotic telescopes. KIT is installed atop the roof of the Science Museum of Tokyo and the YRTs are installed at the Yerkes Observatory. Since 2005 KIT and YRTs have had been good counterparts to each other as the two halves of a mutual agreement between the Yerkes Observatory and the Science Museum. An important feature of this collaboration is the Interactive Camera Network (i-CAN). Noteworthy features of i-CAN are: a wide field of view (about 70 degrees diagonal) best suited for recognizing constellations and asterisms, a color CCD that shows the colors of stars, and an interactive system that engages children in astronomy by giving them the joy of controlling the camera. Collaborating institutions of the i-CAN project are spread over the world. In addition to the authors institutions they include University of Florida, New Mexico State University, Bradford University, and several Japanese collaborators.

2.   From Informal to Formal Education

2.1.   The Kudan Elementary School After-School Program

Starting in 2004, an after-school program was developed by the Science Museum of Tokyo for the Kudan Elementary School. Financial support for three years was provided from the Ministry of Education, Culture, Sports, Science and Technology. The main goals of the program were to acquaint children with the latest scientific research and to enable them to find answers to questions by applying scientific methods. The goals are expected to be achieved through experiments and discussions with instructors. In addition, the program has helped create linkages and partnerships between those who are involved in the program and the parents of the school children.

2.2.   Astrobiology from Kudan Elementary School

The Coordinators group that worked on the after-school program provided Astrobiology for children because this field of research connects the studies of life with the universe as a whole. Twenty-three children from the 6th grade and the 5th grade were exposed to evolution and dinosaurs for biology and to the Big Bang and our solar system for the universe. Although the children did not realize what Astrobiology was at this point, some volunteered an interest about life on Mars, extra-terrestrial intelligence, UFOs, and habitable zones.

At Astrobiology classes, the young thinkers created new lives on various planets by referring to physical/chemical characteristics of "real" datasets of the exoplanets. By learning biology and astronomy in harmony, kids increase their interests and concern about the universe and their lives.

3.   Exchange Between Different Fields and Cultures

Since astronomy encompasses the entire universe, it deals with a broad range of sciences. Astrobiology may be one of the best examples of its interdisciplinary nature since it deals with the origin and evolution of astronomy, biology and geology. In studying astrobiology a student must learn about physical, chemical, and biological processes and how they change. So, needless to say, it is essential that partnerships be made among people in different scientific areas to properly present this.

In this program, different field researchers from different cultures could support and help each other. All had to learn the background science and vocabulary so they could discuss the overall science and contribute on an equal ground with the other disciplines. Within the collaboration the coordinators and Museum educators worked to establish a proper link between researchers and teachers. In addition parents also were included and engaged with teachers, researchers, and the undergraduate/graduate students. The Astrobiology class was an excellent example of how to teach the latest most exciting results to children, and was a successful collaboration.

EPO and a Changing World
ASP Conference Series, Vol. 389, © 2008
C. Garmany, M. Gibbs, and J. W. Moody

Motivating Reluctant Learners with a Big Bang

James C. Lochner

*CRESST/USRA & NASA/Goddard Space Flight Center, Astrophysics
Science Division, Greenbelt, MD 20771, USA*

Geraldine A. Cvetic and Jonathan B. Hall

*Chesapeake Senior High School, 4798 Mountain Rd, Pasadena MD
21122, USA*

Abstract.   We present results of a collaboration between a media specialist,
a science teacher, and an astronomer to bring a modern astronomy topic to at-
risk, emotionally disabled students who have experienced little success. These
normally unengaged students became highly motivated because they were given
an authentic task of presenting research on an intriguing science topic, and
because they witnessed a collaboration brought together on their behalf. This
experience demonstrates that sophisticated astronomy topics can be used to
motivate at-risk students.

1.   Reaching a New Audience

We reached out to a new audience of students through a collaboration between
a media specialist, a science teacher, and an astronomer. This student audience
consisted of at-risk, emotionally disabled students for whom expectations of success are low. The media specialist had worked with both average and honors
students, but desired to extend her promotion of research using online databases
and technology to students who are often left out of main-stream experiences.
For the topic, the science teacher selected the Big Bang, which is part of the curriculum, because he thought it would be a high interest subject for his students,
and it would lend itself well to student research. They joined with a NASA
scientist who could successfully present the latest research to high school students. Together they developed and presented a set of integrated, multi-sensory
activities using a project-based instruction approach.

In this collaboration, the media specialist (Cvetic) provided instruction for
utilizing library resources for doing research and using computer technology for
producing the final project. The science teacher (Hall) provided the science
background as preparation for the visiting NASA scientist, as well as guidance
and assessment of students' final project. The visiting NASA scientist (Lochner)
provided input for the background presentation, and gave an expert content
presentation to the students.

2.   Our Reluctant Learners

This class consisted of nine students who are part of the Chesapeake Regional
Pro-gram. These students are emotionally disabled, often coming from extremely troubled homes and often in trouble with the law. They frequently

exhibit behavioral problems, and are distrustful. School is not important compared to the trauma in their lives, and they feel the educational system has failed them. The Program has its own therapist, psychiatrist, social worker, and law enforcement officer. Each class has a teacher and at least one teacher assistant. It is a separate day school within a regular high school, providing a safe, therapeutic academic environment. Goals of the Program are to "prepare students for transition to general education or to the work-place." In reality, because of their extreme behavior disorders expectations for student success and achievement are low. Their classes are completely separate, and the students are often ostracized in the school.

3.   The Big Bang Unit

We developed a 7 class-period unit consisting of a variety of lessons and activities, including a pretest on their familiarity with library resources and astronomy, a scavenger hunt on astronomy using library resources and online databases, content lessons, the visit by the NASA scientist, a lesson on techniques for avoiding plagiarism, and a lesson on communicating their research results. Under the guidance of the science teacher, students developed 5 essential questions of their own about the Big Bang, and researched answers using library resources and online databases. They also used appropriate citations for each question and developed a bibliography. They created a poster with their research results using Microsoft Publisher, which was printed, enlarged, and displayed outside their classroom. The unit ended with a field trip to NASA/GSFC, where the students toured the facility and participated in hands-on activities.

4.   Student Accomplishments

These student rose to the challenge! The students were initially apathetic on the pre-test, but became attentive and engaged during the science teacher's background lesson. The students then showed great interest during the presentation by the visiting NASA scientist and became highly motivated by this topic. The students were extraordinarily engaged in using the online databases to research their questions and in designing their posters. Their accomplishment was commended and recognized by school faculty and the administrator of the Chesapeake Program.

5.   What Motivated These Reluctant Learners?

The students were motivated by the fact that they were presented a challenging, but interesting topic, with a specific, doable goal. In particular, they reacted positively to choosing their own questions, working with the online databases, and developing their posters using the computer. The students recognized that the visiting NASA scientist took them seriously and didn't treat them differently from other high school students. Most importantly, the students witnessed their science teacher joining with the media specialist and a NASA scientist, and that team working together on their behalf and interested their success. This experience demonstrates that sophisticated astronomy topics can be used in teaching and motivating at-risk students.

EPO and a Changing World
ASP Conference Series, Vol. 389, © *2008*
C. Garmany, M. Gibbs, and J. W. Moody

Astronomy Outreach for Special Needs Children

Donald Lubowich

Department of Physics and Astronomy, Hofstra University, Hempstead, NY 11549

Abstract. While there are many outreach programs for the public and for children, there are few programs for special needs children. I describe a NASA-STScI-IDEAS funded outreach program I created for children using a telescope (including remote and robotic observations), hands-on astronomy demonstrations (often with edible ingredients). The target audience is seriously ill children with special medical needs and their families who are staying at the Long Island Ronald McDonald House in conjunction the children's surgery and medical treatments at local hospitals. These educational activities help children and their families learn about astronomy while providing a diversion to take their minds off their illness during a stressful time. A related program for hospitalized children has been started at the Hagedorn Pediatric Inpatient Center at Winthrop University Hospital.

1. Ronald McDonald House

Ronald McDonald House of Long Island (New Hyde Park, New York) was founded in 1986 and is part of the network of 245 Ronald McDonald Houses in 26 countries throughout the world. It is a "home away from home" for families of seriously ill children undergoing critical medical treatment in area hospitals and is 500 feet from Schneider Children's Hospital. The Ronald McDonald House is a temporary residence where family members can sleep, eat, relax and find support from other families in similar situations. Families are kept united at a time when mutual support is often as critical as the medical treatment itself. The Ronald McDonald provides shelter at minimal fees so that income will not prevent children from obtaining the best medical care and having the support of their families. The Ronald McDonald House of Long Island has served more than 7,500 families from the New York metropolitan area, all 50 states, and 62 foreign countries.

2. Outreach Program

The purpose of this program is to provide daytime and nighttime telescope observations and hands-on astronomy demonstrations for seriously ill children and their families) who are staying at the Long Island Ronald McDonald House. This family learning experience includes activities designed for ages ranging from elementary school to high school along with their adult family members. There are no similar astronomy outreach programs designed for this group in the New York metropolitan region. Innovative edible demonstrations using chocolate,

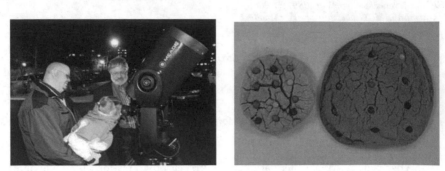

Figure 1.   Jerome family looking through a telescope(l); big-bang cookie (r)
m&ms separated by 3 cm in cookie dough & 7 cm in baked cookie (far right)

marshmallows, and popcorn are used to present astronomy, earth science, and
space science concepts to enhance learning and achieve a greater educational
impact. An important component of this program is training the staff to use
the telescope and to conduct astronomy demonstrations throughout the year to
take advantage of clear weather or celestial events and to be able to continue
this program after the grant period ends.

A Meade 12" telescope is used to view the Moon and lunar craters; the Sun
and sunspots; Saturn's rings and satellites; Jupiter's satellites and atmospheric
belts; Martian polar caps; multiple stars; and star clusters. Visible constellations
are identified along with their astronomical legends. The telescope is equipped
with a digital camera so the children can take an image of what they saw through
the telescope. Each program begins with a description with Tonight's Sky from
Amazing Space (STScI). Remote and robotic telescope observations are used so
that the program can be done in any weather. In the future I plan to expand the
program to additional Ronald McDonald Houses and hospitals and to summer
camps for children with special needs.

Edible demonstrations incldue: differentiation (marshmallows, chocolate,
M&Ms, cereal); plate tectonics (crackers with peanut butter/jelly); convection
(hot chocolate; miso soup); mud flows on Mars (chocolate poured on cake);
formation of the Galactic disk (pizza); Oreo cookie lunar phases; open curva-
ture of the Universe (Pringles); expansion of Universe (big-bang chocolate-chip
cookies); radioactivity and radioactive dating (popcorn); constellations patterns
with chocolate chips; planet cookies; chocolate milk measurement of solar radiation. Hands-on activities include: toilet paper and cardboard scale model of the
solar system; toilet plunger sundial; flashlights to simulate constellations and lunar phases; building a cardboard-tube telescope; building a spectroscope to show
how spectra can identify elements; demonstrating velocity and the Doppler effect
with a radar gun; demonstrating heat and radiation with an infrared temperature sensor; making a comet or rainbow; identifying and naming star patterns.

Acknowledgments. This program is funded by the Space Telescope Science Institute, AURA grant HST-ED-90300.01, from the Initiative to Develop
Education through Astronomy and Space Science (IDEAS) program.

EPO and a Changing World
ASP Conference Series, Vol. 389, © 2008
C. Garmany, M. Gibbs, and J. W. Moody

EuroPlaNet: Improving the Communication on Planetary Sciences

Yaël Nazé[1] & Anita Heward[2]

[1]*FNRS-ULg, Institut d'Astrophysique et de Géophysique de Liège, Allée du 6 Août 17 Bat. B5c, B4000-Liège, Belgium ;* [2] *EuroPlaNet UK node, Braemar close, Godalming, Surrey, Gu7 1SA, UK*

Abstract. EuroPlaNet is an EC-funded consortium. It coordinates the activities of European researchers working in planetary sciences but it is not only aimed at pure scientific activities. Its outreach action involves a networking of the members, in order to promote the planetary sciences in Europe, improve the public awareness of the major European achievements & projects, and stimulate the use of planetary sciences for the promotion of scientific education and culture at large. For more information: http://www.europlanet-eu.org/ or http://www.europlanet.cesr.fr/.

1. What is EuroPlaNet?

The European Planetology Network (EuroPlaNet) was created in January 2005 in order to promote collaboration in the European activities linked to Planetary Sciences, with the objective to enhance the competitiveness of European scientists in the worldwide community. The network initially consists of representatives of 17 countries and 59 institutions across Europe, with associate involvement from a few institutions in the USA, but it has continuously grown since then. With 10% of the budget (about 200,000 euros spread over four years), the outreach plays an important role in this network. It is funded though European Commission FP6 and the Europlanet outreach activities are coordinated by Jean-Pierre Lebreton. (jean-pierre.lebreton@esa.int)

2. Why outreach?

The aims of the outreach action of EuroPlaNet are:
- To increase the knowledge level in planetary sciences across Europe
- To enhance networking between planetary sciences communicators
- To highlight European involvement in planet exploration
- To promote the work of EuroPlaNet The audience is very broad, going from the general public & media, to the science community & schools, but also European science policy decision makers & the European Commission, funder of EuroPlaNet.

3. Let's collaborate

EuroPlaNet tries to trigger collaborations, not only in the scientific field, but also for the outreach. The Outreach Steering Committee makes regular teleconferences, in order to coordinate the outreach projects and to decide of new actions to undertake. A national "node" in each participating country has been identified and that person is the link between planetary scientists, but also between scientists and media or general public; he/she also helps in translating documents.

During the annual European Planetary Science Congresses (EPSC), outreach sessions are organized:
- in 2006: "Venus Express EPO," "Outreach Techniques," "Is Pluto a planet?"
- in 2007: "IAY2009," "Outreach Techniques," "Networking."

Such sessions are aimed at people already involved in outreach, but help the "normal scientists" discover outreach and begin new collaborative networks.

4. Website

Every outreach action has its website, first contact with the public at large - EuroPlaNet is no exception. With so many different countries (and languages!) and limited manpower, it is focused on a few well chosen subjects:
- why is planetary science important?
- what is our current knowledge of the Solar System?
- where are scientists working? A: not very far from your home!
- how is the Solar System studied?
- what missions are used to study planets?
- news of the EPSC & calendar of events
- special activities (e.g. "2007, A very spatial year?")
- FAQ, forum, etc.

5. Training scientists

It is not always easy for scientists to do outreach, but an efficient training can help them understand the "tricks" of communicating science and the way journalists work. For example, in September 2006, EuroPlaNet organized in Greece a training session in collaboration with ESConet. A dozen planetary scientists learned how to improve their communication skills, and they applied it right away through exercises. Also, the EPSC meetings, where a lot of scientists are present, are used to show some working examples of planetary science communication and to give the broad lines for an effective outreach strategy.

6. Acts & Facts

EuroPlaNet has done much over the last two years. It has provided translations of the Huygens descent movie in 11 languages and provided a document entitled "Communicating a Cosmic Vision - Developing an Effective Outreach Strategy" to help scientists answer the ESA CV call for proposals. A DVD presenting EuroPlaNet was also made, and members have participated in big science/non-science fairs (e.g. in Paris last May). A big event is scheduled in October 2007 entitled "2007, A very spatial year?" where EuroPlaNet will organize three contests in nine countries that are open to amateur astronomers, children and artists. It provides a calendar of space and planet-related events, space exploration, a nice poster with planetary images, and promotes other ways to discover science like (g)astronomy & science plays.

EPO and a Changing World
ASP Conference Series, Vol. 389, © *2008*
C. Garmany, M. Gibbs, and J. W. Moody

Results of Modifying Astronomy Curriculum for Special Needs Students Using Best Practices

Julia K. Olsen and Timothy F. Slater

University of Arizona, Steward Observatory, 933 N Cherry Ave, Tucson AZ 85721

Abstract. In early 2006, the Lawrence Hall of Science (LHS) conducted a national field-test of a new GEMS space science curriculum package developed for use with middle school students. During this field-test, we modified a subset of the curriculum materials for use by special needs students, to be delivered via computer mediated instruction. These materials were implemented in a subset of the field-test classrooms and LHS collected pre- and post-test data for each unit. This data was analyzed to determine if students in the classrooms using the modified materials scored differently than students in the larger assessment data base. Data was disaggregated to measure the impact on students with special needs, as evidenced by individualized education plans (IEPs). Results suggest that many students, not just those with special needs, demonstrate greater achievement gains using materials modified using the principles of best practice for special needs students.

1. Introduction

Inclusionary classrooms present a particularly ardent challenge for even the most seasoned science teachers because of the wide diversity in student abilities, modes of learning, and successful experiences of the students included. Teaching science in inclusionary classrooms is a deeply complex and multifaceted process that can place extraordinary burdens on under prepared teachers. Special needs students all too often fall behind in achievement in math and science, especially during the middle school years. Nationally, schools view science as a natural and desirable content area in which to mainstream special education students due to the inherently structured nature of scientific inquiry. Although technology holds promise for enhancing educational opportunities for special education students, there has been little systematic work to date on the actual effectiveness and feasibility of informed interventions. The purpose of this study was to explore technology as a tool for increasing student achievement within the middle school science classroom and specifically to support the learning of special needs students.

2. Methodologies

Utilizing field-test curriculum from the Lawrence Hall of Science's Great Explorations in Math and Science (GEMS) Space Science Curriculum Sequence, software modules were designed to mediate instruction in specific problem areas which special needs students, especially those with learning disabilities, face in learning science. The Space Science instructional materials developed by LHS/GEMS are widely regarded as being highly inquiry-oriented, so it was determined early in the design process that an overriding principle was that the computer-based modifications would make every attempt to not infringe upon any of the inquiry activities in the curriculum. Rather, the modifications would focus on areas known or highly suspected of being particularly difficult for special needs students.

3. Major Findings

While the numbers of students involved are too small for a robust statistical analysis to confirm if significant differences exist, a visual inspection of the raw scores and individual student gains suggest that special education students using the unmodified curriculum experienced great difficulty in learning the concepts involved. Gains in students' pretest to post-test scores were notably higher for the special education students who used computer-mediated instructional approaches designed utilizing best practices. In addition, the proportion of special needs students who provided more scientifically accurate and extended responses was much greater among those who used the modified materials. Most importantly, special needs students in this study who used the modified materials demonstrated more conceptual growth than did the special education students in using the unmodified materials. Some misconceptions repeat among a number of students as seen in the pre-test / post-test responses. It seems plausible that inquiry-based science instruction was able to remediate some misconceptions among students, but not all. These findings are consistent with other studies of students' conceptions and progression along a continuum of conceptual understanding (Sadler 1998).

The major finding of this work is that most special education students demonstrated considerable gains in learning the content using the modified curriculum. Moreover, students using modified curriculum not only increased in the frequency of their responses, but also increased in the quality of their responses to a particular prompt. In addition, responses from special education students in the modified curriculum group were consistently within the range of responses found among the general education population, who also increased. It is evident from both the quantitative and the qualitative analysis of the student work products that the scores and work products of special needs students are indeed substantially different when provided with technology-based instructional activities modified according to best practice for working with special needs students. For more information, see http://caperteam.arizona.edu.

References

Sadler, P., "Psychometric Models of Student Conceptions in Science: Reconciling Qualitative Studies and Distractor-driven Assessment Instruments", Journal of Research in Science Teaching, **35** (3), 265-296 (1998)

EPO and a Changing World
ASP Conference Series, Vol. 389, © 2008
C. Garmany, M. Gibbs, and J. W. Moody

Making Space Science Elementary!: Broadening our Audience to Include the K-4 Classroom

Ruth L. Paglierani and Gregory R. Schultz

University of California, Berkeley, Space Sciences Laboratory, 7 Gauss Way, Berkeley, CA 94720

Shannon L. McConnell

NASA Jet Propulsion Laboratory, 4800 Oak Gove Drive, Pasadena, CA 91109

Abstract. The integration of elementary science with language arts provides a means of keeping science education robust in the elementary classroom. By linking the two subject areas, teachers can take advantage of the highly-motivational content that science provides while using writing as a powerful tool to synthesize science learning. We report on two successful K-4 NASA curricula, *Eye on the Sky and Reading, Writing & Rings!* which suggest a model for the successful integration of science instruction with language arts through inquiry-based learning.

1. Programs that Integrate Science Instruction with Language Arts

The young students who will become tomorrow's scientists, engineers and technologists are currently sitting in elementary classrooms across the country. Yet, elementary educators typically have only limited opportunities to teach science. On average a mere 23 minutes per day go to science instruction while 115 minutes go to language arts instruction. This is due, in great part, to the primary focus on literacy and mathematics instruction in the early grades. It is not surprising then, that the time and resources allocated to science teaching are significantly less than those allocated to language arts and mathematics.

The integration of elementary science with language arts provides one means of keeping science education robust in the elementary classroom. By linking the two subject areas, teachers can take advantage of the highly-motivational content that science provides while using writing as a powerful tool to synthesize science learning.

Two successful K-4 NASA curricula, *Eye on the Sky and Reading, Writing & Rings!* suggest a model for the successful integration of science instruction with language arts through inquiry-based learning. Both were developed by NASA scientists and UC Berkeley educators in partnership with classroom teachers. *Eye on the Sky* focuses on heliophysics for young learners, making the Sun-Earth connection accessible in the primary grades; *Reading, Writing & Rings!* contains a suite of lessons exploring Saturn, Titan and NASA's Cassini Mission.

Each set of activities has been assessed by independent educational evaluators. We have identified the following as best practices for developing materials for the early grades:

- Partner with teachers as co-developers

- Align to both science and language arts standards

- Integrate across the curriculum to include math and visual arts

- Make materials "ready-to-go" for classroom teachers

Complete curricula and examples of K-4 student work are available at http://www.eyeonthesky.org and http://saturn.jpl.nasa.gov/education/edu-k4.cfm.

Teacher professional development is key to implementing such programs in the elementary classroom. Our model for successful professional development includes:

- Teaming E/PO professionals, teachers and scientists as presenters

- Allowing authentic work time to do the lessons resulting in work samples to take away from the training experience

- A post-training point of contact for ongoing support

Acknowledgments. The development partners for these K-4 science and language arts integrated materials were NASA's Project FIRST (UCB), the Bay Area Writing Project (UCB), NASA's Cassini Mission (JPL), the Pre-College Science Initiative (Cal Tech) and a talented team of teacher developers (Northern and Southern California School Districts).

EPO and a Changing World
ASP Conference Series, Vol. 389, © *2008*
C. Garmany, M. Gibbs, and J. W. Moody

Cosmology and Globalization

Kala Perkins

P.O. Box 3733, Los Altos, CA 94024

Abstract. Exploring cosmological concepts and the emergence of life at astronomical scales offers valuable insight on the human role in global evolution. New dimensions of research await cognitive psychology and consciousness.

1. Introduction

Microbes swarming on a sand grain planet or integral complex organisms evolving consciousness at the forefront of cosmic evolution. How is our new cosmology contributing to redefining who we see ourselves to be at the edge of the 21st century, as globalization and capitalism speed forward? How is the evolution of stardust and the universe offering new paradigms of process and identity regarding the role, function and emergence of life in space-time? What are the cultural and philosophical questions that are arising and how might astronomy be contributing to the creation of new visions for cooperation and community at a global scale? What is the significance of including astronomy in K-12 education and what values can it offer modern youth?

Exploring our new cosmological concepts and the emergence of life at astronomical scales may offer valuable orientation toward reframing the human role in global evolution. Considering new insight from astrobiology, each diverse species has a definitive role to play in the facilitation and functioning of the biosphere. Below is a reflection of possible roles of the human dynamic. As well the question arises as to the presence of any sort of ethic inherent in or implied by natural science and offered by our rapidly expanding cosmic frontier.

It may be that what we call ethics is an emergent reality arising out of the inherent nature of cosmos as an expression of (a) singularity, or non-dual undifferentiated integrity. Truth is then the very fabric of reality, -the integral unfoldment, enfoldment and dynamic of the singularity. Goodness is that which perpetuates reality's intent or intension - literally the tensions giving rise to cosmos' emergence, perpetuity, realization, process and rhythmic transcendences. Beauty is perhaps an experiential property of the resonance and harmonics of the fabric, deeply related to wisdom regarding totality. Thus, it is the inherent wisdom in the integrity of the whole that facilitates the arising of the existential experience of that which we call beauty. Other values may be combinations of vibratory complexities arising from the blending of varied principles in space-time, or unique emergent identities or qualities. Future cognitive research will explore the diverse effects on consciousness of our new encounter with cosmos.

Cosmology and globalization are our new frontiers. We are being invited to champion infinity not as an hor d'oeuvre but as a main course. Infinite possibilities, potentially infinite worlds, realms and cosmoi, - and most certainly, infinite co- creativity. We are exploring new ways of revisioning ourselves, our relationships as nations and cultures on our tiny global satellite, our relationships as humanity to the global collective biosphere and biocosm.

Within our bodies and minds, the entire global effort of 4.6 billion years of Earth evolution and 13.7 + B yrs. of cosmic evolution, - perhaps infinite harmonics of infinities of universes, are uttered and reiterated incessantly. Each cell and nerve, all of our actions, thoughts and dynamics, - move, pulse and dance to the cosmic choreography. The entire scope of reality is generated as infinite infinities of interactive fields, iterated and reiterated over cosmic and global histories, continuously converge and omni-suffuse. At the meeting of each converging set of arcs of infinity, multi-dimensional nexus are generated. Complex convergences become causally significant, acting as foci or tension vortices for the emergence of subtler or more complex dimensions of identity and awareness. This is the quantum fabric of reality.

Our most ancient philosophies and sciences discourse upon the interrelationship between the cosmos and the complex human organism. We are beginning to explore these correlations, such as the nature of the heart and surging rhythms of polarized plasma in the orb of our sun and other stars. The entire history of the universe may be traced through each and every particle. Rays of light and energy from the first instants of cosmogenesis surge through our bodies incessantly, along with that from countless stars and galaxies in the continuous spectrum of frequencies. The gravitational direction of cosmos, its dark matter and energy, and galaxy clusters move our moments. Cosmos, it is now being proposed at the edge of modern astronomy, may be a self-aware incessantly emerging fractal; perhaps countless cosmoi are multi-dimensionally superimposed.

We begin to understand the profound integrity of the human life system, its bio-rhythms, the correlations between organs, senses and environment, and its integral nexus of meridians, points and interactive fields with the cosmic scheme as proposed by certain of the ancient oriental medical systems. In Hwa Yen Buddhism, the human is actually transposed through the process and stages of enlightenment, awakening and various practices, into a foundational support for the entire dimensionality of cosmic life expressions. One is literally said to awaken to the universe(s) - infinity - as the fabric of one's cosmic form. On the human stage, the seeds of all the unfolding worlds are said to be the centers, organs, glands, systems and charkas of the bio-organism.

In the realms of the new sciences, movement toward the *singularity* has come to refer to the glitches or phase transitions in our cognitive and bio-technical capability to transcend our mortality and the sense of finitude. Life moves as a wave through varying dimensionalities, assuming the informed states natural to its convergence with those dimensionalities. If how we see things has definite effect on who and what we experience and express as *ourselves*, then new dimensions of research await cognitive psychology: discerning the bio-psychological and creative effects of our visual and intellectual encounter with the span of cosmic identity as we are perceiving it. We are finding that life itself is the most radioactive element: creative mind catalyzing consciousness, culture, the calculated fabric of reality's weave, cosmos' emergent neural net and heartbeat. Our questions now at the scientific frontier: What is *dark energy*, the hidden cosmic magnet impelling cosmos into existence and beyond? And what is *consciousness*?

EPO and a Changing World
ASP Conference Series, Vol. 389, © *2008*
C. Garmany, M. Gibbs, and J. W. Moody

Youth Astronomy Apprenticeship (YAA): An Initiative to Promote Science Learning Among Urban Youth and Their Communities

Irene Porro, Vesal Dini, and Timothy Prol

Massachusetts Institute of Technology Kavli Institute for Astrophysics and Space Research, 77 Massachusetts Avenue, NE80, Cambridge, MA 02139, USA

Abstract. We present an out-of-school time initiative that uses an astronomy apprenticeship model to promote science learning among urban youth and their communities.

1. Introduction

YAA is an out-of-school time initiative to foster science learning among urban teen-age youth and their communities. The goal of YAA is to broaden the awareness of science learning as an effective way of promoting overall youth development and of providing competitive professional opportunities. YAA staff first develop partnerships with professionals at community-based centers to create a mutual understanding of goals and expectations for the program. They then engage high school students in an after-school astronomy training program. After the training is completed, the successful participants become astronomy apprentices who work with educators and other professionals to create astronomy outreach initiatives directed at their own communities. Through the youth's work and their presence among their communities as science ambassadors, we aim to promote involvement and support for science learning among underrepresented communities. YAA is a collaboration with MIT Kavli Institute (MKI), the Smithsonian Astrophysical Observatory (SAO), the Timothy Smith Network (TSN), and the Institute of Learning Innovation (ILI).

2. Youth Astronomy Apprenticeship

2.1. Youth Astronomy Apprenticeship: After-School Program

The YAA after-school program is a 14-week training during which youth engage in astronomy investigations based on images taken with MicroObservatory, a network of robotic telescopes that are controlled via the Internet. Youth learn to use software tools to process astronomical images, and produce reports and presentations about their investigations. In the process, youth develop important skills, including logical reasoning, inquiry, completing self-directed tasks, oral and written communication, and collaboration. At the end of this training program, a group of youth is chosen to participate in a summer apprenticeship at MIT, the core element of the YAA model.

Partnerships   Community-Based Organizations: After-school sites that host the program serve a significant function in both recruiting participants and ensuring effective administration. Four centers from the TSN served as partners for the first year of the program: the Roxbury Multi-Service Center, Inc., Urban League of Eastern Massachusetts, Dimock Community Health Center, and Tobin/Mission Hill Community Center.

MicroObservatory: Urban teens can make actual astronomical observations thanks to this network of four automated telescopes that can be controlled over the Internet. MicroObservatory was developed by a team in the science education department at SAO. The project is funded by NSF with support from NASA.

2.2.   Youth Astronomy Apprenticeship: Summer Program

The objective of the YAA summer program is for youth apprentices to create a portfolio of astronomy outreach projects that they will present to audiences in their communities over the following school year. During the summer program, apprentices are exposed to a variety of astronomy content as they also practice some of the professional skills necessary to complete an outreach project of their choice. In the summer of 2007, YAA youth were mentored by researchers from MIT and SAO, amateur astronomers, by professionals in museum exhibit development and in the performing arts. In August 2007, YAA apprentices presented to the public their first outreach event, "Party Like an Astronomer" that featured three remarkable projects.

Outreach Projects   Telescope Activities: Mentored by members of the Amateur Telescope Makers of Boston our apprentices created interactive activities that describe the 'guts' of a telescope, used lasers to show how a telescope focuses light, and explained magnification, showing that bigger is not always better. These activities will primarily be presented at star parties organized by the apprentices and amateur astronomers.

Black Hole Exhibit: Apprentices worked with museum professionals to develop prototypes for a black hole exhibit opening at the Boston Museum of Science in 2009. One component has young visitors learn that there are black holes of different mass, another helps visitors explore some of the media's interpretations of black holes and in the third, a fun animation explains to visitors how black holes are formed.

Astronomy Theater: Apprentices worked with professionals from the performing arts to write, produce, and perform a play based on the life cycle of stars. In bringing together art and science, the astronomy content came to life for an audience of all ages, and engaged scientists and non-scientists alike. The theater group is eager to tour the greater Boston area with the play.

Acknowledgments.   YAA is a 3-year project funded through the NSF-ISE program.

EPO and a Changing World
ASP Conference Series, Vol. 389, © 2008
C. Garmany, M. Gibbs, and J. W. Moody

The Supernova Club: Bringing Space Science to Urban Youths

Philip J. Sakimoto,[1] Rebecca Pettit,[2] Dinshaw Balsara,[1] and Peter Garnavich[1]

[1]*Department of Physics and* [2]*Center for Social Concerns, University of Notre Dame, Notre Dame, IN 46556-5670, USA*

Abstract. The Supernova Club is an experiment aimed at bringing space science to youths, almost all African Americans, from the most severely disadvantaged areas of the South Bend, Indiana, region. It leverages the National Youth Sports Program (NYSP) that, in Summer 2007, brought 100 children, ages 10-16 and living at or below the poverty level, to the Notre Dame campus for a 4-week non-residential summer program. Six contact hours of space science instruction were added to the core curriculum of nutrition, physical fitness, and academic study. At summer's end, 13 high interest/high potential youths were selected to form "The Supernova Club"-a year-round, after-school, weekly follow-up program.

1. Motivation

The National Youth Sports Program (NYSP) at Notre Dame has brought hundreds of youths, almost all African Americans, from low-income families to the Notre Dame campus each summer for a 4-week non-residential program focused on nutrition, physical fitness, and academic study. In a major restructuring of the program last summer, the idea arose that the program should raise its sights. In addition to providing the basic instruction and services it had always offered, the program should purposefully expose the participants to a wide variety of possible interest areas. It should identify individuals with strong interests and high potential in given areas and provide them with targeted, year-round follow-up activities that would develop those interests and capabilities. *It should aim to ultimately make at least some of the program participants capable of being admitted to and succeeding in a highly selective university like Notre Dame.*

2. Funding

The Notre Dame Center for Social Concerns, which operated the NYSP, and the Center for Astrophysics at Notre Dame University (CANDU) formed a partnership to make space science the special focus area for the first pilot year. Education supplements from three Hubble Space Telescope Cycle 15 research awards were obtained and combined to provide funding. Since each of the parent awards dealt with an aspect of supernova research, supernovae and the story of stellar life cycles became a special focus, and the name "Supernova Club" was coined.

3.   Program

The Summer 2007 space science curriculum began with subjects familiar to the students- basic exercises in planetary motions and distances (Fraknoi 1995)- and then moved on to new activities aimed at familiarizing students with more distant objects in the universe (Universe! Education Forum 2003). A specially created activity on human life cycles was added to introduce the concept of stellar life cycles and build confidence in working with inquiry-based activities. Specially tailored presentations in Notre Dame's Digital Visualization Theater (DVT) supplemented the classroom instruction.

After the end of the summer program, two special family nights for students interested in joining the Supernova Club were held. Talks by role models aimed at increasing comfort with science were given by theologian and Dean Hugh Page, and by summer physics research student Ashley Jackson from Hampton University. By the end of the second family night, through their attendance and attention, thirteen students self-selected themselves to be the initial members of the Supernova Club.

During the 2007-2008 school year, the Supernova Club will meet once a week at Notre Dame's Robinson Community Learning Center for more space science classroom activities, peppered with a variety of special trips and events.

4.   Evaluation

Evaluation of the summer program via pre- and post-testing showed significant increases ($\sim$20% gain) in understanding that stars evolve and that stars more massive than the Sun, but not the Sun itself, will end their lives as supernovae. The impact of the DVT was clear. In response to open-ended questions, more than half of the respondents cited the DVT as the facet of the program that they liked best. Interestingly, the evaluation showed statistically significant gains in *interest* in science, but not in interest in *being* a scientist.

5.   Conclusions

The goals of introducing space science to the hundred students in the summer program, increasing their knowledge of space science, and selecting a dozen high-potential students to be in the year-round Supernova Club were achieved. As we work with the Supernova Club members throughout the year and into the future, our fond hope is that at least a few of them will ultimately pursue careers in science.

Acknowledgments.   Support for this project was provided by the NASA Space Telescope Science Institute grant HST-EO-10934.03-A.

References

Fraknoi, A., *The Universe at Your Fingertips* (Astronomical Society of the Pacific, San Francisco, CA, 1995), activities C-4 and D-7.
Universe! Education Forum 2003, Cosmic Survey,
    http://www.cfa.harvard.edu/seuforum/download/CosmicSurvey2003.pdf

EPO and a Changing World
ASP Conference Series, Vol. 389, © *2008*
C. Garmany, M. Gibbs, and J. W. Moody

Balloon Payload Project at the National Federation of the Blind Youth Slam

Terry Teays

Maryland Space Grant Consortium, Johns Hopkins University,Room206C, Bloomberg Center for Physics & Astronomy, 3400 North Charles Street, Baltimore, Maryland 21218, USA

Mary Bowden and Andrew Ellsberry

Department of Aerospace Engineering, 3181 Glen L. Martin Hall, University of Maryland, College Park, Maryland 20742, USA

Mark A. Riccobono

National Federation of the Blind, Jernigan Institute, 1800 Johnson Street, Baltimore, Maryland 2123. USA

Abstract. Air Slam was an activity to construct and launch an instrument on small balloons as part of the National Federation of the Blind Youth Slam.

1. Youth Slam

In the summer of 2007, the National Federation of the Blind (NFB) conducted a Science, Technology, Engineering, and Mathematics (STEM) leadership academy called Youth Slam. It was the most dynamic gathering of blind youth ever - nearly two hundred blind and low vision high school students spent four days exploring science and engineering. While staying at Johns Hopkins University, the youth were mentored by blind role models during challenging hands-on activities meant to stretch the imagination, build confidence, increase scientific content knowledge and encourage interest in STEM careers. The students selected specific "tracks" with each group focusing on a different type of science or engineering. The Maryland Space Grant Consortium Balloon Payload Project (BPP) conducted a balloon science track called Air Slam.

The BPP is a program in which college and high school students conceive, design, and build payloads that they launch to "near-space" on weather balloons. While these are done from a launch site in rural, Western Maryland, the challenge for this project was to come up with something that could be launched from the Johns Hopkins campus in the heart of Baltimore.

Four mornings were devoted to this track. The twenty four students were divided into eight teams of three students each, along with a mentor for each team. On the first day the students constructed their payload. This consisted of a commercially available kit that was modified by the use of sockets put on the board for each electronic component. This avoided the need for soldering and the time it takes to learn this skill. The students were given the parts and the integrated circuit board and they assembled their instrument. This simple and lightweight instrument continually measured temperature and had a transmitter to send the temperature data to the ground.

On the second day the students tested their payloads and constructed plastic parachutes that they attached to the payload with string. They then had the experience of inflating a full-size weather balloon with helium. They each estimated the lift of the balloon and then compared it to the value that they measured. Students usually overestimate the lift capacity of a weather balloon.

Their next activity was to achieve neutral buoyancy with a party balloon that had a paper cup attached to it. The ballast was provided by jelly beans and other small candies, which allowed fairly precise weight levels. Achieving neutral buoyancy is not easy and takes some patience. This activity also gave the students experience with handling inflated balloons of this size, which prepared them for using the slightly larger party balloons to launch their payloads. The launch balloons used party grade helium and were around 70 cm in diameter when inflated.

On the third day the students heard a talk about ham radio and Morse code. Their data was sent down to the receiving radio as an identifier, which was unique for each team's balloon, and the temperature. Finally, they launched the flotilla of eight balloons, along with a tracker balloon that carried a GPS unit to provide location and altitude data. Normally the tracking module would be on the same balloon, but weight considerations with these small balloons precluded having both the temperature package and a GPS unit on the same payload. Though technically exempt from FAA regulations, the BPP personnel went through the usual procedures for notifying the FAA and contacting the Baltimore-Washington International Airport tower.

On the final day the students heard a talk on scientific, long-duration ballooning, followed by learning about the results of their experiments. The balloons rose to about 30,000 feet and the temperature dropped to zero degrees Celsius. This was precisely what was predicted for that altitude on that day. The students also were given tactile maps of Maryland and small plastic sticks were glued onto the map to show a typical flight path for a BPP weather balloon, as well as the ground track for their flight.

At the close of the workshop a lessons-learned session was conducted with the students to learn what worked well and what needed improvement. The students provided excellent suggestions for improving the activity. Though the instrument boards worked, there were several changes to the design that will be used in future student programs. The coolest part of the activity for many students was the idea that they had built something themselves that flew and collected real data.

For more information on the National Federation of the Blind Youth Slam please visit http://www.blindscience.org/ncbys/Youth_Slam.asp.

EPO and a Changing World
ASP Conference Series, Vol. 389, © *2008*
C. Garmany, M. Gibbs, and J. W. Moody

A Fully Wheelchair Accessible Telescope for the Frank N. Bash Visitors Center

F. Cianciolo, W. Wren, M. Jones, and M. Dubberly

McDonald Observatory Visitors Center, The University of Texas, One University Station 2100, Austin TX 78712

Abstract. We present the design and description of a telescope that is fully wheelchair accessible. It is to be installed at the the McDonald Observatory Visitor Center and will service the needs of the general public at star parties and other night-time observing functions.

1. General Introduction

The McDonald Observatory hosts approximately 30,000 visitors each year at the Visitors Center's popular Star Party programs. An increasing percentage of these guests are mobility impaired or completely wheelchair bound. Such physical challenges can make it nearly impossible for these visitors to comfortably look through traditionally designed telescopes. The new Wheelchair Accessible Telescope (WAT) will soon be installed at the Visitors Center's Telescope Park that will address this need.

Essentially a fixed focal point Pfund design (http://en.wikipedia.org/wiki/Pfund_telescope), the original incarnation of the telescope at McDonald Observatory used to search visually for supernovae was inspired directly from a design independently developed by John Fundingsland (1992) dubbed the "Fundyscope". The modified design now includes two 18" (0.46m) primary mirrors aligned north-south with the steering flat mirror centered between them to allow easier, quicker access to the entire sky. To view the southern quadrant, the flat mirror is pointed towards the south primary with the observer to the north behind the flat. To view the northern sky, only the flat mirror and eyepiece assembly need to be rotated 180° to face the north primary.

Additionally, the relatively small movable portion of the design will allow the telescope to quickly slew to numerous targets in rapid succession while the eyepiece stays fixed. For those visitors who find that they cannot view through the Center's more traditionally designed telescopes, this high speed pointing system will allow a far greater level of participation in the Star Party programs than is currently available.

Thanks to the design and fabrication skills of the WAT team, the system will include several viewing options. A binocular viewer with quickly and easily adjustable intraocular separation was designed specifically to take full advantage of the unique imaging capabilities of the system.

Alternately, to ensure that all wheelchair-bound visitors no matter what their seated height or degree of mobility can look through the telescope, an adjustable "periscope" viewer can be installed in place of the binocular system.

For larger crowds when minimizing the time needed to make adjustments is crucial, a straight-through viewing monocular system can be equipped with a standard diagonal for 2" eyepieces.

Since the system is, by necessity of design, completely open, a site for the telescope was chosen to minimize interference from any potential light source and to allow for construction of ADA compliant paths. The site has been prepared and awaits installation in late 2007 of the system now in final fabrication and assembly at Los Cumbres Observatory. (see http://lcogt.net/telescopes/snst2)

For more information about the history and design of the Wheelchair Accessible Telescope, go to http://idisk.mac.com/rwren/Public/wmwat2/index.htm.

References

Fundingsland, John O., "Easy Viewing with a Fixed Telescope", Sky and Telescope, **84**, 212-215, (1992)

EPO and a Changing World
ASP Conference Series, Vol. 389, © 2008
C. Garmany, M. Gibbs, and J. W. Moody

Hands-On Optics in an Informal Setting: Science Camps

Carolyn Peruta, Constance E. Walker, Robert T. Sparks and Stephen M. Pompea

National Optical Astronomy Observatory, 950 N. Cherry Ave., Tucson, AZ 85719, USA

Erin Dokter

CAPER Team, University of Arizona, 933 N. Cherry Ave., Tucson, AZ 85721, USA

Abstract. To expose young children to optical phenomena that build scientific literacy, Hands-On Optics camps provide an ideal way to encourage interest in optics before career choices are developed. Here, we provide an outline of our pedagogical approach for the camps, specific optics activities, strategies for cooperative learning and what worked best in the camp setting.

1. Introduction

Hands-On Optics (HOO) is a National Science Foundation funded program to bring optics education to traditionally under-served school aged students (ages 8-14). We have developed six activity modules and classroom-ready kits that teach students optics concepts through hands-on, inquiry-based activities. Having been used extensively in after-school settings, science museums, and Boys and Girls Clubs, these modules formed the basis for a full-day, weeklong optics camp that provides students with approximately forty hours of instruction time in optics.

2. An Optics Camp Designed for Under-represented Middle Schoolers

In June 2007, the National Optical Astronomy Observatory (NOAO), in collaboration with BIO5, Tucson Gaining Early Awareness & Readiness for Undergraduate Programs (GEAR-UP), and the Flandrau Science Center, offered three week-long camp sessions in optics to disadvantaged middle school students. Through a combination of hands-on, inquiry-based science activities, campus field trips, and science center experiences, students were immersed and engaged in the process of doing science via optics and exposed to science resources available at The University of Arizona.

The primary goals of this program were to:

- Engage middle school students in the process of doing optics;
- Excite middle school students about science and technology;
- Expose middle school students who might otherwise be unlikely to attend college to educational opportunities available at The University of Arizona;
- Educate middle school students about career opportunities in optics.

3.   Curriculum

The camp program utilized five modules that addressed basic optics concepts. The 5-day camp program consisted of:

Day 1- Laser Challenges: Explored the law of reflection using lasers and mirrors.

Day 2- Kaleidoscope Adventures: Explored multiple reflections using hinged mirrors.

Day 3- Magnificent Magnifications: Learned about refraction by observing lasers passing through acrylic blocks and lenses as well as kinesthetic activities.

Day 4- Peculiar Polarization: Learned about the wave and polarized nature of light.

Day 5- Infrared and Ultraviolet Light: Learned about the "invisible" light that is all around us by using items such as infrared remote controls, black lights, and ultraviolet-sensitive beads.

4.   Participants

About 20 incoming 8th-graders from GEAR-UP schools in Tucson attended each weeklong camp session. GEAR-UP program coordinators worked with the teachers at these schools to identify students who would most benefit from the summer science camp experience.

5.   Strategies for Cooperative Learning

Group project time was developed to encourage cooperative learning, team building, and communication skills. At the end of the week, each group made presentations to the other groups on: *Math Connections* (in-depth math explorations related to the science concepts), *Building a Reflecting Telescope* (Dobsonian telescope built from a kit and scientific journal kept to record progress), *Art Project* (poster depicting concepts learned), and. *Career Research:* (research different optics careers).

6.   What Worked Best in a Science Camp Setting

Guided inquiry activities in small groups worked best in these settings. The most successful activities were those that encouraged *group cooperation* (e.g. challenge stations , games, and open-ended challenges) and creativity (e.g. making their own tape art mural and creating unique kaleidoscopes).

Acknowledgments.   The *Hands-On Optics* Project was funded by the NSF ISE program, PI Anthony Johnson, Director, Center for Advanced Studies in Photonics Research, University of Maryland, Baltimore County. Major funding for the camp came from the Martin Foundation. NOAO is operated by the Association of Universities for Research in Astronomy (AURA), Inc. under cooperative agreement with the NSF. For further information on the HOO Program, contact Dr. Stephen Pompea, HOO Co-I and Project Director at spompea@noao.edu or 520.318.8285. NOAO student workers, Catarina Ubach, Jessica Jorajuria, and Samantha Christiansen were instrumental to the implementation of the camp.

EPO and a Changing World
ASP Conference Series, Vol. 389, © *2008*
C. Garmany, M. Gibbs, and J. W. Moody

Music of the Spheres: Astronomy-Inspired Music as an EPO Tool

Andrew Fraknoi

Foothill College, 12345 El Monte Road, Los Altos Hills, CA 94022 &
Astronomical Society of the Pacific. E-mail: fraknoiandrew@fhda.edu

Abstract. In doing public programs, getting audiences to think about astronomy in the wider culture, or just having some fun with a class or museum group, it's useful to have them brainstorm about all the pieces of music they can identify that have an astronomical connection. We have found over 100 pieces of classical and popular music that draw their inspiration from serious astronomy (and not just the use of a single astronomical term). These include three rock songs about black holes, operas about Einstein and Kepler, an electronic piece in which the players are asked to expand like the universe, and many more. We also highlight several astronomers and physicists who perform science music and discuss how anyone can use music to catch audience interest. The full list of pieces and more information is available at: http://aer.noao.edu/cgi-bin/article.pl?id=193.

1. Introduction

Most audiences can come up with examples of music that includes some astronomical title or idea, whether it is Mozart's *Jupiter* symphony or "Twinkle, Twinkle Little Star." But it's fun to ask them to find music that actually develops from astronomical discoveries and ideas and includes at least some correct science. With the help of students, colleagues, and music catalogs, we have identified over 100 pieces of classical and popular music based (at least in part) on real astronomy. Some are easy to listen to and explain, while others are clever but sound difficult and atonal. Selecting some songs or pieces that resonate with you, you can use them to spice up a talk, illustrate an astronomical point in a web or film discussion, or challenge a museum audience. Members of your audience may also be able to point you to some pieces they know or to think of other ways to capture the latest astronomy results in music. Families sometimes enjoy going home after your class or event, going through their music collection, and getting a chance to contribute more ideas.

A few musicians have even put together CD's of "educational" songs with good astronomy and physics. For example, the Chromatics, a singing group based at NASA's Goddard Space Flight Center, offer a K-12 curriculum guide to the various doo-wop and easy listening type songs they have created. A full discussion of all the music, can be found in an article in *Astronomy Education Review* (AER; http://aer.noao.edu/cgi-bin/article.pl?id=193). Below we give only a few examples.

2. Solar System Music

Kepler had a deep conviction that there was a connection between the mathematical regularities of the orbital motions of the planets and the regularities that give a sense of harmony in music. His work on the "harmony of the spheres" inspired a number of composers over the years, particularly Paul Hindemith, who wrote an opera in 1957 called *The Harmony of the World*, which is now available on a Wergo CD set. Hindemith explores the search for order in politics, science, and music through episodes in Kepler's life and thought. In the 1970's, a geology and a music professor at Yale used a computer and sound synthesizer to construct a piece of music based on the instantaneous orbital speeds of the planets starting on Kepler's birthday in 1571.

3. The Music of the Stars

As you might imagine, rock musicians find the deaths of stars particularly fascinating, and such songs as Epidemic's "Factor Red" (about red giants), Pink Floyd's "Shine on You Crazy Diamond" (about white dwarfs), Rush's "Cygnus X-1" (on the album *Farewell to Kings*), and Amanda Lear's "Black Holes" make for a nice break in a discussion of the lives of the stars. There are also a number of pieces that make use of constellation patterns on our list. An especially bizarre example is *Atlas Eclipticalis* by the contemporary composer John Cage. The composer placed his music score right on top of old star maps and then put the notes where the dots corresponding to stars happen to fall on the page. (We don't endorse these ideas, folks, we just tell them to you!)

4. Quasar Music

Back in the 1960's, there was a brief flurry of public attention to quasar CTA 102, because its radio signals were claimed to include coded information from an advanced civilization. There was nothing there, but the singing group called The Byrds wrote a song entitled "CTA 102" on their *Younger than Yesterday* album. Radio astronomer Eugene Epstein then thought it would be a lark to include the names of the Byrds in a reference in a paper on CTA 102 in the *Astrophysical Journal*. He got it past the editors in proof stage (see vol. 151, p. L31, second paragraph), referring to the song as "private communication."

5. Cosmology Music

The year 1973 was the 500th anniversary of the birth of Copernicus and a number of musical pieces were commissioned for the occasion. Perhaps the most intriguing is *Copernicus: Narrative and Credo* by Leo Smit, which includes a modern declaration of belief written and read by astronomer Fred Hoyle. But by far the strangest cosmology piece is electronic composer Karl-Heinz Stockhausen's YLEM, named after the ancient Greek term for the primordial substance from which everything came (revived in our time by George Gamow.) The players perform a Big Bang, clustered tightly together on stage, and then expand away from their position, much as the galaxies do.

Richard Smith - Las Cumbres Amateur Outreach Award Winner

Part III

Linking Research with EPO

EPO and a Changing World
ASP Conference Series, Vol. 389, © 2008
C. Garmany, M. Gibbs, and J. W. Moody

Engaging Learners with Space Telescope Data: Best Practices and Lessons Learned from Across the Spectrum

Mary Dussault

Science Education Department, Harvard Smithsonian Center for Astrophysics, 60 Garden St., Cambridge, Massachusetts 02138, USA

Denise Smith, Bonnie Eisenhamer, Frank Summers, and Dan McCallister

Space Telescope Science Institute, 3700 San Martin Dr., Baltimore, MD 21218, USA

Michelle Thaller

Spitzer Science Center, California Institute of Technology, 1200 East California Blvd, Pasadena, CA 91125, USA

James Lochner

Astrophysics Science Division, USRA and NASA/Goddard Space Flight Center, Greenbelt, MD 20771, USA

Mark Hartman

Kavli Institute for Astrophysics and Space Research, Massachusetts Institute of Technology, 1 Hampshire St., Cambridge, MA 02139, USA

Abstract. The ever-increasing accessibility of astronomical data has tremendous potential for supporting powerful science learning. In this interactive case-study and panel session, participants explored several different space telescope projects (including NASA's Great Observatories) that have created educational materials and programs that enable student-driven investigations by providing access to professional science data. Participants examined the attributes of the various programs including strategies used to facilitate learning from data; common challenges faced by developers; and lessons learned. Small group discussions led to the identification of key insights and unresolved questions regarding the growing number of projects that aim to engage learners with "real" astronomical data.

1. Perceived Benefits and Challenges

Before the session began, the 36 participants were asked to use three index cards to indicate the following: 1) identify a major benefit of engaging learners with real data analysis experiences; 2) identify a key challenge or potential barrier to doing so; and 3) list one or two good resources that could be "models" for this kind of work. The perceived benefits fell strongly into three categories. First, many participants identified the "real"-ness, "authenticity," and "relevancy" of real data investigations to be key factors in sustaining students' interest, motivation, and engagement in science learning (i.e., more so than learning from the textbook). Second, a significant number of participants noted the value of such experiences in helping learners to understand "how science gets done" – the processes, methods, and nature of science. A few participants highlighted the exciting potential of some of these projects to actually promote original scientific discoveries by non-professional researchers. Notably, none of the participants suggested that student investigations using authentic scientific data were a better way to learn science content, highlighting an issue that came up several times in later discussions.

Participants also identified a number of potential challenges or barriers to successful implementation of real data analysis projects, which ranged from common classroom logistics to issues that are at the heart of *all* efforts to promote student learning of inquiry and scientific reasoning skills. The key challenges raised were:

- Technology barriers: classroom access to appropriate hardware, software and Internet capabilities

- Time/No Child Left Behind/Standards: authentic data analysis projects take time, a rare commodity given classroom obligations to meet No Child Left Behind requirements and an overloaded menu of content standards

- Teacher training: these kinds of projects require substantive opportunities for teacher professional development, which is challenging to scale up

- Developing appropriate and accessible interfaces to data and analysis tools

- Helping learners navigate the complexity and volume of real data archives

- Structuring the learning as a real investigation, not a "cookbook" lab

The most frequently mentioned models for engaging learners with real data were the Sloan Digital Sky Survey's Skyserver projects and the Hands On Universe project, although a greater number of participants noted they were still looking for such a model. A few participants also highlighted the "citizen science" projects Stardust@home and GalaxyZoo.

2. Engaging Learners With Space Telescope Data: Four Cases

2.1. Professional Development for Teachers Using Hubble and Other Astronomy Data in the Classroom

In this case study, participants examined two activities from the Space Telescope Science Institute's Office of Public Outreach (OPO) Formal Education program, Amazing Space. The data analysis activities, the Hubble Deep Field Academy and the Mixed-Up Solar System, are designed as curriculum support tools that are used in OPO's teacher professional development programs.

The Institute's teacher training programs aim to provide both science content and pedagogical strategies, and these field-tested activities are part of OPO's commitment to working with middle school educators to demonstrate how to select and implement data that is appropriate for classroom use. Both activities-which provide opportunities to work with images, numerical and tabular data, and graphical data- are designed to provide authentic learning experiences that specifically satisfy the needs, and meet the various levels of, middle school teachers and students. The data is presented in context and without jargon, the content is geared toward national education standards, and the activities are modular and flexible in order to be used by learners with a range of abilities.

The Amazing Space education team offers the following as its most important lesson learned: it is necessary to determine the types of data middle school educators *need* for the classroom, and provide them with the data and supporting materials that meet their needs, rather than focusing solely on the specific data our mission has to offer.

Reflections and Discussion: Participants noted that Amazing Space materials used both Hubble images and other data to promote data analysis skills such as observing and asking questions, classifying objects, and generating and interpreting graphs. These were the "abilities of inquiry" standards for which middle school educators indicated they needed help. They also noticed the particular "packaging" of data and sequencing of activities in this case study that served to scaffold increasingly sophisticated thinking by students. One participant commented on the apparent disconnect between middle and high school level efforts to engage students with data: *"It seems that there is a better understanding for how to use 'data' at the middle school level that at the HS level. Why do we try to turn HS students into some kind of mini-scientists? Can the approach used at the MS level be useful at the HS level too? (It is not necessary to crunch data!)"*

Questions focused on how much background content information is needed by teachers before they can effectively facilitate these activities, and how best to provide it. Several participants also had questions about any evaluation data that could demonstrate the impact and effectiveness of these materials-a topic that came up for all the case studies as well as in the general discussion.

2.2. Student Hera: Accessing NASA's High Energy Astrophysics Data Archive

Student Hera is an internet-based tool that provides students access to both analysis software and data for studying astronomical objects such as black holes, binary star systems, supernovae, and galaxies. Different segments of the project are aimed at upper middle school, high school, and introductory college level audiences. Through a client tool, students access data and run software on servers from NASA's High Energy Astrophysics Science Archive Research Center (HEASARC). In doing so, students use a subset of the same software and experience the same analysis process that an astronomer follows in analyzing data obtained from an orbiting satellite observatory. Student Hera is accompanied by a web-based tutorial that steps students through the science background, and the procedures for accessing the data and for using the analysis software. The web page tutorial is self-guided and contains a number of exercises; students can work independently or in groups.

Student Hera currently includes two analysis modules: one for light curves and one for images. In the light curve analysis students explore data from a binary star system containing a normal star and a black hole. The objective of the lesson is for students to use plotting, estimation, and statistical techniques to determine the orbital period. Students interpret the shape of the light curve with the nature of the binary system. Students may then apply these techniques to a number of data sets and draw conclusions on the natures of the systems (for example, students discover that one system is an eclipsing binary).

The learning goal for Student Hera is for students to extend basic math and science concepts into real world research applications with easy access to both data and analysis tools. The strategy used to facilitate learning is a guided analysis that steps students through both the science concepts and the analysis techniques. Author Lochner offers the following challenges and lessons learned during the project:

- Focus on what you want the students to learn - Is it the science, the analysis techniques, or a particular software package?

- Use data sets that are as simple as possible. Avoid students from having to implement "calibration" procedures.

- Simplify the inputs to the analysis tools - use default input values where possible.

- Design the lessons with a succession of steps so that students of different abilities may find success. In the Student Hera timing analysis lesson, middle school students can plot the data and estimate the period from the graph. Advanced students can use the more sophisticated plotting and period-determination tools.

- Connection to NASA servers may be blocked by a school's firewall!

- Any lesson or module should be the first step for deeper exploration of the data. Be sure to offer additional data sets.

Reflections and Discussion: Participants discussed the merits and challenges of the particular strategy of the Hera project to adapt and simplify professional research data analysis tools for student use, and also to give students step-by-step guidance to investigate a limited and judiciously chosen set of authentic spacecraft data. The discussion then broadened to general questions of the relationship between data analysis activities and inquiry, and what is meant by the phrase "authentic inquiry." Some of the questions and insights from participants were:

- *"The Hera project brought up the question of true inquiry-based learning. Do any of these [projects], at the middle school or high school level, help students learn the scientific method?"*

- *"It is important to connect data analysis to inquiry-based learning, i.e. interpretation, argumentation, presentation of results."*

- *"Is the potential for a 'new' discovery (new to scientists) required for authentic inquiry?"*

2.3. Chandra Astrophysics Institute

The Chandra Astrophysics Institute (CAI) is a yearlong out-of-school time program targeted at high school students underrepresented in the Science, Technology, Engineering, and Mathematics (STEM) program from the greater Boston area. The goal of CAI is to provide an opportunity for these students to build the background skills and knowledge necessary to understand how research science is done by actually doing it. The program consists of a five week summer session with x-ray data research projects mentored by MIT Kavli Institute (MKI) researchers and educators during the school year. Students develop their own questions based on their summer experience and investigations of patterns in their data. MKI researchers become advisors for the developing projects giving guidance on how to answer those questions.

"Practice-based mastery of skills" and "the importance of student voice" are cited by Boston teens as an important part of what they desire in an out-of-school time program, and these are reflected in several of the intended outcomes of the CAI program:

- Students have learned enough astrophysics and data analysis skills to undertake an investigative project using the methods of research science.

- Students have a clearer picture of the way research science works, including the value of communication, collaboration and argumentation skills in making progress in a scientific community.

- Students become better at practicing and recognizing good implementation of the skills involved in doing research science.

MKI educators identify several educational strategies for engaging students in real data analysis. First, the CAI program science teaching method mirrors the development of knowledge by a working science community. Students are guided to explore key concepts needed for their research through observation and questioning, model building, testing predictions and answering questions, and communicating results. For example, an investigation to observe, characterize, and test a model of a light bulb light glow builds concepts and skills that can be used in an investigation of starlight. Second, the program engages students in repeated practice with a small set of concepts and analysis tools to develop their comfort and confidence. In this way, they can interpret what they observe about a piece of data that interests them, develop their own connections and ideas, and communicate them to others, *regardless of whether others have come to similar conclusions*. A third important pedagogical strategy is to guide students explicitly from their own personal experiences and representations of ideas (e.g. "spectrum" or digital images) towards scientists' conceptions.

The CAI program shared the following challenges and lessons learned with participants. First, be aware that the "rawness" of the data is inversely proportional to the ease with which students can interpret it. Second, don't underestimate the challenge of guiding students through the process of discerning what is really important about the patterns or characteristics of real data. If they already know what to look for, you end up promoting a traditional "cookbook" lab approach. If students *don't* already know what to look for, you can more closely approximate true inquiry - but only at the expense of time and the risk of student confusion and frustration. Finally, the strategy of repeatedly using just a few analysis tools can lead to a limited depth of questions from students, but is *essential* to enable learners to be successful on their own.

Reflections and Discussion: These CAI "lessons learned" stimulated considerable discussion about the scaffolding strategy of first giving students guided exploration experiences that provide them with the tools and skills such that they are then able to pose their own questions and design data investigations to answer them. CAI students pursue an inquiry process that captures many of the features of authentic ("real") science, even if their conclusions are already known (or rejected) by scientists. As one participant noted: *"It is important to differentiate between research-like experiences and authentic research-discovery experiences. Both are useful."*

The amount of time students (and CAI program leaders and scientists) invest in CAI is considerable, however, and participants wondered if such an experience was possible in the classroom environment.

2.4.   Spitzer Space Telescope Teacher Research Program

In this case study, participants learned about what is probably the high-end of engaging learners in authentic science inquiry with space telescope data. The Spitzer Science Center (SSC), in partnership with the National Optical Astronomy Observatory (NOAO), has designed a program for teacher and student research using Director's discretionary observing time on the Spitzer Space Telescope. This program allows a select group of teachers and students to actually observe with Spitzer and work with Spitzer archival data. Following a considerable training program, participants propose for and obtain Spitzer Space Telescope time for educational observations.

Participating teachers attend an initial workshop to become familiar with the Spitzer Space Telescope archives and to receive training in infrared astronomy and observational techniques. The teachers also attend a workshop to learn about the observation planning process, and telescope and instrument capabilities. Subgroups of teachers prepare for and propose their observing projects with mentoring and technical assistance from SSC and NOAO scientists. Finally, the teachers and their students visit the SSC to reduce and analyze their data. They have been able to present their original research findings at professional meetings such as those of the American Astronomical Society.

Spitzer EPO Lead Michelle Thaller noted a key challenge of this ambitious project is that it requires significant resources (funds, extra effort involved in providing support for participants and in collaborating with multiple organizations, time commitment of scientists and program managers) for what is arguably a limited impact. Only a few teachers (and their students) can have this experience, and many of them find it difficult to bring their complex investigations directly into their own classrooms. On the other hand, the ability to conduct original research has had a profound impact on the teachers involved, and in most cases teachers suggest that the experience has transformed their own understanding of science and their approach to teaching it, a change that they indicate does have an impact in the classroom.

Reflections and Discussion: Participants were impressed by the Spitzer program's commitment and ability to provide a transformative experience for teachers. The authenticity of teachers being NASA space telescope researchers is clearly motivational and, most thought, a way to humanize and bring the excitement of real science back to the students in the classroom. The discussion included many questions about how to broaden the impact of the program, and how specifically the teachers' research experiences could be applied to new science learning experiences for students in the classroom.

3. Wrap-Up: Key Insights and Questions For the Future

Participants discussed the fact that the case studies in this workshop represent points on a longer continuum of experiences with data–experiences that can range from cookbook-type labs using canned data designed for students to "re-discover" ideas already taught, to completely open-ended authentic science research investigations that can result in publishable findings. As one group member noted, *"we must carefully define what we mean by 'authentic research' and 'authentic data'. Do we mean original discoveries? Or discoveries by the students?"* Another stated that there is a spectrum of levels of engagement in inquiry processes, and that learners need support and guidance along the way.

Within astronomy education and public outreach there are some programs that enable learners to contribute to the discovery of new scientifically valid results, as well as many that provide teachers and students with high quality classroom inquiry experiences. Our community, however, is still in the early stages of understanding of the relative merits of each of these outcomes and the best practices to achieve these goals using professional astronomical data. We recommend two sources from the educational research literature for developers of inquiry-based experiences with real data. Clark Chinn and Betina Malhotra of Rutgers have presented a theoretical framework useful for designing classroom inquiry tasks that evoke reasoning processes similar to those employed in real scientific inquiry (Chinn & Malhotra 2002). And Carl Wenning of Illinois State University has outlined a hierarchy of teaching practices and intellectual processes that illustrate how one can promote an increasingly sophisticated understanding of inquiry among students (Wenning 2005).

Finally, all participants agreed that we need more community-wide exchange and more robust evaluations to answer our questions about the actual impact of these kinds of programs. Do students understand the nature of science better? What strategies are most effective for helping students learn inquiry skills and thinking processes that are transferable beyond the classroom? Can classroom inquiry experiences based on sources of professional data promote conceptual understanding? We look forward to more discussion, on the "Data in Education" blog (Christian et. al, this volume) and elsewhere.

Acknowledgments. The case studies presented in this workshop are all part of NASA's Science Mission Directorate Education and Public Outreach portfolio. We thank the workshop participants for the lively discussions.

References

Chinn, C. A., and Malhotra, B. A., Science Education, **86**(2), 175 (2002)
Wenning, C. J., Journal of Physics Teacher Education Online, **2**(3), 3 (2005)
    (http://www.phy.ilstu.edu/jpteo/)

EPO and a Changing World
ASP Conference Series, Vol. 389, © 2008
C. Garmany, M. Gibbs, and J. W. Moody

Astronomy Village: Innovative Uses of Planetary Astronomy Images and Data

S. K. Croft and S. M. Pompea

National Optical Astronomy Observatory, 950 N. Cherry Ave, Tucson, AZ 85719

Abstract. Teaching and learning science is best done by hands-on experience with real scientific data and real scientific problems. Getting such experiences into public and home-schooling classrooms is a challenge. Here we describe two award-winning multimedia products that embody one successful solution to the problem: *Astronomy Village: Investigating the Universe*, and *Astronomy Village: Investigating the Solar System*. Each *Village* provides a virtual environment for inquiry-based scientific exploration of ten planetary and astronomical problems such as "Mission to Pluto" and "Search for a Supernova." Both *Villages* are standards-based and classroom tested. *Investigating the Solar System* is designed for middle and early high school students, while *Investigating the Universe* is at the high school and introductory college level. The objective of both *Villages* is to engage students in scientific inquiry by having them acquire, explore, and analyze real scientific data and images drawn from real scientific problems.

1. Introduction

The effective use of planetary images and data in the classroom has been a challenge from the beginning of the space program. The tendency has been to flood classrooms with 'gee whiz' press release images, or to provide access to enormous archives of satellite images or data assuming that classroom teachers will easily incorporate such information into their classroom presentations. Experience has shown that most teachers generally have neither the time nor the expertise to make effective educational use of masses of images, and that the best use of images is in the context of a carefully designed curriculum.

Simply incorporating astronomical images and data into the curriculum is not enough. Most astronomers and planetary scientists "do" science because it is interesting, challenging, intriguing, cutting-edge and exciting. Most children look at and explore the world around them for the same reasons. Yet by the time they get into high school and college, the excitement and intrigue are often gone, and classes in science become chores to avoided whenever possible and endured when not. Why? Partly it is the view of the nature of "real science" as taught in too many K-14 classrooms across the nation. In the perception of one middle school student, "real science" consists of memorizing words and taking tests. For example, students are expected to learn roughly 1500 new words in a typical first year foreign language class. In contrast, the number of new vocabulary words in a typical introductory biology class is closer to 3500! With such a formidable list of words to remember, who has time to get into the spirit of exploration and discovery that drives the typical space scientist?

It has long been recognized that science teaching is more effective when it involves hands-on activities and problem solving using real data and images. Two award-winning curriculum supplements developed at the Center for Educational Technology in Wheeling, WV, deal with both the image and interest challenges by providing an inquiry-based scientific context for selected sets of planetary and deep space images: *Astronomy Village: Investigating the Universe* (hereafter AVIU), and *Astronomy Village: Investigating the Solar System* (hereafter AVISS). Following content guidelines in the NRC's National Science Education Standards, AVIU is designed for high school students and deals with topics mostly in stellar and galactic astronomy, while AVISS is designed for middle school students and deals with topics in astrobiology and planetary geology.

2. Pedagogical Foundations

The objective of both *Villages* is to engage students in scientific inquiry by having them acquire and analyze real scientific data and images drawn from real scientific problems. As stated by the National Committee on Science Education Standards and Assessment, students need to "learn science in ways that reflect the modes of inquiry that scientists use to understand the natural world" (National Committee on Science Education Standards and Assessment 1993).

The basic approach is constructivist and problem-based (Finkle & Torp 1995). In each *Village*, students have a variety of investigations to choose from. Within each investigation is a problem an array of information - images, experiments, informative documents, and digital/graphical data - that can be used to define the problem and investigate possible solutions. Images are used in several different roles: as illustrations, as elements in sets of related images combined in several types of comparative formats, and as objects of detailed image processing and digital analysis. The problems and data sets are designed to foster students' research skills. The design emphasizes the process of scientific inquiry as outlined in the National Science Standards (National Research Council 1996). Both *Villages* can also be used as classroom or teacher resources: each contains numerous grade-level appropriate articles on astronomy and space science, and hundreds of Earth- and space-based images.

The educational goals of the *Villages* are to motivate students to learn concepts in astronomy and space science, to engage them in scientific inquiry, to make use of technology to acquire, explore, and analyze scientific data and images, and to introduce students to cutting-edge scientific problems and issues.

3. The Investigations

The investigations in *Astronomy Village: Investigating the Solar System* are organized into two introductory Core Research Projects and associated sets of focused Investigations. This arrangement grew out of the need to take middle school students with minimal understanding of science to a level where they could comprehend cutting-edge research problems. The Core Projects provide an introduction and general context in which the Investigations are imbedded. Students should work through one of the Core Projects and then tackle one or more of the associated investigations. The Projects and their investigations are:

Core Project Search for Life is an exploration of the nature of life on Earth, and the necessary conditions for its existence.

1. Mars Rocks: investigates the putative fossils found in a meteorite from Mars.

2. Stormy Mars: investigates the geologic evidence for flows of liquid water in Mar's past.

3. It's Alive: uses true and IR color images to search for plant life on Earth and Mars.

4. Space Oasis: explores locations throughout the solar system where liquid water may exist.

Core Project Mission to Pluto examines the nature of planets and the forces that shaped their surfaces to let students puzzle out where Pluto fits in.

1. The Big Smash: introduces impact cratering as a geologic process and its uses in interpreting structures and surfaces throughout the solar system.

2. Fire and Ice: explores rocky and icy volcanism on the Earth, planets, and icy moons.

3. Shake 'n Break: discusses earthquakes and tectonic features in the solar system.

The investigations in *Astronomy Village: Investigating the Universe* are designed as independent units, though they are loosely grouped into four general research areas: stars and stellar evolution, scale: time and distance, searching for other planetary system, and instrumentation. The investigations are:

1. Search for a Supernova: uses neutrino data and time sequences of images to search for exploding stars.

2. Looking as a Stellar Nursery: looks for stars-in-the-making in the Omega nebula.

3. Variable Stars: looks for Cepheid variables as yardsticks for intergalactic distances.

4. Search for Nearby Stars: uses parallax to identify and determine the distances to nearby stars.

5. Extragalactic Zoo: examines the variety of extragalactic objects one encounters in the universe.

6. Wedges of the Universe: examines the view into and perpendicular to the galactic plane to help interpret the structure of our galaxy and the universe.

7. Search for a "Wobbler:" looks for stars with regular oscillations in their paths through space that may indicate the presence of a planet.

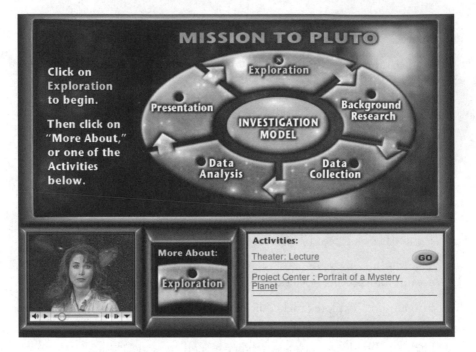

Figure 1.   The Research Path diagram for the Mission to Pluto Core Project. The mentor for this project is seen in the window at lower left.

8. Search for Planetary Building Blocks: looks deeply into the Orion Nebula in search of solar systems in the making.

9. Search for Earth-Crossing Objects: uses image processing to find fast-moving asteroids to look for possible Earth-crossers.

10. Observatory Site Selection: provides data on several potential observatory sites, and challenges students to choose the best one for a variety of telescope projects.

4.   The Research Path Diagrams

Students are guided through their investigations in both Villages by the "Research Path Diagram," a visual representation and interactive model of the scientific process (Figure 1). In AVIU, the "path" is linear and each investigation is independent of the others. In AVISS, the path is circular and investigations are linked, so that students can see how research activities are in a sense cyclical and build on one another. By working through the investigations and by doing "hands-on" activities both on and off-line, students gain an understanding of how science works.

Figure 2. The *Village* map for *Astronomy Village: Investigating the Solar System.* Each named building can be "entered" with a click. The navigation toolbar is on the left side.

An audio-visual "mentor" is provided for each investigation. The mentor introduces the investigation and directs the student through the path diagram, providing helpful suggestions for things to think about during the investigation. The mentors appear in videos. Their verbal comments are also provided in print form.

5. The Village Interface

When entering each *Village*, the student is presented with a clickable picture of an observatory and associated buildings (Figure 2). The *Villages* were designed to simulate real facilities like the Jet Propulsion Laboratory in California and the Mauna Kea Observatory in Hawaii. The buildings in the *Village* can be "entered" by clicking on them to access the various tools, images, and data. Each has an observatory, a library, a lab, a computer lab, lecture hall, and other work areas. There is even a cafeteria where the students can take a break and listen to professional astronomers spin tales of life as an astronomer. For new users, there are also audiovisual tutorials introducing the "workings" of the *Village*. The libraries contain articles, videos, and images. The labs contain both computer-based activities and directions for hands-on experiments to be done away from the computer. Hands-on experiments were added to give students experience in carrying out physical experiments that illustrate scientific concepts in the investigations, as well as to provide flexibility in classroom use where computer access is limited.

"Tools" in each Village include an image browser, computer simulations, virtual instruments, and image-processing programs ("built-in" in AVISS, and a version of NIH Image in AVIU). AVISS also includes the solar System discovery Center where students can compare planets, gather data about them, and play arcade-like games introducing concepts about gravity.

Navigation is also provided by a toolbar on the left side of the *Village* map, which includes a help function.

6.   Classroom Management

The investigations in AVISS are designed to each take a week of class time, so a completed cycle (one Core Project plus one Investigation) can take a little as two weeks. However, by having students go through a number of investigations, classroom time can be extended to about 10 weeks. In AVIU, each investigation is designed to take as little as four weeks or can be extended to as much as 12 weeks. Scope and sequence suggestions are provided for teachers in help materials that come with each *Village*.

7.   Software Requirements

Both Villages are written in HTML with Flash and Java applets. Thus they can be used on a variety of Internet browsers. AVISS works best with Internet Explorer, but is incompatible with some of the newer browsers. AVIU is compatible with Internet Explorer, Firefox, and Safari.

8.   Educational Effectiveness

Both AVISS and AVIU were extensively tested in the classroom during the development phase. After completion, each underwent a formal analysis of effectiveness. During May and June of 1997, questionnaires were sent to approximately 350 registered owners of AVIU. About 80 responded, mostly teachers currently working in the classroom. The teachers indicated that the AVIU materials are of high quality and lead to effective learning outcomes in the areas of content knowledge, technical skill, and attitude towards science (McGee *et al.* 1998). About one third of the budget for AVISS was devoted to development of a formal assessment instrument designed to evaluate student learning. A total of 837 students participated in the assessment study in the fall of 1999, including 590 who used AVISS, 117 in an "alternative treatment" group (same material, standard presentation), and 130 students in a control group. The results of the study indicate that the materials developed in AVISS can be used effectively to promote interdisciplinary understanding and problem solving in planetary science within a relatively short period of time (details can be found in Dimitrov, McGee, & Howard 2002).

In addition to the positive results provided by the assessments, both *Villages* have won educational awards. AVISS earned the 2001 Association of Educational Publishers recognition for being exceptional in its educational content and delivery. AVIU was awarded the Technology & Learning School Winner Software Award, 1996.

9. Future Directions

New Astronomy Village-like modules are being developed at the National Optical Astronomy Observatory as part of the educational outreach for the Giant Segmented Mirror Telescope. Two modules have been selected: Observatory Site Selection and Systems Engineering. Students will examine site selection data from the Thirty Meter Telescope and Giant Magellan Telescope projects including seeing data, cloud cover, temperature, and turbulence data. The environmental issues associated with site selection will allow this module to be tied into Earth science as well as astronomy.

Acknowledgments. This project is supported by the National Optical Astronomy Observatory, and the Giant Segmented Mirror Telescope educational outreach. NOAO is operated by the Association of Universities for Research in Astronomy (AURA), Inc., under the National Science Foundation AURA/NSF Cooperative Agreement AST-9613615.

References

Dimitrov, D. M., McGee, S., and Howard, B. C., "Changes in Students' Science Ability Produced by Multimedia Learning Environments: Application of the Linear Logistic Model for Change", School Science and Mathematics Journal, **102**(1), 15-22 (2002)

Finkle, S.L. and Torp, L.L., "Introductory Documents" (Available from the Center for Problem-Based Learning, Illinois Math and Science Academy, 1500 West Sullivan Road, Aurora, IL 60506-1000, 1995)

McGee, S., Hong, N., Shia, R. and Purcell, S., "Results of a Survey Assessing the Impact of Astronomy Village: Investigating the Universe" (Online Technical Report that can be found at http://www.cet.edu/research/techreports.html, 1998)

National Committee on Science Education Standards and Assessment, *National Science Education Standards: An Enhanced Sampler* SE 053 554(National Research Council, Washington, D.C. 1993).

National Research Council, *National Science Education Standards* (National Academy Press, Washington, D.C., 1996)

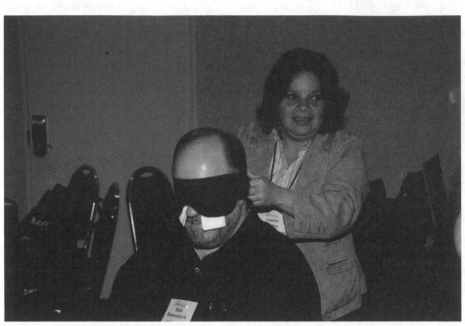

Learning to teach the heavens to those who cannot see

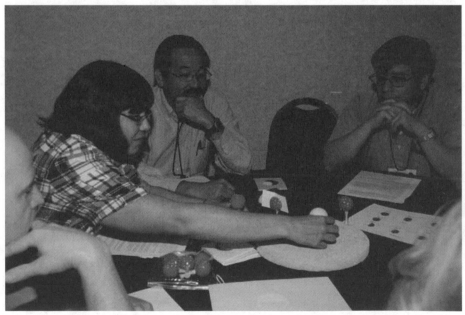

Hands-on learning taught best by doing!

EPO and a Changing World
ASP Conference Series, Vol. 389, © 2008
C. Garmany, M. Gibbs, and J. W. Moody

SpaceScience@Home: Authentic Research Projects that Use Citizen Scientists

Bryan J. H. Méndez

Space Sciences Laboratory, University of California at Berkeley, 7 Gauss Way, Berkeley, CA 94720-7450

Abstract. In recent years, several space science research projects have enlisted the help of large numbers of non-professional volunteers, "citizen scientists", to aid in performing tasks that are critical to a project, but require more person-time (or computing time) than a small professional research team can practically perform themselves. Examples of such projects include SETI@home, which uses time from volunteers computers to process radio-telescope observation looking for signals originating from extra-terrestrial intelligences; Clickworkers, which asks volunteers to review images of the surface of Mars to identify craters; Spacewatch, which used volunteers to review astronomical telescopic images of the sky to identify streaks made by possible Near Earth Asteroids; and Stardust@home, which asks volunteers to review "focus movies" taken of the Stardust interstellar dust aerogel collector to search for possible impacts from interstellar dust particles. We shall describe these and other similar projects and discuss lessons learned from carrying out such projects, including the educational opportunities they create.

1. Introduction

Some scientific endeavors require greater manpower (or computing power) than a team of professional scientists can practically accomplish. This is where the idea of "citizen science" is useful. Citizen science refers to a scientific project that makes use of a large group of volunteers to aid in performing critical project tasks. These volunteers may have no formal scientific training of any kind, but may still be able to aid in making basic observations, measurements, or computations. This is by no means a new concept. The Audubon Society has conducted the Christmas Bird Count (http://www.audubon.org/bird/cbc/index.html) since 1900 where birding enthusiasts across America help ornithologists take a census of early-winter bird populations.

The concept of the volunteers scientist is fundamental to the history of astronomy. For centuries amateur astronomers (those who do astronomy not as profession, but as a hobby) have been making critical contributions to the field. In the last century, their impact on the study of variable stars and minor planets has been staggering (http://www.aavso.org/aavso/membership/impact.shtml).

With the growth of the internet over the past two decades, ever more citizen science projects are taking shape. A great many of these projects are in the fields of zoology, meteorology, environmental science, and geology. For example, the United States Geological Survey (USGS) has been collecting online reports from citizens about the ground shaking following significant earthquakes (http://pasadena.wr.usgs.gov/shake/ca/). The business world has not let this idea go unnoticed either. Amazon.com has created a service called the Mechanical Turk (http://www.mturk.com/). This is an artificial, artificial intelligence service that pays "volunteers" for their efforts in everything from transcribing online videos to searching for Steve Fossett.

With the recent explosion of space science data now being collected world wide, citizen scientists can play a real and significant role in new discoveries. Projects using citizen scientists can not only help solve difficult problems space science, but also hold an enormous educational potential for those volunteers involved.

We will describe several recent citizen science projects in space science and discuss important lessons learned from them. We will also discuss ideas for future citizen science projects in space science.

2.   SETI@HOME

SETI@HOME (http://setiathome.ssl.berkeley.edu/) from UC Berkeley's Space Sciences Laboratory is an early example of a citizen science project in space science. Radio SETI, the search for extraterrestrial intelligence, collects radio data from thousands of stars over a large frequency range looking for evidence of unnatural, narrow-band transmissions. Beginning in the 1990s, the project began generating enormous amount of data that proved too much for timely analysis by the resources of the project.

The team developed a program that runs on an internet-connected personal computer to download data from SETI, perform data reduction and basic analysis, then upload the results back to SETI. This program, SETI@HOME, runs in the background, only using the computer's free CPU cycles. Thus, a person can contribute to the project by volunteering their computer's idle time. The idea and program proved to be enormously popular; over five million people to date have subscribed to the SETI@HOME service. The success of SETI@HOME spawned the BOINC project (http://boinc.berkeley.edu/), which generalizes the SETI@HOME infrastructure for many different applications in massively distributed parallel computing.

The large number of subscribers to SETI@HOME demonstrates the strong interest in space science by the general public as well their strong desire to contribute to space science research. However, one drawback to the SETI@HOME approach is that it makes use of only the volunteers' computers, and does not engage the volunteers themselves in the process of research.

3.   Clickworkers

At the beginning of this decade, the partnership of NASA Ames Research Center and the SETI Institute developed a citizen science project to identify cratering features on the surface of Mars. This project was called clickworkers (http://clickworkers.arc.nasa.gov/top).

In 2000, Clickworkers conducted a pilot test with over 800 volunteers using Martian surface imagery from the Viking orbiters. They compared the volunteers' work to that of professional planetary scientists and found a very tight match. Based on the success of the pilot test, Clickworkers began to make crater identifications in earnest in 2001 using Mars Global Surveyor imagery.

A new version of Clickworkers is now in beta testing using HiRISE imaging from the Mars Reconnaissance Orbiter. Volunteers may be able to request their own observations to be taken in this new version.

There are plans to extend Clickworkers from identifying craters in images of Mars to craters in images of the asteroids Vesta and Ceres which will be visited by the DAWN mission in 2011 and 2015, respectively.

Contact for Clickworkers: Virginia Gulick, SETI Institute, vgu-lick@mail.arc.nasa.gov

4. SPACEWATCH FMO Project

The SPACEWATCH program at the University of Arizona studies various kinds of small Solar System objects, such as asteroids, comets, and trans-Neptunian objects, and searches for objects that could be potential hazards for Earth (http://spacewatch.lpl.arizona.edu). In 2003, SPACEWATCH began a three-year, privately funded, citizen science program to search for Fast Moving Objects (FMOs; http://fmo.lpl.arizona.edu/FMO_home/index.cfm). FMOs move through the sky rapidly because they are close to Earth and are likely to be asteroids in a near Earth orbit. FMOs appear as streaks, or arcs in single epoch images. These streaks are difficult for software to differentiate from other possible features, such as cosmic ray strikes, background galaxies, or artificial satellites. People, however, demonstrate an inherent ability to easily distinguish between such features.

The SPACEWATCH FMO Project transmitted image data from Kitt Peak to Tucson in near real time and made that imagery available to the public on the same night it was collected via the internet, to allow for follow-up observations. It is essential to quickly follow up on possible Near Earth Objects (NEOs) as they can quickly be lost without accurate orbit determinations. Only fresh, unreviewed images were presented on-line.

SPACEWATCH recruited and trained hundreds of volunteers online, worldwide to examine image data. Volunteers were required to view an online training tutorial and pass a test before participating. Potential NEO candidates from volunteers were screened and evaluated and appropriate action was taken on the viable ones.

From 2003 to 2006, 52 volunteers spotted trails in images left by FMOs. Of those trails there were 43 discoveries of asteroids, 3 rediscoveries, 15 recoveries, 7 artificial satellites, and 8 unconsolidated discoveries.

There were some important lessons learned during the project. First, in order to calibrate the efficiency and reliability of the hundreds of volunteers, it would have been useful to inject fake candidates into the images sent out to users. Doing this would have allowed the SPACEWATCH team to prioritize the evaluation of FMO candidates. Candidates from volunteers with higher reliability could be reviewed first. Additionally, it would have been useful to have images reviewed by more than one volunteer, enhancing the efficiency of prioritizing candidates.

Additionally, there were problems with some volunteers who were not content to participate within the collaborative environment of the project. There were instances of volunteers hoarding images under multiple fake user names, and attempts to "discover" objects and send them to the Minor Planet Center as original observations, etc. Again, duplicate image delivery and the use of fake candidates could have helped here as a countermeasure. Other possible solutions might have been to work with specific groups of reliable people rather than the public at large. For example, classroom students could have been recruited to help and incentives given for their collegial participation.

Another important, if mundane, lesson learned was that adequate financial resources are needed to maintain such a project. For this project, the level of effort required to maintain the website, supervise, train, and correspond with volunteers was underestimated.

Contact for Spacewatch: Robert S. McMillan, University of Arizona, bob@lpl.arizona.edu

5.   Stardust@home

In 2006, a new citizen science program was created at the UC Berkeley Space Sciences Laboratory. Inspired by SETI@HOME, Stardust@home (http://stardustathome.ssl.berkeley.edu) uses volunteers to help in the search for interstellar dust collected by NASA's Stardust mission.

NASA's Stardust mission launched in 1999 to collect dust from comet Wild 2 and return the samples to Earth. It was the first ever comet sample return mission. The Science objective of Stardust was to understand the materials and conditions that went into the formation of the Solar System.

Along the way to Wild 2, Stardust also collected Interstellar dust entering the Solar System from outside. Stardust used a two-sided, tennis-racquet-shaped collector with tiles of aerogel to collect star dust. The front side of the collector was used for collecting dust from Wild 2, while the back side of the collector was pointed into the incoming stream of interstellar dust twice during the flight to Wild 2. This was also the first-ever sample return mission from the Galaxy.

The density of interstellar dust is very low, and we expect only about 45 dust particles in total to have been captured in the 1,000 square cm collector. An automated microscope at the Johnson Space Center scans through the aerogel collector taking digital "focus movies." There will be over 1 million of these. Finding the interstellar dust particles will be like searching for 45 ants in a football field looking at one 5cm x 5cm square at a time.

The interstellar dust particles themselves are not visible in the focus movies, only the tracks they leave in the aerogel. We had no knowledge of the condition of the aerogel until it returned, nor do we really know what the particle tracks look like. In order to use pattern recognition software to find tracks we would have to first teach the software to recognize particle tracks and differentiate them from other possible features. To do that we would need to find a dozen or so particles!

We need people to look through the movies. People show a remarkable ability to visually discriminate between various features on the surface of the aerogel and possible particle tracks. However, the task of manually searching through a million focus movies would be overwhelming for a small research group but not for an army of enthusiastic volunteers.

We place the focus movies online for volunteers to examine. We originally estimated that it will take 30,000 person-hours to complete the task (assuming four people view each focus movie). We have had over 24,000 people registered for Stardust@home (leading to hundreds of views per focus movie).

It will take several months to complete the scan of the collector with the automated microscope, that is the limiting time factor. The staff at Johnson Space Center is not able to scan the collector consistently due to other constraints of the Cosmic Dust Lab.

Volunteers use a Virtual Microscope (VM) to examine focus movies. The VM works directly within a web browser. No special software is needed, simply an internet connection and a fair amount of RAM. A simple online training session and test are required for volunteers to learn how to use the VM. Each focus movie is viewed by many people at random. Calibration movies (movies known to have no particle tracks, or movies containing simulated particle tracks) are placed into the data stream to gauge each volunteer's sensitivity (find tracks when they are there) and specificity (find no tracks when they are absent). Each user receives an overall score based on their responses to calibration movies, which make up about 20% of the movies seen through the VM. When viewed in the VM, each real focus movie receives a score based on the number of times it has been seen and weighted by the score of the volunteer who flags it as either containing a track or not. The movies are sorted into a prioritized list based on their scores, and the UC Berkeley Stardust@home team follows up on movies that receive a high enough score.

The first focus movies were made available online on August 1st, 2006. After completing more than 1/3rd of the collector, we have a few dozen candidates, all of which are much smaller than expected and very subtle. So far they appear very different from expectations based on simulated tracks made with test particles fired into acrogel. In August, 2007, Stardust@home began Phase 2 of the search, which revisits the prior focus movies at high magnification. When scanning of the rest of the collector resumes at the Cosmic Dust Lab at Johnson Space Center, a Phase 3 of the search will commence.

The volunteers for Stardust@home (who have named themselves "dusters") have been a remarkable group and are very dedicated. The Stardust@home website features a 'Community' section where dusters can communicate with each other and the Stardust@home team via a bulletin board. This has been an effective way of communicating with such a large number of people. Dusters often answer each other's questions and small group of moderators selected from the dusters help keep things in order on the board.

We provide different kinds of incentives to reward dusters for their efforts. The website features a list of the dusters with top scores. Dusters achieving various score milestones receive a certificate of participation, and we invite top scorers to visit our lab at Berkeley for a tour. Additionally, the first to find a track will have the privilege of naming the dust particle and will also be given coauthorship of scientific papers about the discovery.

To recruit volunteers we initially advertised the project via a press release during Stardust's return in January, 2006. Hundred of news articles around the world were written about the project and dozens of radio and television news spots carried the story as well. Our website collected the email addresses of more than 110,000 people who were interested in the project. Once we began the project more than 24,000 volunteers registered to participate. Our initial analysis of an online survey of 10% of the dusters shows that they are 20% Female and 80% Male, of ages ranging from 6 to 99, and from over 60 countries on 6 continents.

Contact for Stardust@home: Bryan Méndez, University of California at Berkeley, bmendez@ssl.berkeley.edu

6. Systemic

Systemic, which launched in November 2005 (http://www.oklo.org/), takes a somewhat different approach to citizen science. This project from the University of California at Santa Cruz has produced simulated extrasolar planetary systems. Participants download software to observe and analyze and characterize the simulated planetary systems. Their analyses are compared to the original simulations to test for possible biases. The Systemic collaboration also serves as a community center for people to find the latest news about extrasolar planetary research and for some amateur astronomers who are trying to make their own observations of extrasolar planets via the transit method.

7. GLOBE at Night

Most of the space science citizen science projects mentioned so far make use of their volunteers by having them perform analysis on data collected by professional scientists. The GLOBE at Night project (http://www.globe.gov/GaN/) does the opposite. In order to characterize light pollution conditions around the world, volunteers are asked to observe the night sky on specific dates and report counts of stars seen at their locations. The Great World Wide Star Count (http://www.starcount.org/index.html) was another such program carried out in collaboration with GLOBE at Night. Volunteers may participate at various levels depending on their interest. Participants range from avid amateur astronomers to school children. GLOBE at Night began in 2006 and so far in 2007 has recorded nearly 8,500 observations world wide.

Contact for GLOBE at Night: Connie Walker, NOAO, cwalker@noao.edu

8. Galaxy Zoo

A new space science project for the citizen scientists out there has entered the scene in 2007 in the form of Galaxy Zoo (http://www.galaxyzoo.org/). The goal of the project is to obtain morphological classifications for a million galaxies observed in the Sloan Digital Sky Survey (SDSS-II). Morphologies help astronomers learn more about galaxy evolution and large scale structure in the Universe. Images of galaxies are taken for the Sloan Digital Sky Survey by a robotic telescope in New Mexico. The data are automatically reduced by software. The software also automatically searches the images for galaxies. The software can make many basic measurements of the galaxies, including size and brightness. But one property for which software is inadequate is that of determining morphological classification (e.g. spiral, elliptical, irregular, etc.). Here is another case where people are needed because they are better at pattern recognition in images than computer software.

Volunteers are presented with a tutorial and quiz to teach them how to classify galaxies and to recognize erroneous galaxy detections. Then, after registering, volunteers are presented with images from SDSS-II and asked to classify the galaxies as spirals (clockwise spiral, anticlockwise spiral, or edge-on), elliptical, merger, or star/don't know. Images are seen by multiple people for maximum reliability.

Volunteers are able to communicate with each other and the Galaxy Zoo team via an electronic bulletin board. They also may review galaxies they have classified and print images of them. Since the galaxies are initially identified by automated software, the volunteer viewing an image may be the first human being to ever lay eyes on that particular galaxy, a rather romantic notion.

As of this writing there are approximately 110,000 users of Galaxy Zoo who have completed 30 million classifications.

The contact for Galaxy Zoo: Jordan Raddick, John Hopkins University, raddick@pha.jhu.edu

9. Future Projects

Many possible citizen scientists projects in space science are being planned for the future. There are an enormous number of possibilities, especially with new all sky surveys being completed in the next several years (e.g.: LSST, WISE) and ever growing easy access to astronomical data via robotic telescope networks for education and the Virtual Observatories (NVO: http://www.us-vo.org/, and IVOA: http://www.ivoa.net/). We describe one possible project as an example, Asteroids@home.

9.1. Asteroids@home

The Wide-field Infrared Survey Explorer (WISE, http://wise.ssl.berkeley.edu) of NASA will launch in late 2009 and detect many possible Near Earth Objects (NEOs) that will require an enormous effort to confirm. In most cases, NEOs are asteroids in near Earth orbits, possibly in Earth crossing orbits, which raises the possibility of future collisions. WISE will have the advantage of being able to discover NEOs that are too faint to be seen by Earth-based searches, because asteroids are brighter in infrared than in visible light. In addition, WISE will survey portions of the sky closer to the Sun than Earth-based telescopes typically survey.

Candidate detections in the WISE data will be made by automatic software, but the thousands of anticipated candidates will need to be individually confirmed by a trained human eye to find the expected several hundred NEOs that can be discovered by WISE. Candidate NEOs will be identified by comparing sky exposures from one orbit to the next and looking for objects that appear in one frame but at a different location in the next frame. Automated software is effective at finding differences but not in correctly identifying them as moving objects. Software is often confused by artifacts such as cosmic rays, diffraction spikes, and objects at the detection threshold. People have shown a remarkable ability to quickly distinguish real NEOs from other objects.

WISE EPO at UC Berkeley will build on the successful model of Stardust@home to create an online project for WISE called Asteroids@home allowing the public to aid in the search for NEOs in the WISE data. Image data of candidate NEO detections will be served up to Asteroids@home volunteers via the Web, so that they can determine if the candidate is likely a real NEO or some other object. Training tutorials will be put in place to train the volunteers on what to look for in WISE data, and volunteers would need to take and pass a test to be able to participate in the search. We will calibrate each volunteer's responses by randomly adding calibration data into the mix of candidate images. The calibration images would be images that we know a priori are indeed NEOs or are not. NEO candidate detections would be ranked by a score determined from the number of volunteers viewing them weighted by the individual calibrations of those volunteers.

10. Conclusions

Citizen scientists are willing and able to join in the process of discovery and are an invaluable resource for many kinds of projects that, until recently, seemed impractical. For those planning to carry out a new citizen science project it is important to consider some key ingredients: provide ample background information for the volunteers; train volunteers with tutorials and consider requiring a test for participation to insure volunteers do indeed take the tutorials; provide incentives and rewards for volunteers to participate; calibrate volunteer responses whenever possible; promote the project via the media and/or through other projects themselves; provide as much feedback to the volunteers as possible; be sure to budget for the resources needed, because online citizen science projects require significant personnel time to design and maintain websites and software and to communicate with volunteers; people genuinely wish to participate in a real science project but are not interested in gimmicks created solely for the sake of outreach, so be sure that the project is an authentic task. Finally, if you have a project that could benefit from a large number of volunteers who do not need specialized knowledge, do it.

EPO and a Changing World
ASP Conference Series, Vol. 389, © *2008*
C. Garmany, M. Gibbs, and J. W. Moody

Building the World Wide Telescope

Curtis Wong

Next Media Research Group, Microsoft Research, Redmond WA USA

Abstract. The vision of the World Wide Telescope 2.0 is to provide a common infrastructure so that multiple surveys, over time, can all share a common intuitive browsing platform that allows for seamless exploration of the universe augmented by the creation of narratives and paths through the virtual sky and underlying links to related source data.

1. Background

The World Wide Telescope began with a technical paper by Jim Gray (Microsoft Research) and Alex Szalay (Johns Hopkins) titled: *The World-Wide Telescope, an Archetype for Online Science in 2002* that federating astronomy databases will facilitate the creation of a world wide virtual telescope. Both of the authors were instrumental in the creation of SkyServer in 2002 to provide Internet access to the public Sloan Digital Sky Survey (SDSS) data for both astronomers and for science education. The Next Media Research Group assisted in that project by designing the web site but felt that the website was just a foundation for building a comprehensive learning environment of which the SkyServer would form an important foundation data layer.

In the fall of 2006, the Next Media Research group within Microsoft Research began building its vision for the World Wide Telescope with the following components:

1. **Rich Narrative layer** - Enable professional and amateurs to create rich media tours about topics in astronomy which are illustrated and linked into a virtual sky. Tours allow linking to specific objects in the sky as well as to other related tours for further study of specific topics. Initially a number of exemplar tours will be produced by astronomers and education outreach staff as a resource for all WWT users. Users can create their own tours and share those with others on an individual basis and later as a potential resource to all users.

2. **Virtual Sky** - WWT creates a virtual sky using a custom tiled multi-resolution image rendering engine (similar to Virtual Earth or Google Earth) which can seamlessly render multiple sky surveys (DPOSS, SDSS, 2MASS, etc) as well as multiple wavelength object surveys (Hubble, Chandra, Spitzer) etc. Users can go from a wide field multiple constellation view of the sky and seamlessly zoom into the details of a very high resolution space telescope image within a galaxy. Users can pan around the sky easily and switch between surveys seamlessly. Multiple surveys covering

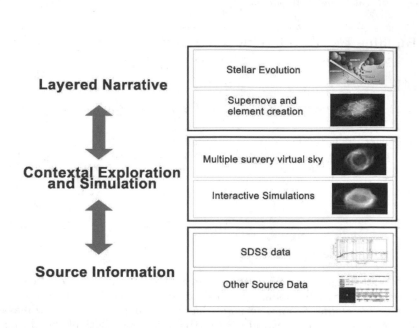

Figure 1.   Interactive Linked Narrative Architecture

different wavelengths can be represented as well as time series surveys to allow spectral or temporal analysis of specific objects. Since all surveys are automatically registered in the virtual sky with WCS co-ordinates, any object or section of the sky could be examined in multiple wavelengths as well as multiple times to view space/time changes over a longer baseline of surveys. WWT is built using a custom 3-D engine so it is possible to view both multiple wavelength and temporal views of the sky as well as planets, moons and other spherical high resolution spherical image data sets. The Virtual Sky will also allow embedding rich media assets and links to simulations as a resource at a specific object or class of objects as needed.

3. **Source Data** - Objects as rendered in the virtual sky are linked to data sources based on WCS coordinates associated with objects. Data from sources like SIMBAD, SEDS and other astronomical web services sources are easily retrieved in context of the sky. These can be adapted for the audience or level of the users.

4. **ASCOM Integration** - WWT has integrated ASCOM telescope control so that examination of any area of the sky can be used to direct a local or remote physical telescope to slew to the same location in the sky.

2. The Vision

The vision of WWT is to provide a common infrastructure so that multiple surveys and studies from multiple sources, can all share a common intuitive browsing platform that allows for the creation of narratives, and paths through the virtual sky, which can assist a new user to effortlessly explore the universe though any wavelength and temporal period and understand what they are seeing. Contextual narratives linked to objects with connections to underlying data provide the user with multiple learning modalities from visual, audio, and interaction to develop and reinforce mental models of information about the sky to foster a deeper understanding of astronomy and science.

Kids who are interested in astronomy but don't have a telescope will learn from the linked narratives, understand what they are seeing and go as deep as they choose, exploring the virtual sky and accessing the source data underneath to potentially make discoveries of their own. Eventually anyone will be able to create and share their explorations though the virtual sky, thereby extending and empowering an ever-growing audience who want to know more about the universe.

Professional astronomers will be able to collaborate with others by creating annotations and call outs within the within the virtual sky and share that annotation with others taking advantage of all the resources of the aggregation of multiple large scale datasets.

Later versions of WWT will allow universities, museums and other communities to host their own localized version of the World Wide Telescope that benefit from the common resource pooling of multiple sky surveys and data while still layering on their own hosting of content specific to their interests. e.g. A University could host their own version of WWT which features annotated lectures and unique content specific to research areas of their own professors. Amateur astronomy organizations could host WWT featuring object images taken by their members as well as creating their own guided tours. Education communities could host their own curricular lessons while leveraging relevant tours from the WWT repository.

Microsoft Research will be releasing WWT as a free resource to the astronomy and science education community.

Acknowledgments. The World Wide Telescope is dedicated to Jim Gray.

References

Szalay, A. and Gray, J., in "The World-Wide Telescope, an Archetype for Online Science" , Microsoft Research Technical Report Technical Report MSR-TR-2002-75 (June 2002)

Poster sessions were a great opportunity to really learn about EPO programs

EPO and a Changing World
ASP Conference Series, Vol. 389, © 2008
C. Garmany, M. Gibbs, and J. W. Moody

No Ph.D. Required: Remote Telescopes Reaching a Wider Audience

Vivian White

Astronomical Society of the Pacific, 390 Ashton Avenue San Francisco, CA 94112 vwhite@astrosociety.org

Steven K. Croft

National Optical Astronomy Observatory 950 N. Cherry Ave. Tucson, AZ 85719, scroft@noao.edu, http://www.noao.edu/outreach/

Alan Gould

Hands-On Universe Project, University of California, Lawrence Hall of Science, Centennial Rd & Grizzly Peak Blvd, Berkeley, CA 94720-5200, agould@berkeley.edu, http://lhs.berkeley.edu/sii

Roy R. Gould

Harvard-Smithsonian Center for Astrophysics, 60 Garden Street, Cambridge MA 02138, rgould@cfa.harvard.edu, http://www.MicroObservatory.org

Tierney O'Dea

Slooh Live Online Observatory, 4901 Avenue G Austin, TX 78751, tierney@slooh.com, http://www.slooh.com

Paul Roche

Las Cumbres Observatory Global Telescope Network, 6740 Cortona Dr. Suite102, Santa Barbara, CA 93117, proche@lcogt.net, http://lcogt.net or http://www.faulkes-telescope.com

Abstract. Remote telescopes are currently being used in many formal and informal educational settings, from museums to worldwide collaborations. The speed and accessibility of the Internet has made remote telescope technology a reality outside of research labs. The mechanisms, interfaces and goals vary between programs, but all use cutting edge technology to deepen public awareness of astronomy research. The National Optical Astronomy Observatory, RBSE program, MicroObservatory, Las Cumbres Observatory Global Telescope Network, Slooh and Hands-On Universe discuss in this paper how they are leveraging the newest technologies to bring opportunities once reserved for professional researchers into classrooms, museums, and living rooms. By partnering with universities, government agencies and commercial enterprises, astronomy educators are giving the public access to advanced telescopes, allowing real scientific discovery to occur.

1.   Introduction to Remote Telescopes in Education

Remote telescopes are not new technology to astronomers. Their use as we know them today - a telescope, mount, and CCD connected to a computer connected to the internet - has indeed brought about a new age in astronomy. Beginning with professional astronomers in the 1980s, remote telescopes were adopted by amateurs in the early 1990s as personal computers and imaging devices became more affordable. The education community soon followed, beginning at the University level and continuing down as young as grade school.

Programs aimed at training high school teachers to take and use real astronomical data began engaging students by allowing them to do real science-finding asteroids and supernovae as well as doing labs that normally rely on pristine local conditions and tools. MicroObservatory and Hands On Universe are two of the pioneering efforts using remote telescopes in education. With the success of these and other projects, the field has expanded to include museum exhibitions, for-profit enterprises, and younger students. Here we examine five of these programs in detail and discuss some of the ways they are collaborating to provide greater access to the night sky for students all over the world.

2.   Use of Remote Controlled Telescopes at NOAO

One of our main educational objectives at NOAO is getting authentic research into the classroom. As part of that effort we developed the Research Based Science Education (RBSE, then TLRBSE, and now ARBSE) professional development program for middle and high school science teachers. In that program, we train a cadre of 15 to 20 teachers each year in basic astronomy content in a 15 week online course, focusing on a few well-defined research projects (currently Nova Search, Open Clusters in the Milky Way Galaxy, Spectroscopy of Giant and Supergiant Variable Stars, Active Galactic Nuclei (AGN) Spectroscopy, and Solar Magnetic Fields - see http://www.noao.edu/education/arbse/arpd). The teachers then come to Kitt Peak National Observatory and use professional-class telescopes in small teams to gather, reduce, and analyze data under the mentorship of the professional astronomer in charge of each project. In this way, the teachers gain first-hand experience with authentic research.

In our original model, the teachers then returned to the classroom and taught their students the relevant astronomy content, and had them analyze the existing data for their part in the research effort. We initiated the use of Remote Control Telescopes (RTCs) to give the students themselves first-hand experience with designing an observing program, running a telescope, and gathering and reducing their own data. We purchased telescope time at the New Mexico Skies Observatory near Cloudcroft, NM, and made that time available to teachers that had participated in our program. The telescope we use is a 14" Celestron equipped with a CCD camera, a 10-color filter wheel, and an easy-to-use online interface by iBisque. The RCT system is real-time hands on, so the students are usually observing outside of school.

We supported the following types of observing activities:

1. Introduction to observing, including basic teaching of celestial coordinates to find objects and digital imaging in white light or different filters to obtain color composites.

2. Research projects that grew out of RBSE projects or the teacher's personal interests or classroom objectives.

3. Research projects that are part of other projects. One of our expert teachers had his students do a series of observations of an AGN in the visible using the New Mexico Skies Observatory (NMSO) while the object was being observed in the infrared by the Spitzer Space Telescope.

4. Asteroid Observing. This is a new initiative in which younger students make paired observations that produce images that can be used to find an asteroid (usually a known asteroid of their choice), and older students do UBVRI photometry of asteroids to determine their mineralogy.

Student projects have included creating color composites, creating a Messier Object album, light curves of variable stars and Active Galactic Nuclei. Most of the projects involved processing the images using ImageJ, which the teachers had learned during their training. Projects have been used for classroom teaching and evaluation, and for a number of award-winning science fair projects.

The program is currently beginning its 5th year, with 12 to 15 teachers signing up each year. Our experience has been that teachers need the training we provide in both content and observing to be able in turn to train their students in the efficient use of telescope time. It is not trivial to design and carry out a research-oriented observing program. While the time investment to learn the skills and tools is great, the potential rewards in teaching astronomy and the process of scientific research are equally great.

3. Real Astronomy Experience: A Museum Exhibit Using a Remote Telescope

The Hands-On Universe (HOU) project at Lawrence Hall of Science received NSF funding to create a museum exhibit that would allow visitors to remotely control a two telescopes: one right in front of their control kiosk in the exhibit hall at LHS (the LHS-scope) and another located at Perth Observatory in Australia (the Australia-scope).

In the original version of RAE, we uploaded FITS files and used an image processing system with IDL developed by New Media Labs in Santa Barbara. But the final version just uploads a JPG file which takes a lot less time, and image processing is done with tools programmed in Flash.

4. MicroObservatory Online Telescopes at the Center for Astrophysics

MicroObservatory is a network of five automated, imaging telescopes that were de-signed specifically for education by a team of scientists, engineers, and educators at the Harvard-Smithsonian Center for Astrophysics (Sadler et al. 2001).

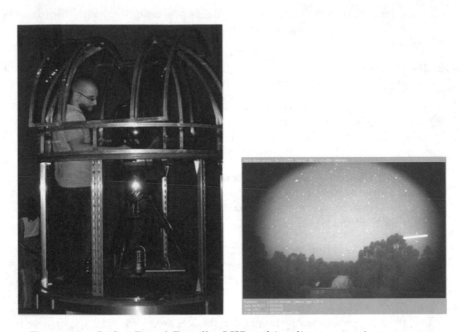

Figure 1.   **Left** - Darrel Porcello, LHS multimedia team project manager, checks out the LHS scope for RAE. An enclosure was made for the LHS scope that gives the impression of a see-through observatory. An awning manufacturer made the enclosure for us to our specification. **Right** - Perth Observatory Skycam shows what the weather is like there. In the future, we would like to add more telescopes and more museums or science centers to the RAE system.

Figure 2.   **Left** - The visitor can choose among 5 activities: Measuring planet sizes, Tracking asteroids, Jupiter's moons, Grouping galaxies, and Name a nebula. **Right** - A ruler tool can be used for measuring size of planets. Introduction to this activity deals with the idea that how big something looks depends on how far away it really is.

Figure 3.   In the Name a Nebula activity, visitors have drawing tools as well as an option to e-mail their image to their home.

The telescopes have six-inch mirrors, are weatherproofed, and sit outside without a dome. To date, more than a quarter-million images have been taken by middle- and high-school students in all fifty states for their projects, as well as by youth in after-school community programs and visitors to the museum exhibition, Cosmic Questions. Students specify the object to be observed, the exposure time, and desired filter. In our new "guest observer mode", the telescope determines the optimum time of night to take the image, greatly increasing the throughput of the system. All images are posted on the Web as soon as taken, and observers are notified immediately by e-mail. The system is completely automated; there is no technician in the loop. Telescopes are sited in Amado, AZ and Cambridge, MA. Telescopes have also been sited at Mauna Kea, HI and Canberra, Australia. (Visit http://mo-www.harvard.edu/MicroObservatory.)

4.1.   Online Telescopes Facilitate Learning

Why would teachers use online telescopes, when professional research images from the world's most powerful telescopes are freely available online? We have found that the benefit of online telescopes comes not from simply looking at images, but from working with them: processing them, and interpreting them in the context of a compelling project. Our image-processing software, developed by Freeman Deutsch, enables students to measure the relative brightness of celestial objects, to create digital movies, and to create full-color images by combining images taken with colored filters. In a series of activities called From the Ground Up!, pre-college students use these tools for a variety of projects. (Visit http://www.cfa.harvard.edu/webscope). We have found that these activities lead to gains in students' understanding of key concepts in physical science, especially the behavior of light and color; size and scale; and selected math concepts (Gould, Dussault, & Sadler 2006). The telescopes are also a powerful tool for improving teachers' classroom practice, for example by helping to reveal students' misconceptions about the behavior of light, and by encouraging teachers to serve as mentors for their students' project work

4.2. Combining Students' Images with Professionals' Images

Thanks to a fleet of new ground-based and space-based telescopes, students can view the universe at virtually any wavelength, from radio and infrared to x-ray and gamma-ray. However, many students have trouble interpreting these images; they have difficulty understanding the nature of false color, or the size, scale, location, and nature of the celestial objects. By working with their own images first, students construct a context for interpreting the "bigger picture" afforded by professional images and data. In our current work, students combine their own images of galaxies with, e.g., radio-wave images that show dramatic evidence for black holes at the centers of those galaxies. Thus, far from becoming obsolete, online telescopes are an increasingly important resource for teachers.

5. Slooh Live Online Observatory

SLOOH.COM is an online network of observatories, broadcast live through patented technology and easy to use web interface. Our flagship observatory is located at the Instituto de Astrofísica de Canarias, with two more online soon in Chile and Australia. Since its official launch in April 2004, we have delivered 223,000 live celestial images to our members.

5.1. Sustainable Educational Outreach Through Learning Communities

With members in over 70 countries, Slooh is a robust astronomy learning community. This past year, we regularly broadcast international outreach events including the Transit of Mercury and Comet McNaught with live radio shows - interactively connecting the public to professional astronomers around the world.

This fall, Slooh and the Astronomical Society of the Pacific (ASP) are launching a joint effort to bring remote telescopes into the classroom. The ASP will design classroom activities and train educators, funded by donations from the Slooh community. A new annual membership, specifically customized for a classroom setting will be available on Slooh.com along with free downloads of the activities.

Additional outreach efforts include: 1) nightly "SkyGuide" broadcasts to explain the telescope views and answer member questions, 2) a promotional partnership with AOL to engage their vast membership in Astronomy, 3) joint outreach events with planetarium and astronomy clubs, 4) a partnership with Scholastic Inc. to distribute 50,000 Slooh memberships to elementary school children 5) and an internationally distributed, family oriented Slooh activity book.

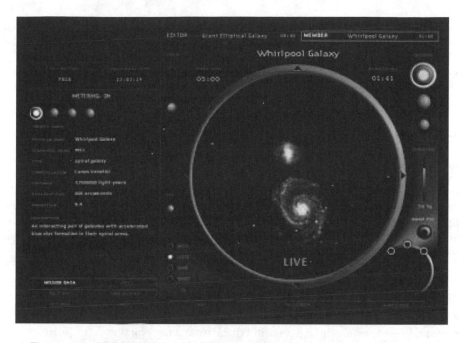

Figure 4.   SLOOH.COM Live Telescope Interface.

6.   Las Cumbres Observatory Global Telescope Network

LCOGTN currently has two 2-metre telescopes, which will be joined by around 18 1-metre telescopes and 28 0.4 metre telescopes, probably located in clusters of 2-4 instruments at professional observatory sites around the world.

6.1.   Specific Programming/Outreach Efforts

The Las Cumbres Observatory Global Telescope Network (LCOGTN) is an independent, non-profit private operating foundation that is building a global network of remotely operated telescopes, to be used for both educational and scientific research purposes.

The initial parts of this network consist of the 2-meter diameter Faulkes Telescope North, at the Haleakala Observatory, Maui, and the Faulkes Telescope South at Siding Spring Observatory, Australia. These instruments have been providing images and data that are being used by schoolchildren in many countries, primarily through the UK-based Faulkes Telescope Project (FTP) since early 2004. Education and outreach programs have initially focused on the UK (with 900 registered users over the past 3 years), with pilot programs running in Poland (Sept. 2005) and Russia (Sept. 2006). FTP has been part of the LCOGTN program since September 2006,

LCOGTN operates the largest telescopes in the world partially, but consistently, devoted to astronomy education. LCOGTN is building a global network of 1-meter diameter telescopes (the Research Network) and will deploy many 0.4m diameter telescopes (the Education Network) distributed around the world, over the next 2-5 years. The exact locations of all these instruments are still undecided, but they will mainly be at professional observatories wherever possible.

An important feature of these telescopes is that will be remotely operable, and one site per hemisphere will always be under dark skies, allowing important observations of transient objects. Children love transient and moving objects, as they provide important connections to the Universe if they can see, measure, and truly experience some astronomical object change in the cosmos in a matter of minutes, hours or days.

Eventually, users with an Internet connection will be able to either control the telescope in real time, or request an observation be made at a specified or unspecified time in the future. Access to the LCOGTN facilities will generally be via collaborative programs - the Institute for Astronomy in Hawaii already has strong links with LCOGTN, and dedicated time on FT North for educational programs. Likewise the Australian National University, working with Swinburne and Macquarie universities, is developing programs in Australia to utilize access to FT South.

7. Conclusion

These five unique remote telescope projects represent some of the ways that remote telescopes are being used in education. They vary greatly in many important features - the size of the telescopes and the individual networks, in how they get images to the user, interfaces, locations, and the end users themselves. Together, they are bringing real astronomy to the public in a way that creates a greater understanding of the process of science and gives the students a fun way to do real science from any location on Earth.

Some of the current work being done on remote telescopes in education is focusing on the synthesizing of various projects into a larger network of telescopes that has a more robust impact on education around the world. Many potential partners in this collaboration attended this session. There were also many interested educators not currently involved in remote telescope technology. More information about this developing network can be found at: http://faulkes-telescope.com/telescopes/ghou.

Acknowledgments. Vivian White would like to acknowledge Mary Kay Hemenway (working with the MONET telescope network at the McDonald Observatory, UT Austin) for her inspiring and patient tutorial on remote telescopes and their applications in education.

References

Gould, R., Dussault, M., Sadler, P.M., "What's Educational about Online Telescopes?: Evaluating 10 Years of MicroObservatory," Astronomy Education Review, **5**, Issue 2 (2006)
Sadler, P. M., Gould, R., Leiker, P. S., Antonucci, P., Kimberk, R., Deutsch, F., and Hoffman, B., "MicroObservatory Net: A Network of Automated Remote Telescopes Dedicated to Educational Use," Journal of Science Education and Technology, **10**, 39 (2001)

EPO and a Changing World
ASP Conference Series, Vol. 389, © 2008
C. Garmany, M. Gibbs, and J. W. Moody

Using Collaborative Environments in Research-Based Science Education

Lucy Fortson and Mark SubbaRao

Adler Planetarium and Astronomy Museum, 1300 S. Lakeshore Dr., Chicago, Illinois 60605, USA

Gary Greenberg

Northwestern University Information Technology (NUIT), NU Library 2EAST #2651, 1970 Sheridan Road, Evanston, Illinois 60208-2323, USA

Abstract.   With the advent of the Internet, the World Wide Web and social networking systems, a number of collaborative environments have been developed that support efforts in online science education. This paper examines the basic aspects of online collaboration, describes two differing types of collaborative environments currently used, and discusses the elements of successful collaborative environments for online projects that enable research-based science education.

1.   What is Collaboration and a Collaborative Environment?

"Collaboration is a process defined by the recursive interaction of knowledge and mutual learning between two or more people who are working together, in an intellectual endeavor, toward a common goal which is typically creative in nature." (Wikipedia 2007)

Indeed, the Wikipedia definition of collaboration recursively describes the main point of Wikipedia. Encyclopedia's are the ultimate product of human collaboration. The innovative aspect of Wikipedia is not that it is another encyclopedia, but that it is imbedded in a collaborative environment allowing open access to the recording and interpretation of human knowledge. In the context of the Internet and the World Wide Web, a collaborative environment provides "...a unified view of the activity context of a member where anything relevant for the progress of his work in the team is directly accessible, for example access to other team members; access to activity resources, planning or goals; requests, events or alarms; activity and data visualization; etc. The collaborative environment shall be responsible for configuring re-sources, select[ing] relevant information or being proactive in the progress of work, removing from the members the burden of configuration and integration of re-sources" (Quemada et al. 2006).

In the context of collaboration for generating and transferring knowledge, there are competing approaches to configuring a collaborative environment. In the two opposite extremes, these are constructing a general-purpose collaborative environment that provides a framework for more than one specific group or purpose, or an environment customized for a specific group or purpose. This paper details two instantiations of collaborative environments - one general-purpose and one customized - in the context of research-based science education. In particular, while the general-purpose collaborative environment has broader application than research-based science education, the example given is specific to an astronomy project that is geared towards engaging high school students in authentic research. The example describing the customized environment was developed for a specific project engaging students and teachers in particle physics research problems. While the authors feel that there is a significant role for research-based science education in promoting greater overall science literacy within the student (and teacher) populations, it is beyond the scope of this paper to detail the education research that supports this concept.

1.1. Collaboration in the Age of the Internet

The Internet, as a functional medium for communication, has been utilized for wide-spread collaborative purposes since the 1980s. Email alone greatly increased the efficiency with which individuals could communicate for collaborative purposes. With the advent of the World Wide Web, the effectiveness of the Internet to enable collaboration between multiple, heterogeneous groups reached a transformative level. At the same time, increasing evidence shows that knowledge generation overall, across fields as disparate as science and art, is obtained through teams of collaborators rather than the single-person, "great-thinker" model of the past (Wuchty 2007). The role of the computer, and in particular the collaborative networks which form the backbone of collaborative environments, in advancing this paradigm shift in knowledge generation is described by Camarinha-Matos:

> "A collaborative network (CN) is constituted by a variety of entities (e.g. organizations and individuals) that are largely autonomous, geographically distributed and heterogeneous in terms of their: operating environment, culture, social capital and goals. Nevertheless these entities collaborate to better achieve common or compatible goals, and their interactions are supported by computer networks. Unlike other networks, in CN collaboration, it is an intentional property that derives from the shared belief that together the network members can achieve goals that would not be possible or would have a higher cost if attempted by them individually." (Camarinha-Matos 2005)

The transformative properties of collaborative networks and environments not only are visible on the largest scales of human collaboration but importantly enable niche groups to build capacity through these virtual networks. Nevertheless, it is these two extremes of use that drive the conundrum in constructing appropriately customized collaborative environments. We now have the situation where collaborative boundaries are fluid and potentially scale-independent - the size and attributes of the target audience changing as the generation and transfer of knowledge within the collaboration evolves. Thus designers of collaborative environments have to somewhat arbitrarily decide the degree to which their design will transition from being useful only to the goals of a very specific problem to being so generic that the clarity and effectiveness of collaborative projects carried out within a general-purpose environment are compromised. Finally, collaborative environments must also be constructed so that there is a process for validating the knowledge generated from the collaboration. Again, the scale-independence brought by the transformation to the Internet allows for the non-expert individual or niche groups to have the same potential authority as the "leading experts" in a given field. While this may at first seem to allow for the insertion of "invalid" sources of knowledge, in practice the validation process can be made to be robust with a self-correcting system as is the case with Wikipedia.

1.2. Properties of Online Collaborative Environments

Online collaborative environment (CE) designs must take into account communication modes, modes of content presentation (video, graphics, animations, etc.), accessibility, level of audience expertise, management, security and many other aspects. Again, the design decisions on which tools to make available rests on the ultimate goals of the CE and as noted above, the extent to which it is intended as a general-purpose CE or a more customized or domain-specific CE.

Certainly, CEs need to be designed for clear communication between constituents and, as appropriate, external audiences. Communication modes are at minimum asynchronous (mail service), but many collaborative environments allow for synchronous communication such as chat rooms. CE designers must also decide how usage tutorials are accessed and presented, which areas may or may not be secure environments, how products are "published" to other audiences within the CE or to the external world and whether the component tools and services of the CE are required to be downloaded or are completely web-based. Particular care must be taken if audiences with multiple experience levels are expected to use the CE and/or inter-act within the CE (e.g. students, teachers and other mentors.) For example, in education uses, CEs must be designed to protect student identity as well as pedagogical methods and "teacher notes" that students should not be able to access.

2. General-Purpose Approach to Collaboration in Research-Based Science Education

Rather than create a project-specific web application with the associated development, delivery, and maintenance costs to enable collaborative research-based science education, one might look at leveraging the resources and services of an existing general-purpose CE. Even though such an environment may not be designed to support science education in general, or astronomy in particular, it can provide needed communication services, offer models for collaboration, and be used to organize content and manage research activities. Extending a general-purpose CE by integrating astronomy resources to support research can offer greater flexibility for the types of projects that can be offered and enable a broader range of learning activities than would be the case with a project-specific application.

2.1. The Collaboratory: A General-Purpose Collaborative Environment

The Collaboratory Project (http://www.collaboratory.nunet.net) is a Northwestern University K-12 technology outreach initiative that is helping educators use the Collaboratory to improve student learning and achievement. The Collaboratory is a general-purpose, Web-based collaborative learning environment that educators are using to develop a broad range of K-12 collaborative project-based learning activities.

Collaboratory Communication Services include messaging, conferencing, discussion forums, invitations, announcements, and calendars to support collaboration among teachers and students. Automatic alerts and notifications keep participants up-to-date about activities, new projects, and events. Search capabilities enable participants to easily find other people and projects. Collaboratory Resources provide the scaffolding to develop innovative project-based learning activities. Collaboratory resources include: The Cybrary (virtual libraries of Internet resources); The Internet Book Club (students write about and discuss books they have read); The Survey Studio (on-line surveys, questionnaires, and data collection forms); ePortfolios (students create, share, and discuss work in binders and folders); and, Nexus Communities (people with common interests come together to create interactive on-line communities).

2.2. The START Collaboratory: Accessing Astronomy Cyberinfrastructure

The START Collaboratory leverages Collaboratory resources and services to access astronomy cyberinfrastructure resources and tools to enable authentic astronomy research by high school students. It was developed over the last five years through funding from the NSF that brought together the Sloan Digital Sky Survey (SDSS) at Johns Hopkins University, Hands-On Universe at the University of California at Berkeley, the Northwestern University Collaboratory Project and the Adler Planetarium.

The START Collaboratory uses Web services to integrate access to terabytes of searchable data and images for over 285 million objects in the Sloan Digital Sky Survey and to SDSS SkyServer tools through Web-based collaborative Research Journals. Students do not have to search through lists of URLs or bookmarks to find a needed tool or resource, copy complex data and information from Web pages, or take screen shots of tables and images in order to organize work in progress or report their findings. Images, data, and tables are added to student journals from the SDSS data-base with only an ObjectID from a SkyServer tool or a SQL query that has been tested using an interactive Search Form. SDSS SkyServer tools are integrated as "viewers" for research journals and return students to the specific image, data, and tool for further investigations.

From these research journals, students can also request remote telescope observations from Internet-controlled telescopes coordinated by Hands On Universe, then view and analyze the resulting FITS files using a Web-based visualization tool created at Northwestern University. All requests and FITS files are managed by the Collaboratory. Students do not need a personal telescope account and there is no teacher intervention to make a request.

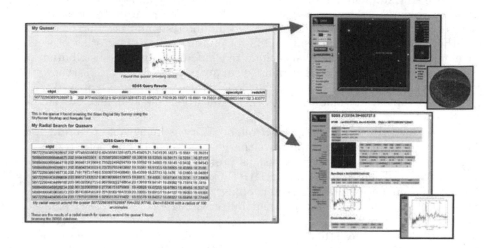

Figure 1. START Collaboratory Research Journal with SDSS/SkyServer Tools as viewers

Research journals also support mentoring and collaborative research. Students can exchange private comments with their teachers and request feedback from professional astronomers through their research journals. They can also contribute to threaded discussions about one another's work that encourage collaboration and peer-to-peer learning. Research findings, summaries, and conclusions can also be shared and discussed in public Nexus Galleries.

2.3. Modeling Collaborative Research

A Research Scenario on quasar variability was developed to introduce teachers and their students to using the START Collaboratory and provide a model for pursuing contemporary astronomy research questions, introducing research techniques, and modeling collaborative research. Activities in this research scenario include browsing SDSS to find quasars and learning about their spectra, creating SQL queries for cone searches that generate (large) tables of quasar data, restricting queries to quasars that are bright enough to be seen by an available telescope, making observation requests to monitor a quasar over time, and measuring the brightness of the quasar and three check stars to create a light curve. On-line mentors and professional astronomers review the quasars students have selected to observe, confirm the location of the quasar in an observation before students begin a monitoring schedule, and are available to respond to questions about the objects, tables, queries, observations, and measurements being dynamically collected and organized in student research journals. Students can review, discuss, and learn from each other's work as their research progresses. Online Collaboratory documentation as well as astronomy content in-formation is available through a Collaboratory Cybrary.

Once educators are familiar with the Collaboratory and the integrated astronomy resources, they can use some or all of these resources to create their own research scenarios to address their specific interests and needs. For example, they might focus on browsing SDSS for quasars, galaxies, or other objects, developing advanced queries that include redshift to explore the distribution of objects, or using telescope observations to survey parts of the sky. These new research scenarios, like any project in the Collaboratory, can be co-managed with colleagues, copied and modified by other educators, and can include remote mentors.

What distinguishes the START Collaboratory is being able to bring real data and real tools to students in ways that engage them in authentic research; generating useful scientific results just as professional astronomers do - learning science by doing science. The START Collaboratory can be extended to expand and enhance student research opportunities by integrating additional datasets, resources, and telescopes and by providing new Web-based analysis tools. This approach leverages the general-purpose Collaboratory to provide "one-stop-shopping" for student astronomy research. Furthermore, once a student uses a Collaboratory resource or service, that experience can be applied to any other project, regardless of subject matter.

3. A Custom Approach to Collaboration in Research-Based Science Education

A custom template-based approach to research-based science education can facilitate both the production and adoption of science education modules. On the consumer side, having a set of projects with similar collaborative environments and consistent approaches to guiding students through the scientific process (delivering background information, acquiring and analyzing data through sharing and discussing the results) enables easy adoption by teachers and students already familiar with this approach as they move from one research project to another. On the production side many large experiments and research projects find themselves in the position of "reinventing the wheel" as they design new educational modules. Providing a toolkit for creating new modules based on solid instructional design should reduce the time and effort needed to get these products into students' hands. A project that is currently working on creating custom templates for science education utilizing authentic data and analyses is Interactions in Understanding the Universe (I2U2). I2U2 enables student collaboration through the publications of results and a peer review process that enables students and mentors to comment on the published results.

3.1. Interactions in Understanding the Universe

I2U2 is an educational virtual organization (http://www.i2u2.org) whose goal is to strengthen the education and outreach activities of scientific experiments at U.S. universities and laboratories by providing infrastructure support and a program frame-work for a rich portfolio of coherent, collaborative science education laboratories. The creation of this virtual organization was a response to shortcomings in the way that education and outreach is currently being done. In particular, having individual experiments and research groups build their education and outreach programs from the ground up results in duplicated efforts and often fails to capitalize on established "best practices" in the field. I2U2's approach is to create a toolkit for creating educational modules for both formal and informal venues (e-Labs and i-Labs respectively). These toolkits share a similar structure, pedagogical approach and evaluation strategy. Research groups use these toolkits to create their own e-Labs and i-Labs, and the I2U2 virtual organization manages the portfolio of projects. The virtual organization consists of an education, computing and science lead as well as educational coordinators and an evaluation consultant. The portfolio serves as a source of "one stop shopping" matching producers and consumers of the educational projects.

3.2. Conveying Science Process and e-Science Process

I2U2 borrows from the intellectual legacy of the QuarkNet project. QuarkNet engaged students and teachers in the construction of cosmic ray detectors, and the taking and analysis of data from the detectors they built. Throughout the programs students engage in the full science process from background research, formulating a question, designing an experiment and analyzing the data to sharing the results of the analysis with their colleagues. Following QuarkNet, all I2U2 e-Labs and i-Labs share an emphasis on supporting science process and using authentic data and analyses. The nature of science process has been captured in the e-Lab workflow, which represents steps needed to fully complete a scientific investigation. A student passing through any e-Lab will pass through the following stages:

- Getting Started: which provides the scaffolding necessary to meaningfully partake in the investigation.

- Figure it Out: where the data acquisition, synthesis, analysis and interpretation takes place.

- Tell Others: which models the publication and peer review process.

Massive datasets, high performance computing and cyberinfrastructure enabled collaboration are transforming the way science is done. It seems logical that we should then start teaching students the process of 21st century research - or the process of e-science. In particular I2U2 is investigating how Grid computing can play a viable role in science education.

3.3. The Toolkits

I2U2 provides toolkits for two types of experiences, e-Labs for formal learning environments and i-Labs for informal environments. E-Labs are delivered as Web-based portals accessible in the classroom and at home, and are implemented with the ever-expanding capabilities of Web based media. Making the analysis tools available through a web browser makes the program more accessible to teachers who may have limited ability to install software on school computers.

The informal learning environment provides unique challenges due to the diverse audience and limited interaction time that museum visitors typically have with any given exhibit. I-Labs address this challenge through interactive interfaces typically located within science museums and similar public venues,

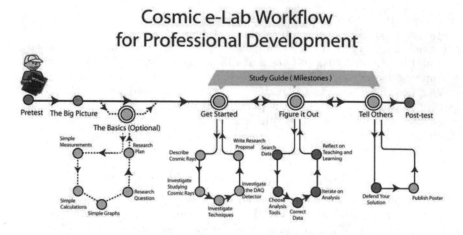

Figure 2.   The Cosmics e-Lab workflow. All e-Labs share the items on the top line (Get Started, Figure it Out and Tell Others) however the specific implementations (indicated by the loops) may vary.

leveraging the latest advances in display technology and human-computer interaction, and bringing the experiences and appreciation of scientific investigation and inquiry to the wide audience of informal education.

3.4.   I2U2 Status

I2U2 is currently finishing up two years of demonstration projects and is nearing full implementation of the project. Significant development has taken place on Grid tools and middleware needed to support the project. Several demonstration projects have been developed as well. In addition to the Cosmics e-Lab which is well into production, e-Labs for the ATLAS, CMS, LIGO and STAR experiments are at various stages of development, and the Adler Planetarium is prototyping the first i-Lab which is based on the successful Cosmics program.

Acknowledgments.   We thank the National Science Foundation for partially funding the START Collaboratory and the I2U2 project.

References

Camarinha-Matos, L. -M., Afsarmanesh, H., Ollus, M., "Ecolead: A Holistic Approach to Creation and Management of Dynamic Virtual Organizations" in Collaborative Networks and their Breeding Environments, edited by L. -M. Camarinha-Matos, H. Afsarmanesh, and A. Ortiz, IFIP Vol. 186, Springer (Sep 2005)
Quemada, J., Salvachua, J., Robles, T., Pastor, E., Pavon, S., and Huecas, G. "A Collaborative Environment Integration Layer for Activity Orientation," *2nd International Conference on Collaborative Computing*, Colcom, IEEE Computer Society (2006)
Wikipedia 2007 link to http://en.wikipedia.org/wiki/Collaboration
Wuchty, S. *et al.*, "The Increasing Dominance of Teams in Production of Knowledge" Science **316** no. 5827, 1036-1039 (2007)

EPO and a Changing World
ASP Conference Series, Vol. 389, © 2008
C. Garmany, M. Gibbs, and J. W. Moody

A Proposal to Make the Dark Universe Visible

Matthew W. Craig

Department of Physics and Astronomy, Minnesota State University Moorhead, Moorhead, MN 56563

Abstract.   Although most of the universe is dark energy, and most of the matter in the universe is dark matter, the typical description of a galaxy, in either informal or formal educational settings, mentions only stars and gas. I describe a proposal to develop a set of museum exhibits on dark matter and dark energy that would serve as a toolkit for others in the EPO community. Preliminary ideas for exhibit components are presented, along with a framework for developing the exhibits rapidly though a collaboration of students, researchers, and informal science professionals. An important part of maximizing the impact of this proposal is to ascertain the need for such a toolkit.

Project Goals

- Develop modular, audience-driven exhibit prototype kits, finished exhibits, and simulations that can serve as building blocks for future EPO efforts.

- Model an exhibit development process well suited for rapid development of exhibits on areas of current research that utilizes teacher, undergraduate, and graduate student interns.

Motivation

A galaxy is roughly 20% atoms (stars and gas) and 80% dark matter. Despite this, galaxies are typically described as though they were 100% atoms. A concise, effective way of describing the dark matter component of a galaxy would be broadly useful.

The EPO efforts that accompany large research on dark matter, dark energy, or the structure and evolution of galaxies would be well served by a toolkit of interactive, flexible, and adaptable exhibit materials and computer simulations.

The proposed development process is well suited to rapid development of exhibits on any topic of current research.

Development Process

The proposed development process is designed to rapidly bring current research to a wide variety of audiences. This is accomplished by developing materials on two scales in parallel with two separate teams exchanging ideas and refinements.

Preliminary front-end research to ascertain audience reaction to and understanding of a small dark matter exhibit displayed at the Science Museum of Minnesota (SMM) in the Science Buzz area devoted to current research.

Gather team of exhibit developers who will guide, train, support, and collaborate with science undergraduate and graduate students, in-service teachers, and scientists.

Parallel exhibit development of exhibit materials at SMM and Minnesota State University Moorhead (MSUM). The development cycle lasts two months. Front-end research drives the initial prototypes. Audience reaction to the prototypes drives appropriate revisions, and there is an ongoing exchange of ideas and revisions between MSUM and SMM.

> **MSUM** develops a small scale, inexpensive version, suitable for prototyping and for informal and formal settings with light supervision. Small scale means each component fits in a cardboard box and inexpensive means less than $100 per component.

> **SMM** develops a larger scale, durable, high quality version, suitable for informal settings with no supervision and replication at other museums.

A final merge of the ideas from the development of both the small scale and the large scale exhibits.

Dissemination of exhibit materials is planned through separate channels for the large and small scale exhibits.

> **Small scale** and all computer and Internet components will be targeted to EPO efforts and to small science centers.

> **Large scale** and all computer and Internet components will be available for replication in museums.

Sample Exhibit Components

Gravitational Lensing caused by dark matter in clusters of galaxies will be illustrated with a hands-on model using plastic lenses that allows users to infer properties of lenses from images and computer-based model allowing user change the amount of dark matter in a cluster of galaxies and observe the effect.

The nature of dark matter is being explored in several lab-based experiments. Components related to dark matter would include a hands-on musical model of dark matter detector, a computer-guided exploration of removal of background events caused by known particles, and a small cloud chamber to demonstrate that unseen particles are common.

   Acknowledgments.   The author wishes to thank J. Newlin of the Science Museum of Minnesota, who is collaborating on the proposal and has spent considerable time developing the ideas presented here.

EPO and a Changing World
ASP Conference Series, Vol. 389, © 2008
C. Garmany, M. Gibbs, and J. W. Moody

Wilderness of Rocks Asteroid Project

Steven K. Croft, Robert T. Sparks, and Stephen M. Pompea

National Optical Astronomy Observatory, 950 N. Cherry Ave, Tucson, Arizona 85719, USA

1. Introduction

Searching for asteroids has been a popular research activity in middle and high school classrooms. It is relatively easy for teachers and students to join forces with an amateur astronomer or outreach group with access to a modest-sized telescope (10" to 20" in diameter), take a small number of images, compare them sequentially, and experience the thrill of discovering a new object in the solar system. The scientific concepts, computer skills and telescope power necessary to make new discoveries are within the grasp of typical students and the rewards are great. That is changing, however. Currently a number of professional asteroid search programs are working hard to reach NASA's goal of discovering 90potential Earth impactors with diameters greater than 1 kilometer by 2008. In the near future, deeper survey programs like Pan-STARRS and the Large Synoptic Survey Telescope (LSST, first light in 2015) will extend the observed limit down to 100 meters. As a result of these programs, asteroid discovery by students and amateurs will become increasingly difficult. Consequently, to maintain the interest and potential for student re-search on asteroids in the classroom, the emphasis will have to change from discovery to follow-up: characterization and classification.

The National Optical Astronomy Observatory Asteroid Project

We continue to develop our pilot educational outreach program on asteroid characterization designed to get cutting-edge astronomical data and research into the Middle School classroom. The project involves students in research using visible & near infrared color photometry to characterize Near Earth Objects, newly discovered asteroids, and other interesting known asteroids (e.g., Vesta and Ceres). The science con-tent fits easily into the Earth Science curriculum, utilizing the exciting research and data of astronomy and asteroids to teach topics including the nature, development, and relations between asteroids, meteorites, and terrestrial rocks; earth processes and origins of rock types, formation of the Earth, Moon, and solar system, the nature and possible use of near earth resources, and, of course, the connection between asteroid impacts and life on earth.

We have created a classroom-ready middle school curriculum (beta version), including three classroom/observation activities, observation protocols, suggested observing lists, and teachers' notes on suggested classroom use of the materials. The materials are flexible time-wise, with formal modules designed to take two days or two weeks, and directions for an observational research project that could continue for a semester. These materials have all been placed online at: http://www.noao.edu/education/asteroids.

On the web site you will find the following sections:

*All About Asteroids:*This section includes short articles for students entitled: What are Asteroids? An Introduction. Where in the Solar System. Sizes and Shapes. Some Cool Pictures. How are Asteroids Discovered? Determining Asteroid Sizes and Shapes. What are Asteroids made of? The Meteorite Connection - Asteroid Colors. Asteroid Spectra. Asteroids, Meteorites, and Geologic Processes.

Activities: This section includes pdf's of the student versions of the three activities:

1. Adopt an Asteroid. This is the basic introduction to asteroids, taking about one hour of class time and a one-hour asteroid-discovery observing experience.

2. Asteroid Spectra. This is one version of a more complete introduction to asteroids, tying them to meteorites and Earth geologic processes. This version takes about one week of classroom time. The activity is paper/computer-based and introduces one of the most important areas of asteroid research today.

3. Asteroid Colors. This is another version of a more complete introduction to asteroids, again tying them to meteorites and Earth geologic processes. This version takes about one week of classroom time. The activity includes observation and analysis of asteroid colors. It is more challenging than simple asteroid discovery, and involves mathematics and graphing. It also introduces another of the most important areas of asteroid research today.

For Teachers: This section contains teacher's notes for each of the activities, and science standards relevant to asteroids in the Earth science curriculum.

Data Archive: This section contains a collection of asteroid images and data that will be gathered by students participating in the project.

Asteroid Resources: This section includes links to asteroid-related Educational Projects, Professional Search projects, and Spacecraft Missions.

About the Project This section contains a description of the project, its origin and educational philosophy, and the people involved.

The activities are designed to range from fairly simple to fairly demanding. The suggested observations for Adopt an Asteroid are a simple pair of images of an asteroid of choice taken 15 minutes or so apart and then compared to show the movement of the asteroid against the background stars. The observations for Asteroid Colors are more demanding and involve imaging an asteroid and a standard star in each of the Johnson UBVRI filters, measuring the intensity in each filter, forming color ratios, and plotting the results in a color diagram to estimate the asteroid type. From that information, the student makes the connection to meteorite types via the colors, and then to terrestrial rock types and geologic processes. From there, the student can construct a simple geologic history of the asteroid that can be compared to the geologic history of Earth.

Acknowledgments.   Universities for Research in Astronomy (AURA), Inc. under cooperative agreement with the National Science Foundation.

EPO and a Changing World
ASP Conference Series, Vol. 389, © *2008*
C. Garmany, M. Gibbs, and J. W. Moody

University / Science Center Exhibit Development Collaboration: Strategies and Lessons Learned

M. Jordan Raddick and Samuel Carliles

Johns Hopkins University, 3400 N. Charles St., Baltimore, MD 21218, USA

Lauren Bartelme

Maryland Science Center, 601 Light St., Baltimore, MD 21230, USA

John Patterson

Educational Enterprises, 1501 Sulgrave Ave. Ste. 300, Baltimore, MD 21209, USA

Abstract.   Through funding from the NSF's Internship in Public Science Education (IPSE) program, Johns Hopkins University (JHU) and the Maryland Science Center (MSC) have worked together to create an exhibit based on JHU's research with the Sloan Digital Sky Survey, a project to map the universe. The exhibit is a kiosk-based interactive presentation that connects to online data about the sky. It is currently displayed in SpaceLink, an area at the MSC that focuses on current events and research in astronomy. The person primarily responsible for the exhibit was a graduate student in computer science in the JHU Physics and Astronomy department. He worked with an EPO professional in the department and two members of the MSC's planetarium and exhibit staff to plan the exhibit. The team also worked with a coordinator in the JHU chemistry department, and an external evaluator. Along with increased public understanding of science, our goal was to create and evaluate a sustainable partnership between a research university and a local science center. We are producing an evaluation report discussing our collaboration and detailing lessons learned. We hope that our experience can be a model for other university / science center collaborations in the future. Some lessons that we have learned in our development effort are: start all design decisions with learning goals and objectives, write goals with evaluation in mind, focus on the process of science, and do not underestimate the challenges of working with the web as part of the exhibit technology.

1.   Project History

Research scientists frequently look for opportunities to share their work with the public. Science museums and centers have a well-understood framework for promoting science learning and designing and evaluating exhibits. It is a logical partnership for science centers to play a role in disseminating research results since so many communities have both a university and a science center.

The partnership described here was funded by the NSF's Internships in Public Science Education (IPSE) program, which promotes cooperation between universities and science centers. The 18-month project consists of three phases;

this paper describes the first. The overall goal is to build a template PIs can use for instructional design collaboration, with examples of how to adapt it. The final template will include exhibit design principles, learning models, tools for measuring knowledge transfer, and reporting tools.

The partnership's first step was to study the available tools and brainstorm possible exhibits. We explored the SkyServer web site (http://skyserver.sdss.org), developed by the research team, which brings Sloan Digital Sky Survey (SDSS) data into formal education. We decided early on that authentic science data should be a key feature of the exhibit.

We chose a narrated computer kiosk exhibit with activities. Next, we designed three learning goals: better technology leads to better knowledge; maps and globes are representations of shape; and scientists often work by comparing predictions of models to observations.

We then designed four activities and a script for the narration. After several drafts, the graduate student (Carliles) began to program the activities. The exhibit is now being used in SpaceLink, an area at the MSC that focuses on current events and research in astronomy, and we have started formative evaluation. Eventually, we will hire a professional narrator, and add sound effects.

2.   Exhibit Structure and Evaluation

The exhibit is an interactive PowerPoint presentation on a touchscreen that uses the LiveWeb add-in to display web pages. The user clicks START to begin, and the presentation plays.

The slide show pauses at certain points for activities: constellation matching, surf through the sky, choose the map (comparing observed data to predicted models), and matching telescopes to the discoveries they made (summative).

Our evaluator (Patterson) is conducting formative evaluations of the exhibit. They include reactions, announced and unannounced observation visits, and tracking of use with web hits. Results showed that school groups found that the activity loading time and narration were too long. Visitors also had difficulty hearing the exhibit.

We have also been evaluating our collaboration process. Our experience shows that scientists need direct guidance from an instructional designer, and that instructional and museum exhibit designers must teach each other principles from their fields.

3.   Lessons Learned

Our goal in conducting this project is not only to increase public understanding of science; we also want to practice and test a collaboration between a research university and a local science center. We hope our experiences can be a model for other collaborations. Some of our lesson learned include: start all design decisions with learning goals and objectives; write goals with evaluation in mind by including measurable visitor behaviors; focus on the process of science in learning goals and exhibit content; and do not underestimate the challenges of working with the web.

EPO and a Changing World
ASP Conference Series, Vol. 389, © 2008
C. Garmany, M. Gibbs, and J. W. Moody

Space Weather Monitoring for the IHY: Involving Students Worldwide in the Research Process

Deborah Scherrer

Stanford University, Solar Center, HEPL-4085, Stanford, CA 94305

Benjamin Burress

Chabot Space & Science Center, 10000 Skyline Blvd, Oakland, CA 94619

Kim Ross

Stanford University, Solar Observatories Group, HEPL-4085, Stanford, CA 94305

Abstract.   Our project explores how new methods of space weather data collection and networks of instruments can lead to innovative and exciting ways of involving audiences in the research process. We describe our space weather monitors, being distributed to high school students and universities worldwide for the International Heliophysical Year. The project includes a centralized data collection site, accessible to anyone with or without a monitor. Classroom materials, developed in conjunction with the Chabot Space & Science Center in California, are designed to introduce teachers and students to the Sun, space weather, the Earth's ionosphere, and how to use monitor data to encourage students to undertake "hands-on" research and gain experience with real scientific data. For more information, see http://sid-stanford.edu.

1.   The Space Weather Monitoring Program

The Space Weather Monitor Project provides a network of scientific instruments worldwide to track solar and terrestrial-storm-related changes to the Earth's ionosphere. Our international collaboration involves scientists, educators, and students who collect and analyze research-quality data to understand how the ionosphere responds to output from the Sun and to internal disturbances. The network consists of a mix of state-of-the-art ELF/VLF receivers ("AWESOME") sensitive to a broad range of ionospheric phenomena and low cost space-weather monitors ("SID") designed for students and sensitive to solar-flare induced VLF sudden ionospheric disturbances. Data formats are similar and both students and researchers can access data from either instrument. Thus the program features both research and educational components and a related data set produced by input from two sensitivities of instruments.

Our program has been designated by the International Heliophysics Year (IHY) United Nations Basic Space Science Initiative (UNBSSI) as a Participating Program and the IHY International Committee for Education and Public Outreach as key interest for use in their pre-college education program. Twenty-five of the more sensitive AWESOME monitors are being placed in universities and 140 of the SID student-targeted monitors are being distributed to high schools around the world.

2.   Research Data

Due to the extremely sensitive nature of the ionosphere, even small changes can be readily detected using VLF methods and one can study an extraordinarily broad set of phenomena, including solar flares, cosmic gamma ray bursts, lightning strikes and related effects, earthquakes, electron precipitation, aurora, and more. Students can compare their data to data from other instruments around the world to determine where certain events might be affecting the ionosphere. For solar events, students compare their spikes to data from the GOES satellite to identify flares. Students can also track down, sometimes to the back side ("farside") of the Sun, the solar active region which generated the disturbance.

A centralized database, freely available to all, exists for the SID sites and many of the AWESOME research sites. This data bank is useful even to students not hosting monitors. Students receive their data as a signal strength value and a timestamp, so the data collected are easily read and graphed. Solar events show up as spikes in the signal strength, with data graphs resembling those from a seismograph. Site data is periodically, usually daily, sent to Stanford via a simple ftp script initiated by the user. A centralized communications hub allows student to discuss data and events.

Our Scientist Mentor program pairs solar and ionospheric researchers and radio experts with classrooms to assist students in understanding their data and developing their research. Mentors communicate with students via email, phone, even letter.

3.   Curriculum Materials and Research Guide

Curriculum materials, designed and tested by Master Teachers, have been developed in conjunction with the Chabot Space & Science Center in California. Activities are inquiry-based and aligned with the American NAS/NRC's National Science Education Standards. Online and CD/DVD/video teacher training will be made available. Extensive background materials are being provided with the instrument distribution.

An extensive Research Guide has been prepared to give students "hands-on" experience with SID data and to suggest various research projects to extend their knowledge. Topics include analyzing sunrise and sunset signatures from different locations around the world and from different transmitters; tracking solar flares back to the Sun; the effective of latitude and/or season on ionospheric response to flares; lightning, gamma ray, and CME effects on Earth's ionosphere; ionospheric predictors to major earthquakes; and ionospheric changes during a total solar eclipse.

Acknowledgments.   This project was originally developed and funded by the NSF's Center for Integrated Space Weather Modeling, NSF contract 00-67. Additional funding was provided by NASA contract NNG05GH15G, supporting the MDI instrument onboard the Solar and Heliospheric Observatory (SOHO). Further funding was provided by NASA contract NAS5-01239 for the Helioseismic and Magnetic Imager (HMI) instrument for NASA's Solar Dynamics Observatory. Support for the IHY distribution is being provided by NASA and by Stanford University.

EPO and a Changing World
ASP Conference Series, Vol. 389, © *2008*
C. Garmany, M. Gibbs, and J. W. Moody

MARSFEST Evaluation - One Year Post Evaluation Results

Andy Shaner, Sanlyn Buxner, John Keller, and Carla Bitter

Phoenix Mars Mission, Lunar and Planetary Lab, The University of Arizona, 1415 N. 6th Ave, Tucson, AZ 85705

Abstract.   The MARSFEST workshop engaged a group of secondary science teachers in authentic planetary science research. We present the one-year post evaluation results.

1.   MARSFEST Evaluation Goals

The goals of the MARSFEST evaluation were to 1) provide the workshop planners with daily feedback from participants regarding the progression of the workshop, 2) determine what changes, if any, participants had in their understanding of Earth/Mars science, including Phoenix mission and 2001 Mars Odyssey GRS science, and 3) determine what changes, if any, participants had in their understanding of inquiry teaching. A longitudinal five-year study is currently being conducted to investigate changes in participants' teaching in the year following the workshop.

1.1.   Evaluation Instruments

Daily Likert-scale surveys elicited participants' attitudes toward the workshop in general, including what they felt did not work and what information they still needed to know. A 12-item pedagogy survey was distributed to participants before arriving in Alaska, at the end of the workshop, and at the end of the 2006-2007 school year. These surveys are meant to measure participants' perceptions of their abilities as inquiry teachers. A six-item pre- and post-workshop content survey was developed to measure gains in the participants' knowledge of the science presented by workshop scientists and from curricular materials. Participants were also asked to write of their experiences over the course of the workshop in reflection journals. Participants were prompted to reflect on:

1. How their experiences had affected their understanding of the scientific process and/or Earth and Mars science.
2. Any revelations and frustrations they had experienced related to their own investigation(s).
3. How they would use their experiences in their classroom and in a professional development setting.
4. Which experiences had been the most useful and why.

A NSES Indicators Survey, a Likert-scale survey which lists all 28 inquiry teaching standards found in the NRC standards, was also given to participants. This survey asked participants to rate to what extent they felt the workshop modeled each of the indicators for inquiry teaching.

1.2. Evaluation Results

Daily evaluations showed that overall, the teachers recognized that the workshop was modeling inquiry and that they were being asked to go through varying levels and degrees of the process from a simple activity of planning a mission to a complete investigation of their own from their original research question through reporting to the community about their findings. Results of the pre-workshop pedagogy survey showed that participants came into the workshop feeling confident about their abilities to teach inquiry science. Post-workshop pedagogy survey results indicate the workshop helped to reinforce this confidence. Results from pedagogy surveys distributed one year following the workshop indicate that participants are still active teachers of inquiry and are implementing lessons learned from their MARSFEST workshop experience.

"I see the value of implementing inquiry and field-based science experiences to enhance and reinforce science concepts e.g., permafrost tunnel experimental design and implementation session."

"The experience in Alaska was a new beginning for me to think about ways to also think about combining different disciplines into my classroom (science, math, English communication) within a meaningful science exploration."

"Because of MARSFEST I have done more professional development this year than all other 8 years of my teaching career combined! For that I'm really grateful. It has caused me to grow professionally and has opened doors and opportunities that I don't think would have otherwise."

The pre and post workshop content survey showed that participants increased in their understanding of Earth/Mars science as well as science from both the 2001 Mars Odyssey and Phoenix missions. Qualitative analysis of the participants' journal reflections reinforced the results of the content surveys and reflected excitement and revelations from the participants' experiences. Participant discussions included their new understanding of Mars science including the exploration of Mars, their revelations of what science is and how it is done, and what they should be doing differently in their classrooms and professional development settings:

"I learned about how we use Earth as an analog to study Mars. Although this may not provide consistent transfer in all areas, it is a good starting point in many cases."

"My understanding of the capabilities of the spacecraft (and its limitations) has been enhanced. I find the instrument design (form and function) really cool."

"Also, this week has made me appreciate and understand the fact that science happens in small steps. It takes a lot of time and effort to collect data and it takes a lot of data to develop a hypothesis. But it takes a lot more time to convince anyone else to be interested."

"[In the classroom] I am better able to describe how to define a problem and how to set up your question for investigation."

"I need to modify my professional development schedule so that I will have time to build in true inquiry experiences."

Results of the NSES Indicators Survey revealed that participants were able to identify the standards for inquiry teaching the workshop did, and did not, model.

EPO and a Changing World
ASP Conference Series, Vol. 389, © 2008
C. Garmany, M. Gibbs, and J. W. Moody

Need for Planetary Science Data in Formal Education Classrooms

Timothy F. Slater, Pebble L. Richwine, and Stephanie J. Parker

University of Arizona CAPER Team, 933 N. Cherry Ave., Tucson, AZ 85721

Stephanie Shipp

Lunar and Planetary Institute, 3600 Bay Area Blvd., Houston, TX 77058

Leslie Lowes

Jet Propulsion Laboratory, 4800 Oak Grove Dr., Pasadena, CA 91109

Abstract. Science education reform documents universally call for students to have authentic and meaningful experiences using real data in their science education. The underlying philosophical position is that students analyzing data can have experiences that mimic actual research. In short, research experiences that reflect the scientific spirit of inquiry potentially can: 1) prepare students to address real world complex problems; 2) develop students' ability to use scientific methods; 3) prepare students to critically evaluate the validity of data or evidence and of the consequent interpretations or conclusions; 4) teach quantitative skills, technical methods, and scientific concepts; 5) increase verbal, written, and graphical communication skills; and 6) train students in the values and ethics of working with scientific data. This large-scale, national teacher survey reveals that far too few teachers are comfortable using authentic data in the classroom. Barriers include, but not limited to: 1) difficulty in finding appropriate data and analysis tools; 2) the perceived length of time it takes students to complete an authentic scientific inquiry; and, most importantly, 3) a perceived lack of expert infrastructure and mentors who can help individual students. These results point to the need for a solution that simplifies the number of pathways for students to access data, reduces the number of analysis tools that teachers and students need to master, provides samples of student work that other students can emulate, and provides a nationwide system of online mentors who are willing and able to help students succeed. at scientific inquiry.

1. Motivation and Context

Recruited initially through the *AstroEd_News@ YahooGroups.Com* listserve of 565 members, and snowballing through personal forwarding from there, more than 600 teachers from across the country completed the online survey in its entirety. Approximately 60% reported they taught high school and about 40% in middle school, less than 5% described themselves as teaching elementary teachers. Approximately half of the respondents had more than 10 years teaching experience, taught in suburban schools, and devote at least one-half of the academic year to teaching Earth & Space science topics. None of the respondents stated that they taught in NASA Explorer schools.

By and large, teachers rarely ask students to look at data more than 30 days per year. In this instance, data can be broadly construed as anything produced from scientific investigations, including graphs, lithographs, online image or numerical databases, CD-ROM virtual tours, etc., although some authors report that there is a wide diversity of opinion among Earth & Space science as to the definition of what actually constitutes scientific data. Assuming that the school year averages about 180 days, this represents less than one day each week. A survey of the science education research literature provides little to no guidance as to how frequently students in science classes should be interacting with scientific data (although common sense suggests more is better). Depending on the exact type of data, 50-60% of teachers ask the students to analyze data 5-30 days each year

2. Results and Implications

The most commonly used data are Internet-delivered images (e.g., Astronomy Picture of the Day and real-time satellite images of forest fires). On the other hand, 40% of teachers rarely, if ever, ask students to look at CD-ROM based data sets (e.g., virtual tours or ocean current models), large Internet-based scientific data sets (e.g., My NASA Data, Sloan Digital Sky Survey Data, and earthquake, volcano, or stream flow records), or data from virtual telescopes or virtual simulator software (e.g., Starry Night or Earth Browser programs). Of responding teachers, 20% report that they access Google-Earth and USGS.gov 5 to 30 days per year and 40% access these online resources one to five days each year. Somewhat surprisingly, about 70% of teachers rarely, if ever, access live web cams, remotely controlled telescopes, VolcanoWorld, or even DLESE.org. In total, the results of this survey suggests that teachers are more apt to access real-time data to engage students in "what is going on right now?" than to access and mine the deeper and larger datasets available either online or via CD-ROM. But even then, not as frequently as one might prefer.

When students are asked to analyze data, the vast majority of teachers report using an instructional approach best known as structured inquiry, in which teachers show student data and give students predetermined procedures and protocols for how to graph or analyze the data. In contrast, the least frequently used strategy reported is open inquiry, in which students design their own questions then pursue additional data to answer their own questions. These survey data can be interpreted as teachers using conventional hands-on approaches based upon an apprenticeship model, which is probably a stronger pedagogical approach than a teacher-centered lecture or demonstration-approach, yet not nearly as strong as more authentic science experiences.

Seventy percent of respondents stated that not enough class time is devoted to students analyzing scientific data. The most frequently reported barriers to including more data included the excessive length of time it takes students to complete an authentic scientific inquiry, difficulty in finding appropriate software analysis tools for existing scientific databases, and the lack of expert mentors who can help individual students. Additionally, survey respondents stated that a barrier to having students do scientific inquiry is a perceived difficulty in finding ways to appropriately include research activities in determining students' overall grades.

EPO and a Changing World
ASP Conference Series, Vol. 389, © 2008
C. Garmany, M. Gibbs, and J. W. Moody

The ALIVE Project: Astronomy Learning in Immersive Virtual Environments

Ka Chun Yu

Denver Museum of Nature & Science, 2001 Colorado Blvd., Denver, CO 80205

Kamran Sahami and Grant Denn

Department of Physics, Metropolitan State College of Denver, Campus Box 69, PO Box 173362, Denver, CO 80217

Abstract. The Astronomy Learning in Immersive Virtual Environments (ALIVE) project seeks to discover learning modes and optimal teaching strategies using immersive virtual environments (VEs). VEs are computer-generated, three-dimensional environments that can be navigated to provide multiple perspectives. Immersive VEs provide the additional benefit of surrounding a viewer with the simulated reality. ALIVE evaluates the incorporation of an interactive, real-time "virtual universe" into formal college astronomy education. In the experiment, pre-course, post-course, and curriculum tests will be used to determine the efficacy of immersive visualizations presented in a digital planetarium versus the same visual simulations in the non-immersive setting of a normal classroom, as well as a control case using traditional classroom multimedia. To normalize for inter-instructor variability, each ALIVE instructor will teach at least one of each class in each of the three test groups.

The ALIVE project evaluates the effectiveness of immersive VEs for introductory astronomy instruction at the Metropolitan State College of Denver (MSCD), using the digital fulldome theater at the Denver Museum of Nature & Science (DMNS). Undergraduate students enrolled in the AST 1040 class are used as test subjects. The three-year study is broken up into two stages. Phase I developed the materials for the experiment, while the experiment and follow-up analyses are now taking place in Phase II. Students participating in the study provide demographic information, which are anonymously cross-referenced to the results from the test suite developed in Phase I and used in the exploration of demographic variations for any metric with statistical robustness. Test classes are divided into three groups, all of which receive regular classroom instruction (including multimedia materials now standard with textbooks). Group I classes serve as the controls. Group II students see VE instruction in the classroom, while Group III students see VE instruction in the immersive Gates Planetarium.

This study is motivated in part by the benefits of VEs: the abilities to show different frames of reference, to switch between ego- and exocentric viewpoints (Salzman et al. 1999), and to increase student engagement and motivation (Dede et al. 1999). Immersive VEs can be more effective than non-immersive ones (Raja et al. 2004, Pausch et al. 1997), and may lead to greater performance gains by women (Czerwinski et al. 2002, Tan et al. 2003).

Phase I

The first phase of the project included prior-to-instruction oral interviews with 120+ students who were enrolled in the Fall 2005 and Spring 2006 AST 1040 freshman astronomy courses. We focused on gauging misconceptions in seven different astronomy topics (phases of the Moon; lunar and solar eclipses; seasons, lengths of day and year; Kepler's Laws, orbits, retrograde motion; scale and structure of the Solar System; outer planet moon systems; scale and structure of the Milky Way galaxy).

These front-end evaluations were used to build new lecture outlines to directly address common student misconceptions. A test database was generated to be used in weekly progressional (curriculum) tests for the classes in the experiment. These quizzes contain questions that cover current instruction, retention of knowledge from previous modules, and pre-test questions for upcoming modules.

Using the new lecture outlines, we have created a suite of interactive visualization modules for our VE software, SCISS AB's Uniview. These contain instructional outlines for the lecturer and configuration files and directions for the real-time VE "pilot."

Early Student Interview Results for Kepler's Laws

Student interviews results are similar to those seen by Sadler (1992). The predominant belief is that planetary orbits are extremely elliptical (66%), followed by circular orbits (20%), and a combination of circular and elliptical orbits (4%) The last category include a mental model where orbit eccentricities increase linearly with distance from the Sun (no doubt from learning that Pluto has the most eccentric orbit—with e=0.245—and imagining a progression among the planets). Other common misconceptions mentioned by students include: planetary orbits often cross each other; planets share orbits; planets have eccentricities that increase with distance; alignments of all of the planets are not rare (occuring multiple times in a lifetime).

Acknowledgments. The authors are funded by NSF ROLE #0529522.

References

Czerwinski, M. *et al.* CHI '02 Proceedings, Minneapolis, MN, Apr 20–25, (2002)
Dede, C. *et al.* in *Computer Modeling and Simulation in Science Education*, edited by W. Feurzeig and N. Roberts, 282 (1999)
Pausch, R. *et al.* in SIGGRAPH Proceedings, **13** (1997)
Raja, D. *et al.*, in *Proceedings of the Immersive Projection Technology Workshop* (2004)
Sadler, P. Ph.D. thesis (1992)
Salzman, M.C. *et al.* Presence, **8**, 293 (1999)
Tan, D. *et al.* in *Proceedings of the Conference on Human Factors in Computing Systems*, Ft. Lauderdale, FL, Apr 5–10 (2003)

Harold McAlister - Maria and Eric Muhlmann Award Winner

Part IV

The Changing EPO Profession

EPO and a Changing World
ASP Conference Series, Vol. 389, © *2008*
C. Garmany, M. Gibbs, and J. W. Moody

Understanding and Learning From Your Audiences

Marni Berendsen, Suzy Gurton, and Anna Hurst

Astronomical Society of the Pacific, 390 Ashton Avenue, San Francisco, CA 94112, USA

Alan Gould

Lawrence Hall of Science, University of California, Berkeley, CA 94720-5200, USA

Abstract.   Educators come in a variety of guises, each with a different set of needs, interests, styles, and venues. This session discusses how these differences affect the development of EPO materials. Participants gain insights into evaluating the needs of the educators they serve to best tailor astronomy-related EPO products their educators will eagerly use.

1. Introduction

This session discusses getting to know your educator, evaluating their needs, and considering factors for adapting astronomy resources to the type of educator.

2. Criteria to consider when developing products, programs, activities, and support for educators

The Astronomical Society of the Pacific (ASP) administers a number of programs which serve specific categories of educators: Science and nature center educators through the Astronomy from the Ground Up program, teacher-astronomer partners in Project ASTRO, and amateur astronomers through the Night Sky Network. We also include insights from experience with planetarium professionals through the Lawrence Hall of Science.

Experience has shown that "one-size-fits-all" regarding EPO activities, materials, and other resources, does not apply. An astronomy activity designed for use by amateur astronomers (such as a star map that highlights the locations of stars discovered to have planets) may be inappropriate or unusable by a teacher or a nature center professional. Adaptation of the activity, additional background information, and/or a change in the materials used may be required to convey the same or a similar message. For example, a planetarium professional might prefer the star maps be used as a reference to create a planetarium show featuring extrasolar planets.

Criteria to consider when developing activities and materials for educators include characteristics of the educator, characteristics of their venues, who the educator's audiences are, and considerations regarding materials used.

2.1. Characteristics of the Educator

The following are criteria to consider regarding the educators themselves:

Level of knowledge about the subject

Volunteer vs. Paid

Style (formal, informal)

The educators' ability to anticipate audience needs and adapt the presentation and materials for the audience

What part of the message to be conveyed is most interesting or important to the educator?

What outside requirements influence the educator? (e.g. state education standards, political, social, or religious considerations)

How far is the educator willing to go outside their comfort zone, outside of their usual mode of communication? (e.g. lecture vs. interactive; at the telescope vs. demo at a table)

2.2. Characteristics of the Educator's Venue

The following are criteria to consider regarding the places the educator conducts EPO:

Venues in which they operate (e.g. outdoors, indoors, day, night, classroom, science center, park, auditorium, planetarium)

Equipment readily available to them (e.g. are scissors, glue, etc normally available in that venue?)

What is the usual mode of communication? (e.g. Planetarium dome, books, blackboard, telescope, exhibits, demos at a hall cart, lecture)

2.3. Educator's Audience

These criteria apply to the educator's audience(s):

Typical length of interaction with their audiences

Size and type of their audiences (fixed or variable, captive or voluntary)

Their audience's demographics (gender, ages, ethnicity, religious, education level; families, students, general public)

What are the expectations of the educator's audience (e.g. level of entertainment, length of activity, what they are willing to do, amount of "work" involved, specific interests or goals, facilities available)

Educator's motivation for interacting with the audience: Does the educator want their visitors/audience to be: Educated? Able to pass a test? Become inspired/excited? Feel the activity was worthwhile? Take some action? (Affective or cognitive experience?)

What part of the message to be conveyed is most interesting or important to the educator's audience?

2.4. Considerations for materials and support

When determining what materials are to be used and what support may be needed:

Consider what materials you provide vs. the materials the educator needs to provide: how much time is the educator willing to invest to prepare for the presentation (e.g. collecting materials, practicing, learn needed background info, setting up)

Methods to reduce barriers to the use of the materials – what different ways need to be provided for the educator to learn how to use the materials (handout, video/DVD, online clips, PDF, face-to-face workshop)

What on-going support can be offered or is needed?

3. Examples of educators and important characteristics to consider when developing EPO

This section examines specific educators and briefly outlines important considerations for each, what benefits they offer, and challenges to providing useful resources.

3.1. Museum and Science Center Educators

The ASP's Astronomy From the Ground Up (AFGU) program provides materials and training to science and nature center educators. The characteristics of the museum and science center educator's venue are varied. They may have exhibits, demonstrations, drop-in stations, school tours, classroom visits, community outreach, and camps. A permanent facility is available to them.

This educator's audience includes:

- The general public who are free-choice learners and generally attend the center to be entertained.
- School Groups who may be concerned about state and local education standards.
- Other community groups such as camps, Girl Scouts, after-school, and teacher trainings.

Considerations for materials and support:

- Should be versatile, easy to adapt to the varied audiences
- Thorough background information needs to be provided.
- Consumables must be easy and inexpensive to replace
- Any reusable items must be durable to withstand constant handling

The benefits of providing astronomy resources to this group are that they are eager and excited to receive such materials and new ideas; they are flexible in what they can offer, generally not being bound by curriculum requirements; they are comfortable adapting materials and activities to different audiences.

Science and nature center educators also present challenges. Each person usually wears many hats, providing EPO on a variety of subjects, often having little or no astronomy background. They lack time and funding for extensive training. Their objective is to quickly engage their visitors' attention, so they need effective "grabbers" to introduce the topic. Their interaction with the visitor is likely to be less than an hour, limiting the depth of topic coverage. They may find it easier to fall back on "edutainment" or just doing make-and-takes without providing any real background science. So giving them ways to keep visitors engaged while providing meaningful interaction is important to this educator.

3.2.   Teacher-Astronomer Partners in the Classroom

Project ASTRO partners teachers with astronomers in the classroom. The teacher-astronomer partnership is intended to take place with just one classroom of students (or one class period for teachers who teach several periods of the same subject). The astronomer commits to at least four classroom visits during the year.

The venue for this partnership is usually limited to the classroom, during the day, with restricted periods of time. The audience is captive and not there by choice but by mandate. Teachers are facing increasing numbers of ESL (English as a Second Language) students. With regards to materials and support, budgets are usually quite limited, so teachers are unwilling to use lots of consumables. The teacher often teaches multiple sessions, but has only one volunteer astronomer for one class.

One of the main benefits of partnering an astronomer with a teacher are primarily that the teacher does not need to be an expert in astronomy and the astronomer does not need classroom management skills. Each partner brings his or her own strengths to the experience. Other benefits are that more hands-on instruction are brought to the classroom and resources can be shared: teachers cover the basics and the astronomers provide the extras.

One of the main challenges to providing resources for this partnership is that state or district science standards frequently dictate what topics may be covered and these standards can change over time. Since the astronomer's time in the classroom is limited, the teacher must have resources to adequately prepare the class for the astronomy lesson and to do appropriate follow-up. Astronomers may use too much jargon, talking "over their heads." Guidance must be provided regarding appropriate levels of communication.

3.3.   Amateur Astronomers as Informal Educators

The ASP has gained extensive experience with amateur astronomers as science educators through our administration of the Night Sky Network program (http://nightsky.jpl.nasa.gov/). The bulk of outreach performed by amateur astronomers is the public astronomy night, also known as a "star party," where a group of amateur astronomers bring their telescopes and share views of the night sky with the public. Amateur astronomers also volunteer in schools, in science centers, and with community organizations such as senior centers and Scouts.

The most important characteristic of this educator's venue is that it is usually outdoors which means no power source, no storage, no chairs or tables. It can be daytime, but more frequently is twilight or darkness where conditions may be damp, cold, or windy. Amateurs prefer low light or red-light-only conditions at night.

The amateur astronomer's audience is fluid and free-choice, meaning interactions are often limited to at most a few minutes. An amateur astronomer normally brings a lot of equipment to a public event (e.g. telescope and accessories, stool, table, binoculars, star atlas) and therefore exhibits a low willingness to hunt for additional needed materials or go to extensive preparation to use an activity. An activity must be "grab and go" or very easy to prepare.

The benefits of amateur astronomers as educators are primarily in what they can provide that other types of educators cannot: telescopic views of the real sky, along with the planets, Moon, and Sun. They have an extensive knowledge of astronomy and have learned to navigate the sky with ease. It is not only unnecessary to provide background on astronomy basics and skills related to observing, for them it would be considered too elementary and almost insulting to do so.

The challenges of providing EPO resources to amateur astronomers mostly relate to the outdoor venue: the activity must not require any power, can be done in low light, and typically can be explained or demonstrated in under five minutes. The materials need to be simple and easily reproduced. Activities related to observing that give the visitor an exciting and stimulating experience are well-received, such as themed telescope tours, simple table-top demos, and models with multiple uses.

3.4. Planetarium Professionals

The venue of planetarium professionals is almost exclusively "under the dome." However, with the large numbers of school groups that generally visit, complementary classroom activities related to the planetarium experience are valued, and even required, by teachers. Without such complementary materials, a planetarium visit is difficult for the teacher to justify.

The Lawrence Hall of Science (LHS) has developed a number of such guides for planetarium educators in the Planetarium Activities for Student Success (PASS) series: http://lawrencehallofscience.org/pass/. For example, in the planetarium show "Our Very Own Star" (PASS Volume 14 – recently released), the activity "A Magnetic Earth Around a Magnetic Sun" can be done either during the planetarium show or outside the planetarium as a classroom activity. In that activity, students use models of the magnetic fields of Earth as a dipole and of the Sun that has sunspots in pairs. They see how magnetism affects space around Earth and Sun using (a) a simple magnetic field detector consisting of a specially bent piece of paper clip loosely fastened to the eraser end of a pencil with a push pin, and (b) tiny washers that act as magnetic field indicators. They see the difference between the structure of magnetic field around the Earth (magnetic dipole) and the magnetic field of the Sun (loops associated with sunspot clusters).

In addition, the LHS Hands-On Universe (HOU) program (http://www.handsonuniverse.org/) and Great Explorations in Math and Science (GEMS) program (http://www.lhsgems.org/) provide extensive resources for classroom instruction.

4.   Comparing educators and their evaluation of resources: A case study

Using an activity relating to representational or "false" color, session participants formed four teams and were given twenty minutes to evaluate what would need to change to adapt the activity and message to different educators: teachers in the classroom, science and nature center educators, amateur astronomers, and planetarium professionals. Participants evaluated the activity in light of these questions:

What part of the message of this activity would your educator be most interested in conveying? Would the materials be appropriate for your educator's venue? If not, what needs to change? Is the activity appropriate for their audience? If not, what would need to change? What background or training would your educator need?

The activity uses a cookie sheet, a small heat source, in this case a small reusable hot pack, and a small dish of ice. The heat source and the ice are hidden in different places underneath the cookie sheet. The visitor is given a number of different colored small plastic tiles and asked to place the colored tiles on the cookie sheet to communicate the pattern of different temperatures the visitor can feel on the cookie sheet. The objective is for the visitor to understand that color, something we *can* see, can be used to communicate something we *cannot* see (in this case, temperature). This is related to why some images of the same astronomical object look so different from each other. The scientist producing the image can use color to communicate the intensity of light detected from the object in wavelengths of light other than visible light, such as infrared or x-ray, to reveal information about the object our eyes cannot detect.

4.1.   Participants report their efforts

Teachers in the Classroom   The Teacher team saw a lot of potential to use the activity to convey other concepts such as modeling, mapping, and resolution. For example to illustrate what is meant by resolution, instead of using the colored tiles, they suggested using graph paper with different sized grids and colored pencils to fill in the squares.

To use the activity to convey the concept of representational color, they felt the teacher would need more background on the concept as well as a full lesson plan. They did not see the activity as presented being used as a stand-alone. Adaptations would be needed along with background resources and a full lesson plan.

Science and Nature Center Educators   The Science and Nature Center team found the activity as presented was quite appropriate for their venue and audiences. They appreciated the message that color can convey information. They suggested it would be used by a docent on a discovery cart with small group or families. Their only concern was if a docent did not facilitate the activity, the small tiles might tend to "walk away."

Amateur Astronomers   The Amateur Astronomer team, in trying to redesign the materials to be more appropriate to amateur astronomers and their venues, discovered that they lost the message that was intended to be conveyed regarding the use of representational color. Among their concerns were there were too many pieces to keep track of, ice would be difficult to transport and maintain and could be messy as it melted, and in low light settings color is difficult to distinguish. For example, they suggested using shapes or textures on the tiles instead of color, which would make it difficult for the audience to understand the message of using color to represent temperature.

They concluded that amateur astronomers would not likely use the activity as designed.

Planetarium Professionals   The Planetarium team struggled to find any useful or practical way to use the activity.

After the Exercise   At the end of the exercise, the session presenters revealed that the activity as presented was developed and tested for use by science and nature center educators – the team that had the fewest issues with using the activity. They also reported that earlier testing of the activity with amateur astronomers had resulted in almost unanimous criticism of the activity for a variety of reasons.

Session participants reported an increased appreciation for the idea that different educators do have differing requirements.

5.   Conclusion

An activity developed for, say, a fifth grade classroom teacher, is unlikely to be appropriate for another type of educator without at least some adaptation. In some cases, the activity as designed can be completely inappropriate to communicate a desired message by another target educator, resulting in the activity not being used. Careful consideration of the circumstances, interests, and concerns of the target educator is critical to produce resources that will eagerly be adopted.

On break in the poster room

Tim Slater, Edna DeVore, and Vivian Hoette

EPO and a Changing World
ASP Conference Series, Vol. 389, © 2008
C. Garmany, M. Gibbs, and J. W. Moody

The Role of EPO Professionals in Communicating and Teaching the Science of NASA and NSF

Daniel Steinberg and Shannon Swilley

PRISM/PCCM, Princeton University, 317 Bowen Hall, 70 Prospect Ave, Princeton, NJ 08540, USA

Jill Andrews

College of Engineering, 2456 Lurie Engineering Center, 1221 Beal Avenue, Ann Arbor, MI 48109-2102, USA

Abstract. NSF and NASA have similar Education and Public Outreach (EPO) requirements and each endorses an important community of outreach professionals to facilitate broader impact goals. EPO professionals hold a critical role in the national quest for a scientifically and technologically literate population, and are often key connectors between investigators conducting cutting-edge research at NASA and NSF centers, pre-college educators and the public. Each owns unique perspectives on how to translate science and engineering research into effective research-based programs. NASA and NSF center EPO professionals could share lessons learned and best practices to promote efficient and effective education program development and implementation that includes leading scientists and engineers. Both groups could explore collaboration opportunities between the Astronomical Society of the Pacific and the National Science Foundation Research Center Educators Network to build on specific strengths and similarities. Through collaboration, each group can better promote recognition of this emerging field and profession. Working together, collaborators will enhance existing expertise, improve job performance, promote standards for this emerging profession, and achieve well-deserved recognition. Collaboration will improve individual ability to meet the higher standards of accountability to which each group is held and improve efforts in this new, flat world.

1. Introduction

On September 5, 2007, Jill Andrews, Dan Steinberg and Shannon Swilley conducted a 90-minute oral session at the 119th Annual Conference of the Astronomical Society of the Pacific (ASP). At the 5th Annual NRCEN (National Science Foundation (NSF) Research Center Educators Network, Appendix A) Conference, and again at the ASP oral session, participants were asked to list skills and duties specific to the EPO Profession. Not surprisingly, both groups created similar lists. As a result, ASP participants recognized that NRCEN and ASP EPO professionals have much in common.

2. Structure of session

Following introductions, Jill Andrews and Dan Steinberg provided an overview
of NRCEN and neo-sphere.org (a NSF-funded, web-based social network and
collaborative tool designed for EPO professionals) (Andrews 2007). The group
then discussed some common issues and differences between the two groups.
They were specifically asked to consider two issues:

1. Describe an effective EPO Professional (Address areas, 1. skills, 2. duties)

2. Record suggestions on potential collaboration opportunities between NSF
   and ASP EPO Groups.

For each, the participants broke into small groups and shared impressions of
the skills and duties necessary to promote effective, best practices in educational
outreach, with the intent of comparing these responses to those compiled at the
5th Annual NRCEN Conference. Each group presented its responses, followed
by a second brainstorming session to determine possible collaborations between
NSF and NASA EPO groups. The authors compiled these responses for questions 1 and 2 from both NRCEN and this session and found many similarities
between the responses of both groups. The results are presented in this paper
and will be discussed with the members of NRCEN to explore how ASP and
NRCEN might form a working partnership. Tables containing the complete list
of compiled responses from this session are available on request.

3. Comparing NRCEN and ASP lists of their skills and tasks

Participating ASP experts shared ideas on the types of tasks and skills of EPO
professionals, and offered opinions on how to collaborate. The following information resulted from the participants' responses to questions 1 and 2 and
the responses from NRCEN. Both groups face similar challenges in developing
programs, engaging research scientists, engaging the public, training teachers,
and evaluating the results of our programs. Both can benefit from sharing best
practices and lessons learned.

   Among both ASP and NSF EPO professionals, most have a science and/or
education background, coupled with strong communication skills. Communication skills, especially with diverse groups, were identified as highly important
by both groups. In addition, both value science content and pedagogical competence; the ability to "translate" research and scientific jargon for the public;
creativity; flexibility; resourcefulness; and networking skills. (Many respondents
used "skills" and "duties" interchangeably; the authors believe the duties and
the skills necessary to complete those duties are strongly linked and were not
easily separated in people's minds.)

   Many of the duties performed by both groups are similar. As both must
disseminate information to the public and work in pre-college education communities, the tasks are much the same. This is not a comprehensive list of all
tasks, but are those provided by the participants from the ASP and NRCEN
meetings. Duties in common include: designing and conducting education programs, writing proposals, fund raising, designing curricula, conducting program

evaluations, reporting, conducting professional development for teachers, and recruiting activities. Similar challenges emerged as well. The authors propose that collaboration will help each group overcome common challenges.

4. Next Steps

The authors propose to launch a cross-group dialogue. New ideas, tools, literature and profession-related advice are examples of potential benefits. New connections to educators in museums and schools, and scientists and engineers in colleges and universities would enhance each group's efforts. ASP session participants suggested each group learn more about the other as a starting point for the partnership. This session has begun the process of introducing NRCEN and NSF center education initiatives to ASP. Likewise, NRCEN members should be made aware of opportunities to collaborate with ASP. A more comprehensive survey of EPO professionals would be highly instructive. The authors suggest a formal survey be conducted among EPO professionals from ASP, NRCEN, AGU, and possibly other organizations. A formal survey with broader participation would increase efficacy and produce uniformly formatted results. The sessions were informal and more intimate as a preliminary foray into these issues but the data suggests an opportunity for growth.

5. Summary

- There are similar tasks and skills among both ASP and NRCEN EPO professionals

- There is a need to explore further these similarities

- There is a need and desire among the two groups to collaborate

6. Conclusion

The session conducted by the authors at the 2007 ASP meeting clearly demonstrated many similarities between the ASP EPO professionals and the NRCEN Center educators. The two groups share similar skill sets and similar tasks to perform. Both groups have very good ideas on how to use a combined knowledge base to help improve the science education and outreach profession.

Jeff Nesbit, NSF director of the Office of Legislative and Public Affairs, closed his talk at NRCEN the evening of April 13, 2007 by stating the work that education and outreach professionals, do is probably the most important work that NSF supports. Mr. Nesbit based this conclusion on solid indicators related to the decline in the nation's science understanding at all levels. In the public arena, for example, two-thirds of Americans don't understand the scientific process at all and more than half firmly believe in pseudoscience such as astrology, ESP, and UFOs. In our schools, only 58% of U.S. 8th Grade Science teachers were science majors in college. This compares to 90% in Asia. The U.S. 12th graders' knowledge of math and science consistently ranks just 22nd in the world. In higher education, more than 40% of Science and Engineering

Doctorates went to non-U.S. citizens in 2005 and the U.S. share of high-tech exports has fallen from 31% to 18% in 20 years. NSF supports Science, Technology, Engineering and Mathematics (STEM) education at all levels, and the work conducted by community in Integrating research activities into the teaching of science, math and engineering at all educational levels (Nesbitt 2007). As indicated in Rising above the Gathering Storm "An educated, innovative, motivated workforce-human capital-is the most precious resource" and is critical to the economic survival of our nation (Rising above the Gathering Storm 2005). Improvements in science education is the key factor succeeding in educating creating a scientifically literate society.

As Daniel Steinberg urged in his talk at the NRCEN Conference, there is a need to focus on EPO professional development and recognition. A dialogue about this emergent profession must begin (Steinberg 2007). Many EPO professionals come from diverse backgrounds with unique sets of skills. EPO professionals continue to play a crucial part in increasing the public understanding of science and ASP and NRCEN can join as advocates for the profession. Andrew Fraknoi (who was present in the 90-minute oral session presented by the authors at the 2007 ASP meeting) has pioneered these ideas in his paper "Steps and Missteps toward an Emerging Profession" (Fraknoi 2005).

More information about NSF centers, as well as the NSF "broader impact" guidelines, is included in the appendices B and C. Princeton University's Materials Research Science and Engineering Center (MRSEC, a NSF center and member of NRCEN) PCCM presented a poster at the 2006 ASP meeting in Baltimore, which led to successful collaborations at Princeton University's Science and Engineering Expo. Another poster at the 2007 ASP meeting was presented and a corresponding paper is currently in press. By advertising our programs at each others' meetings, an increasing awareness between the groups will develop to encourage new partnerships. The subject of this poster, PCCM's Science and Engineering Expo, is a program in which PCCM is making an effort to increase astronomy participation. There are obvious things to pursue from this point: lessons learned, best practices, new collaborations, etc. This is the beginning of a productive exchange. Ultimately, future funding opportunities may be pursued together.

Appendices

Appendix A: What is the National Science Foundation (NSF) Research Center Educators Network (NRCEN)?

NRCEN's Mission is to "facilitate and promote communication and collaboration within the National Science Foundation's Research Centers Educators Network (NRCEN) and serve as a resource for the wider Education and Outreach community." (http://www.nrcen.org)

NRCEN is an organization of NSF center educators who work together to gain access to information about high quality education and outreach programs. This is accomplished primarily through face-to-face interactions, but also in virtual mode. Armed with shared best practices and "lessons learned" from colleagues, we continuously improve Center education activities (Andrews 2007).

(Issues addressed include):

1. how to increase professionalism among E&O personnel in centers;
2. how to increase collaboration and communication among E&O personnel across centers and disciplines;
3. how to improve access to state-of-the-art E&O methods and model (best) practices; how to mi-nimize duplication of effort;
4. how to create and sustain internal and external partnerships;
5. how to effectively reach the "broad and diverse" audiences NSF requires of its centers;
6. and how to increase our ability to attract supplemental funding for other sources (http://www.nrcen.org)

Appendix B: What is an NSF Center?

NSF funded centers include organizations such as MRSECs, ERCs, NSECs, STCs, etc.

The description of a MRSEC as stated on the nsf.gov site follows: (see http://www.nsf.gov/pubs/2007/nsf07563/nsf07563.pdf)

> "(A MRSEC) supports interdisciplinary materials research and education while addressing fundamental problems in science and engineering. MRSECs require outstanding research quality and intellectual breadth, provide support for research infrastructure and flexibility in responding to new opportunities, and strongly emphasize the integration of research and education. These centers foster active collaboration between universities and other sectors, including industry, and they constitute a national network of university-based centers in materials research. MRSECs address problems of a scope or complexity requiring the advantages of scale and interdisciplinary interaction provided by a center. A MRSEC may be located at a single institution, or may involve two or more institutions in partnership."

More information on MRSECs, ERCs, NSECs and STCs can be found at:

http://www.mrsec.org/ (MRSECs),
http://www.erc-assoc.org/ (ERCs),
http://www.nsf.gov/crssprgm/nano/info/centers.jsp (NSECs), and
http://www.nsf.gov/od/oia/programs/stc/ (STCs).

Appendix C: What are NSF's requirements/guidelines for broader impact?

The components of the broader impacts criterion, as defined by the National Science Board, are listed below.

- How well does the activity advance discovery and understanding while promoting teaching, training and learning?

- How well does the proposed activity broaden the participation of underrepresented groups (e.g., gender, ethnicity, disability, geographic, etc.)?

- To what extent will it enhance the infrastructure for research and education, such as facilities, instrumentation, networks and partnerships?

- Will the results be disseminated broadly to enhance scientific and technological understanding?

- What may be the benefits of the proposed activity to society? (http://www.nsf.gov/pubs/policydocs/pappguide/nsf08_1/gpg_index.jsp)

References

Andrews, J., "Creating Positive Influence: The Role of Education in NSF Centers", presented at NRCEN Workshop 2007, April 13, 2007, and selected slides at ASP 90-minute session, September 5, 2007

Fraknoi, A., Steps and Missteps Toward an Emerging Profession, Mercury, **34**, 5, 19-25 (2005)

Nesbit, J., Communicating Science Broadly (2007) http://www.nrcen.org/2007/Communicating%20Science%20Broadly.pdf

National Academy of Sciences, "Rising above the Gathering Storm, Energizing and Employing America for a Brighter Economic Future,", National Academy of Engineering, Institute of Medicine, Augustine, October 2005)

Steinberg, D. "The Emerging Education Outreach Profession: NRCEN's Role for the Education Professional", presented at NRCEN Workshop 2007, (April 14, 2007)

NRCEN website: http://www.nrcen.org

MRSEC Program Solicitation: http://www.nsf.gov/pubs/2007/nsf07563/nsf07563.pdf

Broader Impact Guidelines link found in NSF's Grant Proposal Guide (effective June 2007) http://www.nsf.gov/pubs/gpg/broaderimpacts.pdf, GPG: http://www.nsf.gov/pubs/policydocs/pappguide/nsf08_1/gpg_index.jsp

EPO and a Changing World
ASP Conference Series, Vol. 389, © 2008
C. Garmany, M. Gibbs, and J. W. Moody

A Community Conversation: Developing a Master's in Astronomy/Space Science Education and Public Outreach

Michael G. Gibbs

Astronomical Society of the Pacific 390 Ashton Avenue; San Francisco, CA 94112, USA

Lindsay Marie Bartolone

Adler Planetarium & Astronomy Museum 1300 S. Lake Shore Drive; Chicago, IL 60605, USA

John Mickus

Benedictine University 5700 College Road; Lisle, IL 60532, USA

Abstract.   As the astronomy/space science education and public outreach profession continues to expand, is there a need to provide a formalized academic credential? The Astronomical Society of the Pacific (ASP) feels the time is right for an online master's program in this field. This paper summarizes the discussion from members of the education and public outreach (EPO) community who gathered to explore this topic. Participants were asked for their input regarding possible learning objectives and the desired outcomes for such a degree program.

It is proposed that a master's degree program could serve the emerging population of formal and informal educators, scientists, volunteers and others who are now engaged or wish to engage in astronomy/space science EPO and provide them with the knowledge and skills to be successful. Candidates for the degree could use the pedagogy of inquiry-based learning and technology to create an effective teaching/learning environment.

1. Purpose for the Community Conversation

The desired outcome for the community conversation was to obtain initial input from the EPO community regarding the possible need and feasibility of establishing a master's degree in astronomy/space science EPO. This paper provides a summary of the conversation. Over twenty individuals attended and were invited to answer a set of initial questions upon entering the room in order gain an understanding of those participating. The following are the questions and the responses:

1.1. Are you interested in the possibility of receiving a graduate degree in the EPO field?

Nine individuals indicated yes, four said maybe, and six said no with one of the six indicating they already have a graduate degree in this field.

1.2. Do you currently have an advanced degree related to astronomy/space science EPO?

Nine individuals indicated yes, 10 indicated no.

1.3. Which of the following areas would you like offered for professional development or continuing education?

Table 1.   Areas for Professional Development or Continuing Education

Item	Number of Responses
Science Content	11
Education Content	12
Education Technology	10
Program Evaluation	12
Project Management	6
Presentation Skills	7

1.4. What else should we have asked?

A number of answers to this question were provided, such as: could someone both teach and take classes; what is the market for the degree; should the degree be limited to space science EPO; would the program be available online; what about a certificate program rather than a master's degree; what about a research component and what about practical, hands-on telescope/observing work.

2. Five Questions for the Community Conversation

The conversation focused on discussing five primary topical questions relating to the overall theme. Each table was assigned two questions to discuss and then report back to the entire group.

2.1. In addition to the program at Wheeling Jesuit University, what else is currently available to the EPO community for either professional development or a degree program?

Charles Wood, with Wheeling Jesuit University, informed the audience that Wheeling does not currently have a master's degree program but rather is offering a for-credit class through the Center for Educational Technologies at Wheeling Jesuit University (http://www.cet.edu). Other programs were also listed such as Prescott University in Tucson, Arizona, along with the Montana State University master's of science in science education, and the online degree program from Swinburne University.

2.2. In addition to the information listed in the appendix, what additional elements should be included in this possible master's program?

It was thought the initial outline was indeed a good start and the following could also be added: internships; working with scientists; understanding how to apply for grants and other funding; credit should be given for prior experience; nonprofit law and copyright law would be good to include; program evaluation; and instructional design.

2.3. What skill sets for professional development should be included?

Items such as providing grant writing, negotiation, facilitation skills, human resource skills, organizational management, leadership development, and partnership development were all listed as being important. When addressing the issue of astronomy content, the question was asked, "what does this mean?" Educators need to gather data, analyze it, and present it. Inservice educators do not need pedagogy, for this is something they have already been trained in. Therefore, there should be different tracks for different types of people pending their background and area of interest such as concentrations in content, education, business or mass communication. It was stated that scientists may need a master's to obtain the education content and educators need science content...etc. (i.e. "there's a table with three or four legs...you tell us which one you have and we'll teach you the other three.")

2.4. The target audience - who would benefit from receiving such a degree?

The master's degree could be beneficial to individuals who are or wish to be professionals within the EPO field and this could transcend beyond the astronomy/space science community - pending how the degree program is developed. Additionally, those who already work within the field and wish to advance could benefit from the degree. These places include but are not limited to: museums, planetariums, science centers, nature centers, observatories, after-school programs, science writers, artists, and youth group coordinators. Also, individuals looking to enter the field, maybe more so with informal education than inservice K-12 teachers, could also find this to be a valuable degree.

The field is rather wide open as to possible individuals who could be interested in such a degree, but having a master's from an accredited university was felt to be very important along with the program being accessible (online). It was indicated that there is currently an increase in online certificate and degree programs and that online degrees are becoming more and more accepted by employers.

Additionally, it was suggested that regardless of the focus, the degree needs to provide a real world application that is usable within the work place.

2.5. What would be the ideal format for such a master's program?

In general, the consensus was that an ideal program would be part-time, evenings or weekend and primarily online with some classroom or personal interaction. Because the nature of the degree involves working with the public, individuals stated it is important to incorporate a human element, just not all online. One suggestion for how this could happen would be through an internship or mentorship component to the program. If the degree is online then the "human element" could occur through facebook.com or other new media. Also, the program would need to be financially reasonable for both the organization offering the degree and for the students who may wish to enroll in the program.

3.   Conclusion

The astronomy/space science community was invited to provide initial input and recommendations regarding the establishment of a master's of science in astronomy and space science EPO. Some of the recommendations included offering a degree program that is online and incorporates an opportunity to gather in person, provides a level of mentorship for students to learn from those already in the field, and ensures there would be real world applications that could be easily applied to the work place. A graduate program on education and public outreach could very well prove to be beneficial not just for the astronomy and space science community, but for other professions that engage in EPO activities. Expanding beyond astronomy and space science and providing different tracks could be beneficial to assist in the program's sustainability. These recommendations can provide assistance to those considering establishing a degree program. Additional comments can be sent via email to mgibbs@astrosociety.org.

Appendix

It is proposed that participants in a master's of science degree in astronomy and space science education and public outreach would use the pedagogy of inquiry-based learning and technology to create an effective teaching/learning environment for both formal and informal educators. The program would integrate content knowledge in astronomy/space science utilizing the resources of the local and national astronomy/space science community. Faculty could include Ph.D.-level professors, noted EPO practitioners, and guest lecturers.

What will this degree accomplish?

- Develop appropriate demonstrations and activities related to astronomy/space science.

- Understand, avoid and debunk common misconceptions in astronomy/space science.

- Understand the impact of educational technology available to the EPO community (e.g. remote telescopes) and anticipate future trends.

- Overview current topics and future trends in astronomy (e.g. what happens when NASA states we are going to the Moon, how that changes the focus) and possible future discoveries in the solar system, with stars and galaxies, and the the exploration of space.

- Understand project management, community relations, budgeting, public relations and fundraising.

- Develop public speaking and presentation skills customized for a variety of audience levels and formal education.

- Apply educational research to program evaluation.

Program requirements: A total of 36 semester hours of graduate coursework (12 classes) for the MS degree with the 12th class being the original thesis and presentation of the research at an ASP conference.

EPO and a Changing World
ASP Conference Series, Vol. 389, © *2008*
C. Garmany, M. Gibbs, and J. W. Moody

Checking Your Alignment: EPO Activities and National/State/District Science Education Standards

Kristine Larsen and Marsha Bednarski

Physics – Earth Sciences Department, Central Connecticut State University, New Britain, CT 06053, USA

Abstract.   In this workshop, participants gained familiarity with the specific science content and pedagogical standards at the national, state, and local district level. Through the use of case studies, participants gained concrete experience in developing and revising EPO astronomy activities for alignment to specific, grade-related standards.

1. Introduction

In an effort to improve science education at the K-12 level, Project 2061 of the American Association for the Advancement of Science (1993) and the National Research Council (1996) published seminal works setting forth national science standards. These works set the bar for what all students should know to be considered scientifically literate at various stages in their education. These age-appropriate standards not only dealt with scientific content in the physical, life, and earth/space sciences, but also the nature and history of science, inquiry in science, science and technology, and personal and social perspectives of science. These standards have been used by state departments of education as the foundation for their own science frameworks, policy documents which establish the scope and sequence of science education.

This has predictably led to variations among state requirements for K-12 science education (Palen & Proctor 2006). Freedom is then given to local school districts to develop their own science curriculum, defined by the NRC(1996) as "the way content is organized and emphasized; it includes structure, organization, balance, and presentation of the content in the classroom." Local curriculum developers have the flexibility to reorganize the content standards of the state frameworks (for example, covering the phases of the moon in 4th instead of 5th grade), so long as all students have successfully mastered the necessary content prior to any state testing mandated by *No Child Left Behind*.

In addition to establishing a set of age-appropriate standards for national science education, the NRC(1996) emphasized the need for ongoing and dedicated partnerships between scientists, educators, and administrators in order to continually improve the nation's science education at all levels. In this vein, a number of authors have sounded the clarion call for practitioners of science to become part of this important process (Moreno 1999, Laursen 2006).

To this end, NASA has integrated into its proposal evaluation process for Education and Public Outreach initiatives the requirement that all proposals "must demonstrate a substantive and informed alignment with educational standards appropriate to the target audience," namely either national standards (such as those of the NRC and AAAS) or state frameworks (2006). A significant problem is that many scientists are either unfamiliar with standards and frameworks, or have serious misconceptions as to how they are to be utilized in the development of educational/public outreach materials and activities (Morrow 2003, Laursen 2006, NASA 2006). In the words of the NASA guide (2006), true alignment to the standards/frameworks "is a challenging prospect that is often underestimated... [and] *linking is not the same as aligning.*" Scientists' lack of experience in creating true alignment in their educational products and activities not only contributes to a problematic disconnect between science education at the K-12 and collegiate levels, but also reduces the effectiveness of educational enrichment and public outreach opportunities offered by professional and amateur astronomers to their local school districts and community organizations. This workshop is a direct response to this highly relevant and important national issue.

2.   The Workshop

After an introduction to the concept of national, state, and local standards, and their importance in developing relevant EPO activities and products, participants were divided into six groups. Each group was given a case study in which they were asked to develop an astronomy activity aligned to a specific set of standards (national, state, or local) and a specific age group. The resulting proposals were then shared with the workshop at large and discussed. The six case studies and the proposed activities developed by each break-out group now follow.

2.1.   Third Grade Activity

Case study 1: You receive an excited phone call from your brother, a 3rd grade teacher. He's been asked to take part in a state curriculum grant which will allow his school to create an after-school series of science enrichment activities (and $5000 for the entire program to pay for materials). He asks you for help in proposing a series of astronomy activities and offers you $1000 of the materials money for your portion. The one catch is that the activities must be done right after school and can't last more than an hour each. They must also be aligned with the district frameworks. You promise him to have a preliminary idea for one activity the next day.

   Participants in this group were given a specific portion of the Juneau, Alaska 3rd grade Earth Science curriculum which centered around the essential question "How is the earth like other objects in the night [sky]?" (http://www.jsd.k12.ak.us/district/inst_ser/Science_Curric.pdf).

   The group first developed an activity which aligned with the curriculum key element "The rotation of the earth on its axis every 24 hours produces the night and day cycle." In the first part of this activity, students would role-play the rotating earth while the teacher would hold a flashlight to represent the sun. Afterwards, students would investigate sundials, including what they measure, how the shadow moves, and the history of sundials. The culminating experience would be the construction of Project ASTRO sunclocks and observing the motion of the sun's shadow. Given the money allotted for this program by the district, it would also be possible to purchase one or more Sunspotters.

The workshop group then outlined a second activity aligned with the curriculum key element "The patterns of stars in the sky stay the same, although they appear to move across the sky nightly, and different stars can be seen in different seasons." In this proposed activity, each student would plot a different constellation on a 17×22 piece of black paper. These would be placed in a sequence around the classroom. The students would then revolve around a central light source representing the sun, rotating as they go. Afterwards the students would discuss their observations as to which constellations were visible at what positions (relative to the "sun" and their location in the classroom).

2.2. Sixth Grade Activity

Case study 2: You've been approached by the principal of the local middle school about working with their gifted and talented program for 6th graders. The students are interested in the "demotion" of Pluto, and especially about Eris (which they openly blame for Pluto's demise!) The students have learned about the other eight planets in their science class and are looking for you to take them beyond the regular curriculum. However, the principal has to write a report every year on how the gifted and talented "enrichment" curriculum still fits with the state frameworks for that grade. Develop an activity which will meet the needs of this program.

Participants in this group were given selections from the Utah Science Core Curriculum for 6th grade (http://www.uen.org/core/core.do?courseNum=3060) and selected the following key concepts to frame their activity: [Students should] "use classification systems," "understand the cumulative nature of science knowledge," and "understand that science investigations use a variety of methods." The relevant content standard was "Students will understand the relationship and attributes of objects in the solar system." The main thrust of the activity was to have the students collect information about the various members of the solar system, organize their "research" on cards, and devise (and justify) their own individual classification systems. Student learning would be assessed either by having the students classify a new object according to their system, or to debate their classification with other students. As part of these assessments, students would have to decide for themselves where Pluto would fit in. A review of all students' classifications might lead to an interesting discussion of consensus as a method of discourse.

2.3. Seventh Grade Activity

Case study 3: Your sister-in-law teaches at an inner-city middle school which has (in the opinion of the teachers) clearly inadequate materials and technology. The city's 7th grade curriculum includes the properties and structure of the solar system. For the past ten years, they've been doing the same old paper maché planets (to scale) and scale model of the distances from the sun to the planets (to scale) involving running a string down the hallway with little nametags where each planet should be. Frankly, both the teachers and the students find this BORING! You offer to work with her in developing new activities which will cover the same items in the curriculum, cheaply, but in a more exciting manner.

As in case study 1, this group also used the Juneau, Alaska curriculum, but for middle school (http://www.jsd.k12.ak.us/district/inst_ser/Science_Curric.pdf). The overarching theme of this portion of the curriculum is Systems, and the essential question is "How can we understand a complex world through its systems?" Part of the suggested assessment in the curriculum is to build a model of the size of the solar system. The participants in this group divided the unit into five activities. In the first, the distance scale would be investigated. Here, it was decided to use a tape measure to represent the distance between the sun and Pluto, and the students would calculate the necessary fractions of the tape measure which would correspond to the location of the eight classic planets. In the second activity, the size of the sun is taken as a standard measurement and the relative sizes of the individual planets would then be calculated by the students. Suggestions for materials included using seeds for the planets, or using the Project ASTRO play-doh activity. Activity 3 addressed the third of four general science outcomes for the Juneau system, that "All students will understand the nature and history of science." Students would investigate the role telescopes had in discovering Uranus, Neptune, and Pluto, as well as the history of Bode's Law (comparing our solar system to predictions). Activity 4 would begin with a question "Can we build a model with both distance and size on the same scale?" Answering this question would require that students combine mathematical skills with science content (such as the ratios used in activities 1 and 2). In the final activity (which could be used as a culminating assessment), students would reflect upon the properties which make the solar system a true system.

2.4. Fifth Grade Activity

Case study 4: You've been asked by the principal of your son's elementary school to work on a state grant which will propose a collaborative outreach program for the fifth graders for your town plus two neighboring towns. The teachers in the schools have requested that money be earmarked in the grant to purchase one 8-inch portable telescope (non-computerized) for each town. For the moment, he asks you to come up with an outline of one telescope-centered activity to bring back to the teachers before the next planning committee meeting.

Observation of Apollo lunar landing sites with the unaided eye, binoculars, and the 8-inch telescope was selected as the relevant activity. Students would research the sites and determine when during each lunar phase cycle each site might be visible. Participants closely aligned their activity to the Connecticut State Frameworks (http://www.sde.ct.gov/sde/lib/sde/word_docs/curriculum/science/framework/sciencecoreframework2005v2.doc), both frameworks for "Inquiry, Literacy, and Numeracy" (including making observations, designing and conducting experiments, using data to construct explanations, and organizing and communicating data) as well as specific content standards. The content standards aligned were "describe how light is absorbed and/or reflected by different surfaces," "describe how light absorption and reflection allow one to see the shapes and colors of objects," "describe the monthly changes in the appearance of the moon, based on the moon's orbit around the Earth," and "describe the uses of different instruments, such as eye glasses, magnifiers, periscopes and telescopes, to enhance our vision." Key concepts/questions include the phases of the moon, the affect of shadows on the appearance of lunar features, the visibility of the moon during the day, and the affect of various optical aids.

2.5. Grades K-2 Activity

Case study 5: The local science museum asks you to be part of a grant proposal seeking funds to host after-school astronomy enrichment activities for grades K-2. The granting body demands alignment with the NRC National Science Education Standards. Your task before next week's committee meeting is to brainstorm one activity which could be included in the proposal.

Participants in this group were given the K-4 (NRC 1996) standards as their guidelines, including the Science as Inquiry (A), Earth Space Science (D), Science and Technology (E) and History and Nature of Science (G) content standards. Unlike the other case studies, this study's group chose a narrow focus, in the areas of Science and Technology ("Women and men of all ages, backgrounds, and groups engage in a variety of scientific and technological work") and History and Nature of Science ("Men and women have made a variety of contributions throughout the history of science and technology"). The proposed activity is based on an earlier (1994) idea by Jean Jacobs of the Whitefield Elementary School (New Hampshire) to construct an alphabet book of women astronomers. Such a book could be a coloring book or reading book, and would also include the country of origin of each woman as well as a picture of her country's flag. Students could construct one page each, and could act out the life of their astronomer as a capstone assessment activity. It would be helpful for teachers if a guide of supporting material could be published (including lists of possible women astronomers to include, especially for certain difficult letters). During the project the student could email or write to their astronomer if she were still living, and each living astronomer would be send a copy of the completed booklet.

2.6. Grades 5-8 Activity

Case study 6: Congratulations! Your proposed mission to land a space probe on Miranda, Uranus's "Humpty Dumpty" moon, has been approved! Now you have to develop educational outreach materials to submit with your NASA grant proposal. After some discussion, you and your colleagues decide to target grades 5-8 and to align with the NRC National Science Education Standards. As a beginning, you and your team members brainstorm one activity to include in your proposal.

Participants in this break-out group were given the NRC 5-8 standards as their framework, including Earth and Space Science (D), Science and Technology (E), and Science in Personal and Social Perspectives (F). The group elected to align to the following content standards:

- "The earth is the third planet from the sun in a system that includes the moon, the sun, eight other planets and their moons, and smaller objects, such as asteroids and comets."

- "Gravity is the force that keeps planets in orbit around the sun and governs the rest of the motion in the solar system."

- "Science and technology are reciprocal."

- "Perfectly designed solutions do not exist. All technological solutions have trade-offs."

The proposed activity had students designing their own probe to safely (and permanently) land on Miranda. Students would investigate the necessary background material, including the history of planetary landers and the bodies visited, as well as the different landers and landing techniques used on different bodies. Students would also research Miranda's unique properties in order to decide which properties would have to be addressed by their design. Students could test their basic understanding by designing a "lander" which would safely deliver an egg from a certain height to a ground landing (and conducting the experiment as a contest), and/or by using computer simulations to see how changing the properties of a landing (gravitational force, angle of approach, speed of approach, etc.) might change the outcome of a landing.

3. Conclusion

Participants in the workshop were able to draft activities in alignment to the given standards, frameworks, and curricula. However they agreed with the warnings of the NASA Grant Guidelines that the creation of such activities is not trivial. Participants were also successful in combining astronomical content with the other types of content standards, such as scientific process and history.

References

Palen, S. and Proctor, A., Astronomy Education Review **5**(1), 23 (2006)
National Research Council 1996, *National Science Education Standards* (Academy Press, Washington D.C., 1996)
Moreno, N.P., Bioscience, **49**, 569 (1999)
Laursen, S.L., Astronomy Education Review **5**(1), 162 (2006)
Morrow, C., Astronomy Education Research, **1**(2), 85 (2003)
NASA (2006), http://science.hq.nasa.gov/research/SMD_EPO_Guide_v2.pdf

EPO and a Changing World
ASP Conference Series, Vol. 389, © 2008
C. Garmany, M. Gibbs, and J. W. Moody

Professional Development for Education-Engaged Scientists: A Research-Based Framework

Sandra L. Laursen

Education/Outreach Group, Cooperative Institute for Research in Environmental Sciences, 449 UCB, University of Colorado, Boulder, CO 80309-0449, USA, and Ethnography & Evaluation Research, 580 UCB, University of Colorado, Boulder, CO 80309-0580, USA

Heather Thiry and Anne-Barrie Hunter

Ethnography & Evaluation Research, 580 UCB, University of Colorado, Boulder, CO 80309-0580, USA

Abstract. New research findings from a study of scientists participating in education-related workshops reveal scientists' needs for professional development that can enhance their EPO work and help to sustain their involvement. (Last revised 9-07.)

1. Introduction

In his plenary talk (this volume), George Nelson argued that science teaching should strive to reach not just the 20% of students who can learn on their own, but all students in every lesson, every day. Likewise, he argued, professional development for K-12 teachers should target not just "space groupies," but a much larger group of teachers not already attracted by the subject matter itself. We make a parallel contention: To change the culture and practices of scientists' participation in EPO, we need to offer professional development not just for committed scientist-educators, but for the much larger group of scientists who will not make careers in EPO but can contribute productively and enthusiastically in numerous smaller ways. While the development of today's science EPO professionals has occurred largely through bootstrap approaches (Fraknoi 2005), we will need to find more deliberate and efficient means to prepare the broader community of scientists that we seek to engage in EPO.

Given today's context of increasing emphasis on science EPO, the need for professional development for scientist participants is more acute than ever before. For this group, intrinsic motivations remain important, such as the belief that public science literacy is important, a desire to "give back" to their own communities or support children's education, and interest in sharing their own enthusiasm for science (Andrews et al. 2005). Added to these in recent years, however, are pressures from U.S. research funders such as NASA (1996) and NSF (2003) for scientists to communicate the "broader impacts" of their research. Highlevel concerns about maintaining the numbers and diversity of the scientific and technical workforce have raised science education to greater public awareness, and national leaders have called for scientists' participation in education (Alberts 1991; Bybee 1998; Colwell & Kelly 1999; Leshner 2007). In this context, effective participation in EPO becomes a professional expectation of scientists, not just a hobby—an expectation that requires specialized knowledge and skills but for which most scientists have not been trained.

In order to support scientists in meeting these new expectations, the ReSciPE Project—Resources for Scientists in Partnership with Education—has undertaken a two-pronged effort, taking action to address this problem but also seeking greater understanding of it. Our goals have been:

- To increase involvement and effectiveness of scientists participating in K-12 education,

- To draw scientists into further professional development for their EPO work,

- To identify knowledge, motivations, and needs of these scientists, and

- To understand how they respond to professional development opportunities.

To enhance scientists' participation and effectiveness, we have developed a traveling, introductory workshop on "Scientific Inquiry in the Classroom." In 2.5 years, 18 workshops have reached some 400 scientists and their EPO collaborators. We also developed the ReSciPE Book, a web-based collection of annotated resources that address common needs of scientists as they work with teachers and students. To better understand this group, we have taken advantage of our workshop participants as a study population. Our evaluation-with-research study has explored the readiness, response, and needs of scientists for professional development to support their education work. In this report, we summarize findings from this study, focusing on scientists' professional development (PD) needs. We present these findings in the form of a framework that can guide development of future PD offerings. As an example of how this framework can be used, we apply it to one professional development model, ReSciPE's own inquiry workshop. Our aim is to inspire and guide those who work with scientists to apply the framework in planning professional development for their own EPO collaborators.

2. Study Methods

The study drew on data from multiple sources: online pre-surveys conducted when participants registered for a workshop; immediate post-workshop surveys; semi-structured follow-up interviews; and observations of workshop facilitators. Only participants who provided informed consent for use of their pre/post-survey and interview data were included in the study. A total of 276 participants completed the pre-survey, and the number of matched, consented, pre/post surveys was 147. Thirty follow-up interviews were conducted by telephone several months after workshop participation. The interview transcripts and open-ended responses to survey questions were coded for thematic content and the frequency of occurrence of codes or code groups across the data set was tallied. Quantitative survey responses were analyzed with descriptive statistics, using t-tests to analyze group and pre/post differences.

All study samples were drawn from the population of about 350 scientists and science educators attending a half-day professional development workshop on "Scientific Inquiry in the Classroom" between December, 2004, and April, 2006. Overall, workshop participants were a diverse group, with 60% women and 9% underrepresented minorities. They represented working scientists (70%) and graduate students (18%), predominantly from doctoral institutions (36%) and government labs (21%). Importantly, 73% were already doing some EPO–most (66%) in organized programs–and 51% said they spent more than one day per month on EPO work. In general, demographics of the survey (n=147) and interview (n=30) respondents closely mirrored the overall population (n=276). The interview sample included 50% research scientists and equal numbers of men and women. More on the samples and methods, and a review of prior work, is found in Thiry, Laursen and Hunter (2007).

While only a subset of findings is presented here, the study examined both evaluation questions of interest to our team in refining our program and measuring its effectiveness, and research questions of general interest to the EPO community:

- What do participants know already and learn from the ReSciPE workshops?

- In what ways is the notion of inquiry helpful as a starting point?

- What were the lasting outcomes of the workshops, e.g. use of workshop ideas, pursuit of additional professional development, or other outcomes?

- What are the current activities of education-engaged scientists?

- What motivations and barriers influence their involvement in education?

- What are their professional development needs?

3. Research Findings: Scientists' Professional Development Needs

Here we highlight evidence on scientists' professional development (PD) needs from the interview data, though survey data offer confirmation. A total of 113 observations on PD needs were identified in the 30 interviews and categorized into six types:

1. Motivation to engage in professional development, constituting 5% of all observations;

2. Accessibility of training (13% of observations)

3. Knowledge and skills (29% of observations)

4. Applicability to own work (18% of observations)

5. Broad participation in training (14% of observations)

6. Support for involvement in outreach (21% of observations).

These six types of needs can be arranged progressively across three stages in time: Categories 1 and 2 describe needs that influence how scientists can be drawn into professional development experiences to support their EPO work. Categories 3, 4 and 5 address needs that must be addressed by the professional development experience itself: the content, audience, and connections to their own work that will foster a meaningful professional development opportunity. Category 6 identifies the follow-up support that is needed to deepen and sustain scientists' ongoing EPO work. We discuss each category briefly and outline the implications for EPO practitioners as they consider the PD needs of their scientist colleagues.

3.1. Need for Motivation to Participate

The research scientists and EPO professionals interviewed saw a need to increase scientists' motivation to participate in EPO activities, and to pursue professional development to do this well. For example, one speaker said, "I'd say the biggest problem is one of motivation. And talking about scientists... the motivation to go to workshops, learn something about inquiry, and try to use inquiry, is extremely low."[1] Without participation, professional development will have no impact. Thus, those planning PD for scientists need to consider local, disciplinary, and national factors that will motivate participation, and identify recruiting strategies to identify and pique interest among potential participants.

3.2. Need for Access to Professional Development Opportunities

Interviewees wanted more opportunities to learn about education but recognized that these could not demand extensive time commitments, at least initially, if they were to reach a wide array of participants. They felt training in EPO should be standard training for science graduate students, while conferences should provide ongoing opportunities.

> Make [professional development] available. We get very little of it. ...It just has to be more available, I would say. And I don't know, this is next to impossible to do, but it needs to become part of the curriculum for masters and Ph.D. students. I think it would help tremendously if such a class was required in all colleges, and universities.

In addressing this need, professional developers will need to assess what form of PD will be most accessible for their intended audience. Structures may include a short workshop or intensive course (Morrow & Dusenberry 2004), seminar series, study group, video/teleconference, online tutorial, or one-on-one coaching. The location and timing should optimize access to the PD opportunity. Strategies may be adapted from those used with other professional groups (Loucks-Horsley et al. 2003) but should be customized to fit scientists' workplaces and cultures.

---

[1]It is clear from context that many statements in the interviews about "inquiry" are, like this, references to science education in general. Such conflation is ascribed to the ReSciPE workshops' focus on inquiry (see Laursen 2006 for arguments supporting this choice of topic).

3.3. Needs for Knowledge and Skills

Needs related to the content of a PD experience were noted often, at 29% of all observations made by 47% of interviewees. Participants wanted to build their knowledge of "best practices" in education and become aware of the research base supporting such practices. They sought to develop their presentation and teaching skills. As one put it, "It's always a benefit to me to learn about resources for scientists to use, and also to understand better what good teaching is all about."

To address this need, professional developers will need to identify their goals for content and skills they wish participants to learn, and attitudes or beliefs to be influenced. They will need to consider how PD activities will address content goals, who will facilitate the PD experience, and what forms of presentation will be used.

3.4. Needs for Content that is Applicable to One's Own Work

Respondents strongly stated their need for content that was readily applicable to their own EPO work. Experiential learning was one way to make content applicable, when PD offered the chance for participants to learn in the same manner as recommended for students. They also suggested several ideas to aid transfer to their own settings: resources and tips to apply in their own EPO activities; examples of activities in their own disciplines; and help in connecting with EPO programs that would make use of their expertise and interest at the level of involvement they desired, for example:

> Providing tips and guidance for how [scientists] can be useful, and a guide... Give a heads-up of what ten-year-olds need, in terms of their educational level. ... If people don't know about something, it can seem very over-whelming and too much of a task. And so, to make it [easier], give the guidelines on how they can do it.

Transfer of learning to a new setting is hard (Bransford et al. 1999)–as true for scientists as for students. Professional developers can use varied learning strategies to reach their audiences and select examples from familiar areas, or out-of-field examples to focus participants on the methods used rather than the content covered. Some PD experiences may directly prepare scientists to participate in a specific program, while others address broad issues that apply across many settings. The handbook by Franks et al. (2006) and the ReSciPE Book (2005) are two resources that attempt to communicate EPO information in a manner relevant to scientists.

3.5. Needs for Broad Participation in PD

Many respondents (57%) observed that scientists and educators need to collaborate in EPO and felt that such collaboration should likewise take place within professional development for EPO. They called for participation by educators in PD for scientists and had benefited from educators' perspectives in their own PD experiences, including the ReSciPE workshops. One speaker advocated:

> Getting scientists and teachers together... I think a lot of times they really sort of need to get together to understand, when they have a

mutual respect for each other, but they don't always really understand each other's needs, and thought processes. So actually getting
them together would be useful. It's just like in inquiry-trying to
do science the way scientists do it–and scientists may need to do
education the way educators do it.

Professional developers should be inclusive in their thinking and consider
potential benefits from involving educators as well as scientists, as well as differences in their needs that may be better addressed separately. Approaches
that value the contributions and expertise of all, while recognizing differences
in perspectives, will be most successful (Tanner, Chatman & Allen 2003; Bower
1996).

3.6. Needs for Follow-up Support

Respondents identified a number of needs for support following a professional
development experience that could help them make use of new learning and
encourage ongoing participation in EPO. Key among these was collegial support-
networking with others involved in EPO, and mentoring by more experienced
colleagues.

I think it's having somebody who does that kind of thing . . . to be
available– that they could show me how others have done it, and
then I can incorporate it into what I'm doing. 'Cause I'm kind of
alone in this thing, and I'm trying to figure out, "What could I do?"
that would make it better

Scientists wanted to be able to plug in to existing programs that would use
their expertise and provide this support, and sought meaningful, visible support
from institutional leaders for their efforts. Indeed, follow-up support may be the
most difficult challenge faced by professional developers, as they consider how
to foster community, link people with ongoing programs, sustain individual and
institutional involvement, and engage leaders in recognizing and rewarding EPO
involvement.

4. Applying the Framework in Practice

To gain experience with the framework and to test its utility, conference participants analyzed a case study, the ReSciPE Project's half-day workshop on
"Scientific Inquiry in the Classroom." First they read a short description of
the workshop, using a "jigsaw" approach to divide the reading and share information among group members. Then, for each of the six types of needs listed
above, they considered what features of the workshop addressed this need and
the extent to which this need was met by this particular workshop. This analysis demonstrated the use of the research framework in assessing the strengths
and weaknesses of an existing PD opportunity to judge its effectiveness or to
improve it. The results of this analysis are summarized in Table 1.

As for any real-world educational offering, it is impossible to meet every
need expressed by every individual. Tradeoffs are inevitable as developers make

Table 1.   Comparison of the Research Framework with a Real-World Case Study

Research Framework: Scientist PD Needs & Contributing Factors	*Case Study of ReSciPE "Scientific Inquiry" Workshop: Features that Address Scientist PD Needs*
1.Motivation to engage in PD - Personal, local, disciplinary & national context	Self-selected; 75% already engaged in EPO. NSF 'Broader Impacts', NASA EPO interests. On-site recruitment was personalized at labs.
2.Access - Format & length - Where, when, how many - Recruitment & visibility	Half-day workshops short enough for busy people. Go where scientists are: conferences & labs. Hosting societies helped with advertising. Hosting labs coordinated logistics & recruitment; off-site presenters helped make it a special event. Endorsed by local lab leaders. Diversity of attendees shows that access was broad.
3.Content - Knowledge - Skills - Beliefs - Presenters & presentation modes	Chose inquiry as introductory topic for all fields.Used mix of presentation modes & activities. Summarized evidence base on 'How People Learn'. Targeted to novice level; not program specific. Offered conceptual framework but not 'how-to'. Modest number of examples in any discipline. Data show learning gains, attitude changes.
4.Applicability to own EPO work - Relevance of content - Experiential learning - Chance to work on own projects	Linked student inquiry to scientific inquiry process. Presented by scientists & educators. Mix of activities supported varied learning modes. Brief opportunities to share work & apply; no extended personal planning time. Not tied to a specific EPO program.
5.Broad participation - Mix of participants - Involvement of educators - Network-building	Focused on scientists, with some teachers present. Mix of career stage, age, discipline. Chance to meet kindred souls interested in EPO. Discussion and social time included.
6.Follow-up support - More PD, coaching - Content-specific resources - EPO programs to join - Institutional visibility - Sustainable involvement	Offered online resources, email listserv. At lab sites, local coordinators could follow up. At professional meetings, little follow-up provided to individual attendees from widespread institutions.

choices about their PD approaches and strategies. However, this empirical framework can help professional developers recognize those tradeoffs and make more informed and deliberate choices. For example, conference participants identified some of the tradeoffs evident in the ReSciPE half-day workshops:

Thorough vs. accessible: the choice to offer a half-day workshop made the workshop available to more participants, who were willing to commit a modest amount of time, but limited the opportunity to go into topics in depth.

Broad vs. disciplinary: the choice to offer a general, introductory workshop appropriate to scientists from many disciplines was balanced against scientists' desire to see examples from their own field that they could apply directly to their own work.

National vs. local: the choice to offer a traveling, nationwide workshop weighed against the opportunity for local follow-up, yet the "special event" nature of visiting presenters attracted participants who might not otherwise have attended.

With this background, participants then reflected on the framework as a tool for planning scientists' professional development to benefit their own EPO programs. "It certainly helped me organize my own thinking," said one participant. In adapting the general framework to their own setting, the role of local institutional factors became particularly evident in certain areas. Local initiatives and contexts were seen to influence scientists' motivations; the needs of local programs for scientists' expertise shaped the types of opportunities for scientists to participate and the skills and knowledge they would need to do so effectively; and potential collaborations were identified with other local programs that might wish to co-host professional development activities. Participants recognized that sharing of PD models from diverse EPO providers could help improve PD offerings more widely and increase the professionalism of scientists' EPO participation.

5.   Conclusion

We have proposed a framework, based on empirical data, for addressing the professional development needs of scientists as they begin to engage in EPO. Analysis of one real-world case study in comparison to the framework shows that it is possible to design a professional development opportunity to meet many of these needs, but tradeoffs will inevitably arise. It is clear from this analysis that no single professional development model can meet all the needs of all education-engaged scientists. EPO leaders will need to provide a range of PD offerings to meet the needs of both novices and those plunging deeper into EPO, to address concepts that cut across fields as well as within disciplines, and to support specific EPO programs as well as address broad concerns. We offer this framework to assist professional developers in designing and evaluating such offerings.

Acknowledgments. S. L. thanks her co-facilitators Lesley K. Smith and Carol Schott. We are grateful to the ReSciPE participants who contributed their ideas, interest, and enthusiasm and to the workshop hosts. We also thank the ASP conference participants who considered the framework and shared their ideas, particularly Mark Hartman. This work was supported by the National Science Foundation's Geo-science Education program under grant EAR #0450088.

References

Alberts, B. M., "Elementary Science Education in the United States: How Scientists Can Help," Current Biology, **1**(6), 339-341 (1991)

Andrews, E., Hanley, D., Hovermill, J., Weaver, A., and Melton, G., "Scientists and Public Outreach: Participation, Motivations, and Impediments," Journal of Geoscience Education, **53**(3), 281-293 (2005)

Bower, J. M., "Science Education Reform: How Can We Help?" Issues in Science and Technology, **12**(3), 55-60 (1996)

Bransford, J. D., Brown, A. L., and Cocking, R. R., (Eds.), *How People Learn: Brain, Mind, Experience, and School* (National Academies Press, Washingotn D.C., 1999)

Bybee, R., "Improving precollege science education, the role of scientists and engineers, Journal of College Science Teaching, **27**, 324-328 (1998)

Colwell, R. R. and Kelly, E. M., "Science Learning, Science Opportunity," Science, **286**, 237 (1999)

Fraknoi, A., "Steps and Missteps Toward an Emerging Profession," Mercury, (September-October), 19-25 (2005)

Franks, S., McDonnell, J., Peach, C., Simms, E., and Thorrold, A., *EPO Education and Public Outreach; A Guide for Scientists* (The Oceanography Society, Rockville, MD, 2006)

Laursen, S. L., "Getting Unstuck: Strategies for Escaping the Science Standards Straitjacket," Astronomy Education Review, **5**(1), 162-177 (2006)

Leshner, A. I., "Outreach Training Needed," Science, **315**, 161 (2007)

Loucks-Horsley, S., Love, N., Stiles, K. E., Mundry, S., and Hewson, P. W., *Designing Professional Development for Teachers of Science and Mathematics* 2nd ed. (Corwin Press, Thousand Oaks, CA, 2003)

Morrow, C. A. and Dusenberry, P. B. "Workshops for Scientists and Engineers on Education and Public Outreach," Advances in Space Research, 34, 2153-2158 (2004)

NASA, *Implementing the Office of Space Science Education/Public Outreach Strategy* (1996) http://spacescience.nasa.gov/admin/pubs/edu/imp_plan.htm

NSF, *Merit Review Broader Impacts Criterion: Representative Activities* (2003) http://www.nsf.gov/pubs/2003/nsf032/bicexamples.pdf

ReSciPE, *The ReSciPE Book* (2005) http://cires.colorado.edu/education/k12/rescipe/collection

Tanner, K. D., Chatman, L., and Allen, D., "Approaches to Biology Teaching and Learning: Science Teaching and Learning Across the School-University Divide–Cultivating Conversations Through Scientist-Teacher Partnerships," Cell Biology Education, **2**, 195-201 (2003) http://www.lifescied.org/cgi/content/full/2/4/195

Thiry, H., Laursen, S. L., and Hunter, A.-B. "Professional Development Needs and Outcomes for Education-engaged Scientists: A Research-based Framework and its Application, (Manuscript in review, 2007)

Intently listening to a presentation

A place to relax under the stars!

EPO and a Changing World
ASP Conference Series, Vol. 389, © 2008
C. Garmany, M. Gibbs, and J. W. Moody

A Field Trip to the Moon: A Research-Based Model for Creating and Evaluating a Visualization-Based Museum Program

Rachel Connolly[1]

College of Education and Human Development, University of Louisville, Louisville, KY 40292, USA

Carter Emmart and Rosamond Kinzler

American Museum of Natural History, Central Park West at 79th St., NY, NY 10024, USA

Laura Danly

Griffith Observatory, 2800 East Observatory Rd., Los Angeles, CA 90027, USA

Abstract. The American Museum of Natural History (AMNH), in partnership with NASA's Marshall Space Flight Center (MSFC), has developed, delivered, and evaluated a new educational program, A Field Trip to the Moon, for school groups on field trips to informal settings. The development of this program included an integrated evaluation track that has deepened our understanding of the following three areas: how students are engaged by and learn in museum workshops, how teachers can be supported in their science curricula by lunar exploration, and the role that visualizations can have in engaging students and teachers to participate in and continue their learning. The methodologies for evaluating the program are included.

1. Project Overview

The following report details findings from the research and evaluation of A Field Trip to the Moon (FTM). Through collaboration between the American Museum of Natural History and NASA's Marshall Space Flight Center, this program was developed and piloted for school groups on field trips to the AMNH. The program was piloted with 10 student groups and a total of 270 students over a six-month period. Outcomes from these pilot sessions were evaluated through both quantitative and qualitative methods, and results and outcomes were triangulated through the evaluation of teachers, students, and other museum partners. Through this approach, the effectiveness of the program was measured for all intended audiences.

The program breaks new ground in museum educational programming by combining classroom pedagogy that is based in educational research with an ex-

---

[1]Email: rachel.connolly@louisville.edu

periential "journey" to the Moon in the immersive environment of a planetarium dome. Today's children are sophisticated in their understanding and consumption of digital media through video games, movies and television. Leveraging their comfort with visual technology, A Field Trip to the Moon takes them on a memorable journey to the Moon using cutting-edge scientific visualization techniques.

1.1.   Program Overview

The Field Trip to the Moon program consists of an introduction, where students are informed that they have been selected to be astronauts for NASA next mission to the Moon, they then watch a brief 'pre-show' video on a flat screen that provides historical context for human exploration of the Moon. Following the pre-show, they enter the Dome where they are guided on a 'virtual journey' to the Moon by a live 'mission commander'. Upon leaving the Dome, having just 'landed on the Moon', the students participate in a workshop experience where they break up into teams to conduct a series of investigations of how best to set up a viable lunar colony (the teams included medical, life science, engineering, navigation, habitat, and geology).

1.2.   Uniview and FTM

Uniview is an interactive real-time graphics software package that was developed through a series of graduate internships at AMNH to visualized data across the entire scale range of the universe with seamless magnification, radial, traversal, and rotational examination control. The purpose of Uniview is to display the AMNH Digital Universe database, a collection of many academically published astronomical catalogs of objects with distance information. The Swedish company SCISS, AB was founded by former AMNH intern programmers who wrote Uniview, which is now available as a product. Recent authoring tools were developed by SCISS for Uniview in order to produce FTM from AMNH specifications. Scripting of flight paths and event keying to time line allowed production versioning and segment review before final recording of frames to master final product as a movie.

The flexibility of Uniview was crucial to integrating the evaluation into the production process of FTM. In the formative stages it allowed the production team to fly "live" through the Earth-Moon system and gather feedback and questions from representative student groups. In the production stage, it enabled the modification of flight paths based on feedback received during pilot sessions.

2.   Evaluation

2.1.   Purpose

These studies served both as a formative needs-assessment to guide the development of the program, as well as a summative measure of its success. It also yields a characterization of the elements of successful education and public outreach programs that can be used by NASA to focus its resource development on those areas of greatest effectiveness and fully leverage their technological assets to match the needs and interests of the educational community.

2.2.   Overarching Methodology

In order to evaluate the program effects and measure outcomes, we utilized a mixed-methods approach. We included quantitative and qualitative instruments and audio and video techniques in our data gathering. Almost every pilot workshop was videotaped and reviewed by museum educators and evaluators for evidence of higher-order thinking and collaborative team discussions, two particular goals for the workshop experience. A strong evaluation of an educational program seeks to triangulate results and confirm that the findings are valid for all invested audience members, in this case students, classroom teachers, and museum educators. We triangulated our results by evaluating FTM with all three audiences invested in the program: middle school students (section 3), teachers (section 4), and other museums and science centers (section 5). What follows are the narratives and results of each of these three evaluation components.

2.3.   Initial Development

An evaluation feedback loop was integrated into the program design and development process by having educational researchers observe every pilot workshop. The observers conferred with museum educators immediately following the pilot workshop to determine any recommended adjustments to the program. Changes were then implemented into the next pilot workshop, and results immediately assessed in subsequent follow-up discussions. This created a constantly evolving program that could be evaluated in real-time, as well as a low-risk environment for museum educators to make adjustments to the program that increased the chance for program success with each pilot group. The museum educators presenting the workshops and the observers also provided ongoing feedback the guided the development of the visualizations and script elements that comprised the Dome program that accompanies the workshop.

3.   Evaluation with Middle School Students

3.1.   Participants

We sought to pilot test the complete workshop with middle school students from grades 5 though 8. In order to establish a good sample, at least one student group from each of these 4 grade levels was selected for a total involvement of 270 students. Also included in the pilot groups are a bilingual class of English Language Learners (ELL) and a Spanish-speaking class. For these classes, we delivered the entire program in Spanish by a fluent museum educator.

Pilot classes were identified from a range of schools, including our local NASA Explorer School, as well as a selection of middle schools located throughout New York City. Pilot workshops in November and December were offered for school groups with teachers who had attended the Election Day FTM program (see section 4) and had expressed an interest in bringing their class to the museum for the program.

3.2.   Methodology

Once a pilot workshop was scheduled, the classroom teachers were sent a letter of preparation. The workshop component of each pilot session was observed by a minimum of one educational researcher. The classroom teacher was informally interviewed during the course of the workshop session in order to get their initial feedback on the success of the program with their class. Following the completion of the workshop, all classroom teachers were emailed a letter and written survey.

3.3. Results

There was a 50% response rate for the Pilot Teacher Survey (see Appendix A for selected responses). All responses were analyzed for patterns and are summarized in the following findings:

Finding 1: Success of program does not appear to hinge on pre-program preparation of students. Almost every teacher who responded is new to teaching, and their success with this program supports the finding that this is a good program for newer teachers who might not be familiar with field trips. It can also be a good choice for a very busy teacher with little flexibility to fit pre-program lessons and/or activities into their curriculum.

Finding 2: The outcome of the program experience for the classroom teacher was that the workshop served to model a new way of teaching for them that utilized the team groupings and collaborative discussions. Teachers mentioned during the workshops that they had never had a chance to observe their own class "in action," and that they saw many of their students in a new light. They found out new things about their students as the listened to the team discussions, and many of them were excited to try this model of lab or workshop again back in their own classrooms.

Finding 3: The FTM program experience sparked many questions in the students, and the discussions continued back in their classrooms. For this reason, it is important to give the classroom teachers techniques and follow-up resources so they can build upon the momentum and experience. The survey responses supplied some resources that the teachers would like to have, including handouts, interactive websites, specific museum exhibits, follow-up lesson plans of enrichment activities, and some websites with background information. Upon the completion of the Field Trip to the Moon program, a website has been launched to meet this need at www.amnh.org/ftm.

4. Evaluation with Classroom Teachers

A middle school class does not go on a field trip to a museum that includes a workshop experience unless the teacher decides to take them. Often, this decision rests on how closely the field trip or program reflects and supports the science standards and curriculum that the teacher needs to teach. The developers of the FTM program referenced all relevant Science Education Standards (national, state and city) throughout the development process, for both the Dome program and the workshop. We hypothesized that this strong alignment would increase the ability for a teacher to justify bringing their students to the program and therefore expand our audience base.

4.1. Participants

Every election day AMNH offers a Professional Development Day to provide educators at all levels with opportunities to deepen content knowledge in different areas of science and social studies. In order to test the success of this program in supporting and interesting science teachers to use the program with their class, FTM was field tested with a group of nearly 200 K-12 science teachers during an all-day professional development program on Election Day, November 7, 2006. The FTM program served as the core activity during this professional development program.

4.2. Methodology

An outline of the Election Day FTM agenda and evaluation methods utilized follows:

1. As the teachers arrived for the program, they selected one of the six teams from the workshop portion of the program as their focus: medical, life science, engineering, navigation, habitat, and geology.

2. We began the program by explaining to all participants that they were going to be testing and evaluating a new program that the museum had developed. We asked that they keep this in mind throughout the day, and at the end of the program they would be asked to complete a survey (See Appendix A) to provide feedback on the program.

3. The program introduction and dome program, guided by a live presenter, were delivered to the entire group of teachers.

4. At the completion of the dome program, teachers divided into their teams, with about 30 teachers in a team.

5. Each team went to a museum classroom for their team's activity and discussion.

4.3. Results

What follows in Table 1 are the results for each component of the Election Day program. Total respondents to Election Day survey, N = 168.

Score is on a scale from 1 to 4, with:
1 = Very interesting and connected to my teaching
4 = Not interesting or connected to my teaching

4.4. Selections from open-ended answers

What follows are the open-ended questions and a selection of the answers:

1. How would this program support what you teach?

- It will help to bring current "real world" space science into the classroom, and get students more engaged in planetary science.

- Excellent motivation tool.

Table 1.   Pilot Workshops

	Habitat	Engin-eering	Medical	Naviga-tion	Life Science	Geology	Overall
Pre-show	1.59	2.46	2.0	1.71	2.14	1.7	1.94
Dome Presentation	1.31	1.6	1.56	1.21	1.29	1.26	1.37
Team Activity	1.6	1.84	2.09	2.0	1.81	1.58	1.82
Hall Exploration	2.03	1.63	2.06	1.85	1.65	1.58	1.8
Resource Packet	1.48	1.86	1.92	1.64	1.7	1.59	1.7
Additional Resources	1.34	1.61	1.6	1.45	1.14	1.56	1.45

- Supports my earth science curriculum and brings the curriculum to life.

- It would create a connection from class discussion to a visual experience.

- I like the way this program connects many disciplines via a topic that interests many middle school students, SPACE.

- It will assist my effort to always keep science current and infused with new scientific findings.

- Presents an opportunity for students to connect learning to resources outside the classroom.

- It was a well-put-together, fabulous visual. Loved it! Interesting and Educational.

- I believe it would "spark" student interest.

- It provides the visual simulation that can't be received in the classroom.

- Excellent eye-opening demonstration of lunar travel and how it ties in to so many areas of science.

2. Would you bring your students to see Field Trip to the Moon if it were offered on Tuesdays at 10:30 AM from January to May? Why?

127	YES
13	NO
6	Maybe
22	Didn't respond

4.5.   Analysis of Teacher Responses

Data and feedback from teachers was analyzed for patterns. Key findings follow:

Finding 1: The majority of teachers mentioned how the program "supports" or "connects" with their curriculum, often mentioning specific units or topics that they cover. This confirms our initial hypothesis that for a field trip program to be successful in drawing school groups and their teachers, it needs to specifically link to concepts that the teachers address in their curricula. This means that museums utilizing the FTM program will need to "localize" – which involves aligning their workshop activities with the needs of the regional science standards and curricula. One approach that AMNH has found successful is to convene a working group of classroom and museum educators, distribute copies of applicable Science standards along with the FTM workshop write-up, and discuss strong connections that already exist as well as new ones that can be developed.

Finding 2: The majority of teachers who viewed the FTM program desired to bring their students to the Museum for the program. Almost all "NO" responses were related to operational difficulties. Reasons offered included: cannot go on field trips (school doesn't allow them), cannot get to museum that early, it doesn't fit into their curriculum (see finding 1), they have autistic student's who cannot be in the dark of the planetarium, they are not a classroom teacher and do not have a class to bring.

Finding 3: The highlight of the program for them was the virtual journey experience in the dome. They felt that it helped to make some concepts visual and understandable that can traditionally be difficult for their students to grasp, including the scale of the Earth-Moon system and the magnetosphere.

5. Evaluation with Informal Educators

A representative sample of interested museum and planetarium educators were invited to review and comment on the FTM workshop. Once a working draft of the workshop portion of the program was available, it was posted at a publicly available url on the Museum's website. A letter of invitation that included this link was sent to each pilot institution. The survey instrument was developed using Surveymonkey.com and the link to it was included with invitation and the draft of the workshop.

Appendix: Selected Results from Classroom Teachers

Each survey question is followed by selected, representative responses from classroom teachers who responded.

1. Was there a specific curriculum need you hoped that the Field Trip to the Moon program would meet?

- There was not a specific curriculum needed to be met. We were studying the moon and its atmosphere as well as the magnetic fields. The Field Trip to the Moon helped me, and my students make connections, relate and build upon their prior knowledge from our lessons about space, the Moon, the atmosphere, and the magnetic field. The program solidified the lesson taught and it gave them hands-on experience from which they can now build upon and ad to their experiences. These concepts of atmosphere, the moon, and the magnetic fields, is being thought in 6th, 7th, and 8th. Also, the magnetic field of the Earth, And the Ocean floor.

- I was more interested in motivating my students. Up until the time we did the FT to the Moon I had been drilling my kids with a fast-paced regents curriculum and without much hands on. Since the FTTTM, we've been having richer discussions.

- This program was a great introduction to astronomy, a unit our seventh grade Earth Science students will be studying in June. Since the trip they have generated many thought provoking questions about moon exploration.

2. Did you or your students do anything special to prepare for this experience (curriculum, projects, activities, etc.)?

- Yes, when I went to the workshop Trip to the Moon directed to teachers, I looked for a way to connect that experience with the concepts that I was currently teaching. I made connections to the atmosphere and the possibility to live on the Moon, and also we were working with parts of the Moon and dark spots. Also we were working with the Earth as a big magnet and the magnetic field, as well the ocean floor, and its ecosystem. I devised an entire lesson as a preview to what they would experience during the field trip to the museum.

- No, we didn't have time because it was last minute.

3. Did you or your students do anything special to follow-up or continue this experience after your field trip?

- Yes, I had a writing follow-up assignment in which the students were asked to write about their experience, how they felt about working with other students from another school in relating the material with each other, what they learned and what inquiries they now have about the moon, the atmosphere, the magnetic fields, and the ocean floor.

- We had a great discussion directly after the field trip when we got back to school.

- Yes. Students wrote reflections about their experience at the museum. Other than that, it mainly provided enrichment for our study of the solar system.

- Student work has been posted in the room, and we have followed up the trip with many student-led discussions about the experience. We will continue with this topic later in the semester.

4. a) Do you notice any changes in your students (academically, behaviorally, personally) as a result of this experience? b) If yes, how do these changes impact your classroom (short/long term)?

a) Yes, from a personal perspective I feel that some of them now know that in the museum they can find valuable information to answer any type of question. This is a change that will help them personally and academically as well.

b) Most of them want to behave better to be considered for future trips. They know how to use their experiences and put it in writing. They are able to participate in making oral presentations. As I had answered earlier any exposure to different kinds of social events like, museum exhibits, fields trips, etc, can really help them in their personal development and growth as well as academically.

a) During the group activities I noticed one student participating more than he had at school. I'm so happy to report he has continued to participate more, and I believe it is in part due to the field trip!

b) Having a student more engaged can positively affect other students' engagement during lessons. The student who has participated more after the field trip has influenced another student at his table to work more diligently during class. Additionally, my other classes who weren't able to attend have been asking about when they'll get to go, too.

5. What was your favorite part of the program (activities, being in the museum, the planetarium show, etc.)? What do you think your students liked the most?

- Overall, the experience was excellent. The experience in the planetarium was unique. My students expressed the same. Participation in the classroom was great. My students had the chance to participate in cooperative leaning activities with others students from another school, under the same language acquisition (Spanish-English) conditions.

- My favorite part of the program was the groupwork. I enjoy visiting groups of students working, asking them questions and watching them work. Since this experience, I've actually done more similar groupwork in my classroom. I recently set up a lab with seven different stations. I think my students were more prepared to work at each station after having the initial experience at the museum. It's hard to tell what my students liked the most. Some of them loved the planetarium experience, others thought it was cheesy. They're hard to know and they're opinion often depends on that of their friend's.

- I think the students really liked the show and the hands-on experience of opening the boxes and solving the problem presented. Each class that I took really liked the medical team and the team who had to solve the landing site/cargo in the shuttle.

- I enjoyed the workshop itself in which students led their own discoveries of the moon. I believe students enjoyed the planterium, which was a first for many as well as learning information from their peers in the workshop setting.

6. What would make it easier for you to support this experience (any kind of handouts, museum activities, websites, etc.)?

- Handouts are always great, and a specific exhibit/activity we could attend on our own (after the planetarium show and moon colonization activities) would really allow us to take full advantage of a day at the museum.

- I think this experience would work well nestled into the Sun-Earth-Moon system unit. A current events article about NASA's plans to build a space station on the moon also might help make the experience more relevant.

Acknowledgments. We would like to thank Jerry Hartman and Paula Rodney from NASA for their strong collaborative participation in the development of the Field Trip to the Moon program. We also want to acknowledge the important contributions of the following individuals who made important contributions to the development of all elements of the Field Trip to the Moon program: museum educators Suzanne Morris, Zohar Ris, Minna Palaquibay, and Ryan Wyatt; members of the Museum's production and educational materials group: Michael Hoffman, Monica Philippo, Armistead Booker, and Karen Taber; educational consultant to the Museum Chris Economous, and, members of the museum's Rose Center Engineering group: Benjy Bernhardt, Russ Baird and Loretta Skeddle.

EPO and a Changing World
ASP Conference Series, Vol. 389, © *2008*
C. Garmany, M. Gibbs, and J. W. Moody

Family Astronomy: Improving Practices and Developing New Approaches

Jacob Noel-Storr

Rochester Institute of Technology, Center for Imaging Science, 54 Lomb Memorial Drive, Rochester, NY 14623, USA

Emilie Drobnes

ADNET and Heliophysics Science Division, NASA Goddard Space Flight Center, Code 671, Greenbelt, MD 20771, USA

Sara E. Mitchell

SP Systems and Astrophysics Science Division, NASA Goddard Space Flight Center, Code 661, Greenbelt, MD 20771, USA

Abstract. We present effective strategies for family astronomy programs based on the experiences in recent years developing programs around four key elements: child and parent engagement in the process of science; family cohesiveness and cooperation; parent "professional development"; and continuity of learning beyond the programs we create. We present strategies developed by workshop attendees to implement or improve family programs that can be facilitated in a variety of settings, with an emphasis on creativity and innovation to push the field forwards. We discuss the design of evaluation tools and education research questions centered on family learning that will ensure the value that family astronomy programs add to Science, Technology, Engineering and Mathematics (STEM) education in a range of communities is increased and better understood.

1. Introduction

It has been demonstrated that parent involvement in a child's education has positive results in school performance, such as better attendance and higher scores on standardized tests (Henderson & Mapp 2002). This holds true for families of different cultural and income levels, as well as across male and female students (Bogenschneider 1997). Research-based best practices in involving families in out-of-school time activities include: providing family supports; focusing on family assets; and developing family-focused program facilitation (e.g., Kakli et al. 2006).

By involving whole family groups it is also possible to tackle motivational issues and barriers to participation in informal science and out-of-school time programs for groups who do not usually participate in such events (Shartrand 1996; Huebner & Mancini 2003; Little & Lauver 2005).

In this paper we present the results of our work and discussions on the important issues in family learning that are essential elements for developing the richest possible experiences for all members of the family groups that participate. Initial evaluations of the experiences of different age groups at astronomy related events conducted by Noel-Storr (2002) found that family members of different ages had vastly different experiences, often outside of expectations. Stemming from the results of that investigation we have paid deep consideration to the experiences of every member of a whole range of family groups, and the experience of each family group as a whole (though small) learning community. In §2 we discuss guiding principles and goals for family learning; in §3 we describe key questions important to the development of family programs; in §4 we present examples of family programs from the field. In §5 we explain a program evaluation strategy and we draw our conclusions in §6.

2. Guiding Principles and Goals for Family Learning

We have distilled four central guiding principles for the development of family science programs, based on experiences in program development and on evaluation and feedback from program participants and facilitators. The four principles are:

- Child and parent engagement in the process of science

- Family cohesiveness and cooperation

- Parent "professional development"

- Continuity beyond the family workshops

Using these principles it is possible to design programs that bring children and parents together as learning communities that the parents are trained to support beyond the "class time" of each particular programs. These programs are sufficiently engaging that the families involved continue to seek out science learning opportunities beyond the hosted events, both in organized formal and/or informal settings, and truly informally as experiences crop up in their everyday lives.

As a result of family programs it is important for families to develop their attitudes and behaviors such that they go on to: engage in science related discussions "around the dinner table"; appreciate the connections and common themes between the sciences; take part in a range of science learning opportunities together; develop a positive attitude to science and science learning at all levels; and develop new perspectives on the ways in which they can spend time together, with an emphasis on science rich activities.

Further, we have identified value in giving parents the educational tools they need so that they can support their children as questioning, inquiring scientists and allow them to develop a lasting rapport with scientists and science educators. The children who participate must feel empowered to have science discussions with their parents and family groups and be encouraged to share their experiences with their peers, siblings and classes – through which means the impact of every event is broadened.

3. Key Development Questions

As a result of the evaluation of programs run by Noel-Storr in Southern Arizona (Noel-Storr 2006, and §5.1 below) and by Drobnes and Mitchell in Maryland (Mitchell, Drobnes, & Noel-Storr, 2007, and §5.2 below) we have developed a set of key development questions for consideration by teams who propose or plan family science programs.

- How can we attract a range of family groups? (we see many one-parent, one-child groups)

- What long term attitude and behavior changes are initiated by participation in this type of event? What gains should we realistically hope to see?

- How can we develop "continuity events" that are well attended by the same families but are in different locations / contexts / etc...?

- We have success with this model for 7 - 12 year olds, what lead-in and -out strategies can we develop for families with younger or older kids?

- How do we attract families that are not already frequently engaging in science / learning activities as a family group?

These issues were discussed during the interactive workshop at the 2007 Annual Meeting of the Astronomical Society of the Pacific to which this paper relates, though as an outcome of the discussion it was clear that these remain critical issues in the field which should be considered in depth during the development of new programs. In that way it will be possible to develop strategies that treat the family as a whole, rather than just targeting individual children in a particular age bracket within family groups, while the rest of the family members sit and passively regard what is going on.

4. Examples from the Field

We present two examples below of astronomy centered family science programs that the authors have been the developers of in the past. The first— "Families of Scientists Discovering the Universe"— was a program developed by Noel-Storr in collaboration with the Ventana Vista Elementary School in Tucson, Arizona; the second— "NASA Family Science Night"— was a program developed by Drobnes and Mitchell and run at NASA's Goddard Space Flight Center (GSFC) Visitor Center in Greenbelt, MD.

4.1. Families of Scientists Discovering the Universe

In 2005 and 2006 three sequences of family programs were offered to families at the Ventana Vista Elementary School in Tucson, Arizona. Each sequence was themed around an astronomical topic ("Moons", "Mars", and "Discovering New Worlds") which were then broken into four 2-hour long monthly workshops, each of which was based on a central science theme underlying the topic (Physics,

Chemistry, Biology, and Earth Science). The choice to connect to specific sciences was made to allow parents to more easily see the connections beyond the engaging astronomical theme into more "down-to-earth" sciences that parents and children alike will recognize later in school.

Each event accommodated 8 or 9 families (or 20 people), and was co-facilitated by an astronomer (Noel-Storr) and the school librarian / science resource coordinator. The content was primarily designed for 7-12 year olds, but had extension activities for older or more advanced children, and activities which could be easily simplified and supported by parents for younger family members. A key component of each event was to offer "parent professional development" to the adults to train them, much as we would do when working with teachers, to support inquiry, to develop questioning behaviors, to recognize and utilize teachable moments, and to develop their family into a science learning community.

Over 80% of the families returned to each workshop during each sequence, thanks in large part to the connection felt with the school (and in particular the efforts of the librarian to strengthen those connections). In this way it was possible to deliver a rich program of activities building on each other through the sequences, rather than a set of disparate activities that could "stand alone"; this was particularly important for the parent professional development components of the program which was able to introduce parents to different best practices in science education each month, allowing them to grow a more complete skill set to use with their children in supporting learning.

4.2. NASA Family Science Night

The FSN pilot program, hosted nearly each month of the 2006-2007 school year at the GSFC Visitor Center, inspires discovery and instigates enthusiasm in the wide variety of science and engineering research conducted at GSFC. During two hours of hands-on activities and discussions, NASA education and outreach professionals, scientists, and engineers work with local middle school students and their families as they explore various science, technology, engineering, and mathematics (STEM) themes.

Each event accommodates 15 families (or 50 people). The content is developed for middle school students and their families. The activities are geared toward children in the 7th and 8th grades (12-14 years old), though participating family members range from 4th graders to grandparents. Family members that are younger than 10 years old participate in separate activities better tailored to their age group.

Each two-hour event consists of a series of activities led by NASA GSFC education and outreach professionals, with the assistance of volunteer scientists and engineers who serve as "resident experts" throughout the night. We are showcasing the wide variety of science and engineering research conducted at GSFC to raise awareness of the importance of STEM-related topics in our everyday lives. Topics covered in previous FSNs have included:

"How Big? How Far? How Old?" (size and scale of the Universe)

"Tis the Seasons" (movement of the Earth, reasons for the seasons)

"Batteries Not Included" (building a solar car, circuitry and engineering)

"Living in the Atmosphere of the Sun" (solar activity, space weather)

The entire FSN program is developed around NASA Science Mission Directorate science and engineering, more specifically the Heliophysics Science Division and Astrophysics Science Division objectives and missions. Care is taken to utilize existing materials and resources already developed by the education and outreach community in collaboration with the scientific and engineering community, rather than the development of all new materials. Some adaptations are being made in order to ensure that activities are using current educational pedagogy and current NASA content and results whenever possible.

Anatomy of a Family Science Night Each FSN event explores a single topic or theme in depth, through a variety of methods. The evening begins with an opening discussion, to introduce the concept and engage the families. Each event explores a topic through discussions and activities – demonstrations, building challenges, kinesthetic activities, experiments, modeling, etc. Events build upon the existing knowledge and interest of participants, incorporating familiar concepts along with new ideas and skills. Each evening concludes with a group discussion about the main concepts and conclusions of the evening. Families are encouraged to continue learning outside of the event, and receive materials and information on extended activities to pursue at home.

During the "Tis the Seasons" event, held in December 2006, families learned about the movements of the Earth and the reasons for the seasons. Families were divided into two groups for the main portion of the evening – one group explored the scale of the Earth and Sun and the relationship between temperature and distance, and the other group did a kinesthetic activity about the tilt, rotation, and orbit of the Earth with relation to the seasons. The groups switched at the middle of the event.

4.3.   Preliminary pilot program data

The pilot events have proved extremely popular and are filled to capacity every month. The public interest far exceeds the program's capacity – for the first event, over 200 people responded to the announcement. Advertising for the pilot events has been placed in GSFC educator electronic mailing lists and the Visitor Center, but local schools and community calendars have also publicized the program.

Since its inception, 27 families (over 100 total participants) have participated in FSN events, with many returning attendees. Of the families attending one event, approximately 50% also attend the next event. Families that attend two consecutive FSN events generally attend all subsequent events. If they were unable to return, it was reported to be due to circumstances largely beyond their control. We held phone interviews with participants who did not return. Results show that most families were unable to attend for reasons not related to the nature of the event (relocation, family emergencies, changes in schedule, etc.). The interviewed participants consider FSN a very useful event in their children's learning process and expressed interest in learning science as a family.

The program has been so popular that we have been approached by a number of internal and local organizations to discuss expansion to fulfill the current need and enthusiasm for such programs.

5.   Evaluation of Programs (and of the Evaluations)

We have developed and are in the process of reviewing and refining a series of evaluation tools to use to determine the outcomes of family programs. A key goal of our evaluation program is to establish which strategies encourage families to engage in science beyond the experiences that we facilitate. By following families from month-to-month we are able to track what they did in the period between workshops, and what they plan to do in the future as a family to learn science.

Our evaluation strategy is centered on post-workshop surveys given to each adult and child participant. These data are complemented by observations of what the participants and facilitators do during each workshop, and by follow up phone interviews with the parents and focus groups with the child participants.

Our surveys are designed around several organizing themes to help us better understand the effects of what we do in each workshop. Below, we give examples of the types of question in each category. "Family" refers to questions we ask the whole family on a survey at the start of the workshop when they arrive; "Adult" to the adult participants at the end of each workshop; and likewise for "Child".

Participation in the event:

(Family) Do you have other family members that did not join you tonight?

(Adult) How likely are you to come to another event?

(Adult) How likely would you be to recommend this event to others?

(Child) What would you have been doing tonight if you weren't here?

Engagement in science:

(Adult) What did you like most about the event?

(Adult) How can we make the next event even better?

(Adult) Can you tell us something new that you learned tonight?

(Child) How much did you like this event?

(Child) Is there something you would have preferred to be doing tonight?

(Child) Can you write something new that you learned tonight?

Continuity beyond the event:

(Family) Have you done any science activities or visits as a family in the last month?

(Family) Do you have any science equipment in your home?

(Adult) What 'science things' do you plan to do as a family over the next month?

(Child) Are there any sciencey things that you hope your family will do before the next Family Science Night?

By working with groups of families that we see from month-to-month we are also able to tie together responses from questions such as "What 'science things' do you plan to do as a family over the next month?" to responses the following month to the question "Have you done any science activities or visits as a family in the last month?". This allows us to track the extent to which our programs motivate families to go out and "do" more science, and how well we are able to inspire them to actually follow through.

We have defined a set of measures of success that we hope to meet in our programs that we measure through our evaluation strategies:

- 100% of Families observed to describe at least one element related to their everyday life during the workshops

- 80% of the family members are observed to be engaged in the activities more than 50% of the time during the workshop

- 90% of the participants are able to state something new that they learned at the conclusion of the workshop

- 75% of Families report in follow up interviews and surveys that they have completed follow up activities as a family

- 90% of the families work together as family groups for at least some part of each workshop

- 70% of the families report that they engaged in a science activity following the workshop they attended, as a result of attending the workshop

Paying attention to this type of evaluation strategy, and having clearly defined measures of success, programs can be developed that provide richer experiences for whole family groups, as well as for each individual family member within the group.

6. Conclusions

Family programs can work as a powerful tool to support the STEM pipeline, by encouraging families to act as learning communities that are supportive of STEM education and STEM careers. Programs are more effective when they take into account the different experiences of all members of a family group and encourage and support those individuals to work together as effective groups of learners.

Key questions remain regarding the most effective strategies to involve every member of each family in every family event. Programs that pay attention to such questions in their development and have a carefully designed program of evaluation reflecting the program goals for each family member allow for richer experiences for every individual, and every family group.

References

Bogenschneider, K., "Parental Involvement in Adolescent Schooling: A Proximal Process with Transcontextual Validity", Journal of Marriage and the Family, **59** 718-733 (1997)

Henderson, A. T. and Mapp K. L., "A New Wave of Evidence: The Impact of School, Family and Community Connections on Student Achievement", (National Center for Family & Community Connections with Schools, Austin, TX, 2002)

Huebner, A. J. and Mancini, J. A., "Shaping Structured Out-of-School Time Use Among Youth: The Effects of Self, Family, and Friend Systems", Journal of Youth and Adolescence, **32** 453-463 (2003)

Kakli, Z., Kreider, P. L., Buck, T. and Coffey, M, "Focus on Families! How to Build and Support Family-Centered Practices in After School", Harvard Family Research Project (2006). Available from www.gse.harvard.edu/hfrp/projects/afterschool/resources/families

Little, P. M. D. and Lauver, S., "Engaging Adolescents in Out-of-School Time Programs: Learning What Works", The Prevention Researcher, **12** 7-10 (2005)

Mitchell, S., Drobnes, E., Colina-Trujillo, M.S., Noel-Storr, J., "Family Science Night: Changing Perceptions One Family at a Time" Advances in Space Research (submitted 2007)

Noel-Storr, J., "Effectively Engaging Family Groups in Learning Astronomy", Amer. Astron. Soc. 209th Meeting: Abstract #94.13, Bulletin of the American Astronomical Society (American Astronomical Society, Washington, D.C., 2006)

Noel-Storr, J., "The Generation Gap: Experiences of Various Age Groups at Outreach Events", American Astronomical Society, 201st AAS Meeting, #28.04; Bulletin of the American Astronomical Society, **34**, p.1149 (2002)

Shartrand, A, 1996, "Supporting Latino Families: Lessons from Exemplary Programs," Harvard Family Research Project (1996). Available from: http://www.gse.harvard.edu/hfrp/pubs/pubsbyauthor.html

EPO and a Changing World
ASP Conference Series, Vol. 389, © *2008*
C. Garmany, M. Gibbs, and J. W. Moody

Designing and Teaching to the Standards, and Beyond!

Greg Schultz

*UC Berkeley, Space Sciences Lab, MC 7450, Berkeley, CA 94720-7450,
USA*

Alan Gould, John Erickson, Jennifer King Chen, and Traci Wierman

UC Berkeley, Lawrence Hall of Science, Berkeley, CA 94720-5200, USA

Abstract. This professional development (PD) session brought together participants interested in space science curriculum and teacher PD, and fostered learning and discussion around EPO strategies for designing resources targeted at science standards and, when appropriate, teaching beyond such standards. We used the case example of the new GEMS *Space Science Sequences* (GEMS-SSS) for grades 3-5 and 6-8, and emphasized how others can adopt and adapt strategies for implementation with their own products and programs. The session presenters represent diverse backgrounds in astronomy research, curriculum development, teacher PD, NASA EPO, science writing, and planetarium/science center programs. We outlined the design process employed in the development of the GEMS-SSS, beginning with analysis of space science concepts and scientific inquiry strategies appearing in the national standards/benchmarks and dozens of state standards documents. Then a panel of ten NASA science/education advisors convened to make further recommendations for the GEMS-SSS. This panel strongly urged the inclusion in the 6-8 sequence of content related to objects and structure outside of our solar system, even though this content is rarely found earlier than high school in most standards documents. From the advisory panel's recommendation, and a desire to feature more current scientific discovery, a "Beyond the Solar System" unit was developed and field-tested in middle school classrooms. These results were shared with workshop participants. Our session included interactive activities illustrating teaching both to the standards and beyond them, and featured group discussion of the power of this approach in different contexts – ours and participants'.

Session Outcomes

Participants came away with greater understanding and appreciation of strategies for (1) addressing standards in elementary/middle school science curriculum, (2) going beyond such standards when appropriate (including why and how), (3) capturing current scientific discovery within a structured curriculum, and (4) collaborative, iterative design involving scientists, educators, and NASA.

1. Introduction and Overview

This manuscript is an attempt to best capture and summarize the presentation and discussion that ensued during our 60-minute Interactive Workshop on

September 7, 2007, at the Astronomical Society of the Pacific (ASP) conference in Chicago. There were essentially four parts to the workshop session: (a) a short opening activity/demonstration, an interactive "human orrery", to illustrate a classroom activity based on fundamental standards in space science education (i.e. scale and motions in the solar system); (b) a series of "two-minute" descriptions from each of the five workshop presenters, conveying each of their perspectives and roles in the design and teaching of a new space science curriculum; (c) another hands-on activity, this one a transit/planet-finding activity based first on core standards (more on scale and motions in space), but also addressing an exciting new area of astronomical discovery, extrasolar planets; and finally (d) a closing interactive discussion with workshop participants, gathering and capturing their insights and experiences with designing and teaching to the standards and beyond. The sections that follow in this paper describe these four workshop components, including both hands-on activities, the descriptive statements from each presenter, and a summary of the input and feedback from participants during the closing discussion.

2.   The "Human Orrery" Activity in Brief

We opened the session with a quick interactive demonstration of a modeling activity strongly rooted in standards-based ideas: "The Human Orrery." Note that an orrery is a mechanical model of the solar system that illustrates the relative motions and positions of bodies in the solar system. In our workshop, participants and presenters worked together, like students would do with their teacher's guidance, to create a human-powered orrery to model the movements of the inner planets.

This "human orrery" is a model of the solar system in which students act out the model and set it in motion. Students measure out orbits for the inner solar system (Sun, Mercury, Venus, Earth, and Mars), and place "footstep" markers along the orbits, to indicate the position of each planet in 2-week intervals. Students take turns in teams of four to "walk the model", setting the planets in motion, and seeing vividly how the speeds of the planets in their orbits depend on distance from the Sun.

In the interest of time for the workshop, we set up the markers in advance, concentrated on the three inner planets only, and quickly debriefed the activity's goals and purposes for participants. Standards-based key concepts that are addressed in this classroom activity are: (a) planets closer to the Sun have smaller orbits and move more quickly than planets farther from the Sun; (b) objects in the solar system are in regular and predictable motion; and (c) as seen from Earth, the positions of the planets and the Sun are always changing.

3.   Perspectives and Roles of Each Workshop Presenter in a Collaborative Curriculum Project

3.1.   Greg Schultz

Our group has been collectively involved in the development of a brand new space science curriculum project designed for teaching to the standards and beyond, in grades 3-8: the GEMS *Space Science Sequences* (GEMS-SSS). More details on this curriculum, its design, its testing, and its implementation will be described in sections that follow from the other presenters. GEMS stands for Great Explorations in Math and Science (http://www.lhsgems.org/), and it is an award-winning curriculum and teacher professional development program of the Lawrence Hall of Science (LHS), the public science education center at the University of California, Berkeley (UCB). I am a collaborating scientist based just up the road from LHS, at the Center for Science Education at UCB's Space Science Laboratory (CSE@SSL; http://cse.ssl.berkeley.edu/).

At the outset, I should highlight the very favorable review and commentary on GEMS-SSS from George "Pinky" Nelson in his keynote presentation at this ASP 2007 EPO conference. Pinky's opening slides included commendation for myself and our CSE@SSL director, Isabel Hawkins, in making the wise decision to use NASA EPO funds to partner with LHS in the development of a core science curriculum project such as the GEMS *Space Science Sequences*. He, like our GEMS-SSS team, sees this product as an example of the needed development of "3rd generation" instructional materials, which are cognitive research-based and provide explicit support for teachers with assessment and other pedagogical strategies (Nelson 2006).

I have been involved in the GEMS-SSS as the scientist on the lead development team, and this has been made possible through the NASA Sun-Earth Connection Education Forum (SECEF), for which I am an Education/Outreach Scientist and Teacher Educator. NASA EPO partners, including SECEF, the Kepler and IBEX missions, and the Origins and Solar System Exploration Forums, have contributed funding, science advice, text and graphics contributions, and review feedback to the *Space Science Sequences* development.

The idea for the GEMS-SSS grew from some precipitating activities, including the prior collaborative development of GEMS space science teacher's guides such as *The Real Reasons for Seasons* and *Living with a Star*. When a 2003 NASA external task force report reviewed the NASA/OSS (Office of Space Science) EPO Support Network and its programs, and their first recommendation called for more accessible and coherent K-12 instructional materials (NASA 2003), this spurred us to come together to discuss the development of a coherent curriculum in space science for grades 3-8. Subsequent early work involved the detailed analysis and "deconstruction" of fundamental space science concepts and science inquiry strategies found in standards and benchmarks documents at national and state levels. After focusing on what the real core concepts are that most need to be addressed, we decided to prioritize these as ideas that students should gain "enduring understandings" of (inspired by Wiggins & McTighe 1998).

We soon thereafter convened a meeting of ten NASA science advisors to the *Space Science Sequences*, and this panel unanimously urged the inclusion in the 6th-8th grade sequence of content related to objects and structure beyond the solar system. They reasoned that it was impossible to portray the breadth of space science, its currency, or the vastness of this formidable frontier without inclusion of content related to the Universe. Based on the strength of their recommendation, we decided to include this content, in spite of the fact that, at this time, very few states include standards related to content other than our own solar system at the pre-high school level. From successful field test results, it is anticipated that this component will be welcomed by educators because of high student interest and may well be on the cutting edge of standards in the future.

3.2. Alan Gould

LHS and the SETI Institute (with Edna DeVore and Pamela Harman) are the Co-Leads for EPO for NASA's Kepler mission. For formal education, we have always tried to help channel NASA EPO funds into projects and products that best serve the real needs of classroom teachers. In the past, LHS-GEMS worked with NASA-SECEF to identify the subject of seasons as a teaching topic in much need of improvement nationally. This resulted in *The Real Reasons for Seasons* GEMS teacher guide, rather than a guide narrowly focused on NASA Sun-Earth missions. Later, GEMS worked with the Swift mission EPO team (led by Lynn Cominsky) to produce the *Invisible Universe* GEMS teacher guide, focusing on general understanding of the electromagnetic spectrum, rather than something narrowly focused on gamma ray astronomy and the Swift mission alone.

Rather than use Kepler EPO funds to create a product that only describes the science of the Kepler mission, we decided to contribute the funds towards a broader effort to serve the needs of teachers in elementary and middle schools. The idea behind the *Space Science Sequences* was to take existing standards-based GEMS space science activities, including some from *The Real Reasons for Seasons*, add some new activities to fill in some standards gaps that we identified, and arrive at a sequence of activities that could be the "bare minimum" needed for teachers to use and still meet most of their "standards needs." Of course, we also wanted a storyline or set of themes that would tie everything together for coherence.

A common way that space science curricula are arranged is to progress from Earth outwards: the Moon, then solar system objects, then stars and objects beyond the solar system, and finally galaxies and large scale structure in the universe. In that scenario, the planet transit activity that we quickly did in the latter part of this workshop is a natural bridge between the solar system and "beyond the solar system." However, for Unit 4 of the 6-8 *Space Science Sequence*, we decided to take a slightly different tact. We first focus on distances and units of distance measurement, for things beyond the solar system compared with things in the solar system, taking this all the way out to the realm of galaxies. We then address the question, "Are there planets out there with intelligent life with whom we might converse?" Suitable stars are the first issue, and so we approach characteristics of stars before moving to the methods of finding planets suitable for life. That brings us finally to the Kepler mission that uses the transit method to detect Earth-size planets around other stars.

The transit/planet-finding activity that we did in this workshop is a good example of an activity that is firmly rooted in standards because it reinforces the concept that "planets move in regular and predictable ways" – one of the key astronomy standards for middle school. But it also gives students a chance to look at cutting edge NASA science, and as such allows for a bit of going beyond standards. [Both this activity and the "human orrery" activity described in this paper have write-ups posted on the Kepler mission EPO website which is at http://kepler.nasa.gov/ed/activities.html.

3.3. John Erickson

I am a science educator and curriculum developer at LHS, and have been involved in astronomy and planetarium education for many years now. Both curriculum development and teacher professional development for GEMS have been major activities of mine while at LHS.

GEMS has primarily been a supplementary curriculum for elementary and middle school classrooms, with individual teacher's guides including lessons meant to run typically over a 1-2 week period. GEMS was derived from the best of museum programs for visiting schools, with activities tested and re-worked for classroom use. Over the years, some teachers have adapted GEMS to be their main curriculum, presenting units in sequence in an effort to build a coherent experience for students. With the GEMS *Space Science Sequences* for grades 3-5 and 6-8, we have *intentionally* developed this as a coherent curriculum sequence for teachers. There are obviously consequences and new design strategies needed in this move from the supplementary realm to the realm of the curriculum sequence. What follows is a summary of some of the key features behind the design of the GEMS-SSS:

Limited length of instruction time to what teachers can realistically devote to space science. Sequence for grades 3-5: Four units, 4 to 9 class sessions for each unit, 24 sessions total.
Sequence for grades 6-8: Four units, 6 to 11 class sessions for each unit, 33 sessions total.
These are the units for the elementary and middle school *Space Science Sequences*:

SSS for Grades 3-5

> **Unit 1** - How Big and How Far? (9 sessions)
> **Unit 2** - Earth's Shape and Gravity (6 sessions)
> **Unit 3** - How Does the Earth Move? (4 sessions)
> **Unit 4** - Moon Phases and Eclipses (5 sessions)

SSS for Grades 6-8

> **Unit 1** - How Does the Sun Affect the Earth? (9 sessions)
> **Unit 2** - Why Are There Seasons? (6 sessions)
> **Unit 3** - The Solar System (11 sessions)
> **Unit 4** - Beyond the Solar System (7 sessions)

Flexible instruction implementation for this larger curriculum. Depending on how a school or district chooses to teach space science, SSS units can either be taught across different grade levels (vertical model) or taught in the same grade (horizontal model).

Careful choice of key concepts in space science.   Space science key concepts were chosen based on (a) state and national standards, (b) common misconceptions, (c) what is current in space science for the present and near future, and (d) what else do students need to know for fully rounded space science literacy (e.g. some basic physical science concepts). Standards are the minimum core knowledge, while the SSS goes beyond minimum. There is still room for supplemental space science education.

Design of curriculum driven by desired learning outcomes.   This is as opposed to outcomes driven by the activities we thought we wanted to do with students (we were influenced again by Wiggins & McTighe 1998). This general "backward design" approach was modified by iterative collaboration between curriculum designers, NASA partners, and teacher field testers.

Assessment is more explicit and frequent, with a variety of strategies included for teachers to use.   These assessment strategies include (a) pre- and post-tests for every unit, to assess student learning gains, and (b) embedded assessments, to help measure understandings of the nature of science and inquiry. Assessment is necessary and useful for teachers, and it's also been a valuable tool for us as developers.

In summary, we've tried our best to make the GEMS-SSS easily usable, helpful, flexible, and adoptable. We also have kept and updated "old favorites" from GEMS guides, where appropriate. We were not starting from scratch. Activities have been carried over and adapted from *Earth, Moon and Stars*, *The Real Reasons for Seasons*, *Messages from Space*, and *Living with a Star*. Another trademark of GEMS that has been utilized in the development of the SSS (and described further in the next section) has been extensive field testing by classroom teachers, with feedback and data from this testing directly influencing revision before publication. The *Space Science Sequence for Grades 3-5* was published in early 2007, with the *Space Science Sequence for Grades 6-8* on course for publication in spring 2008.

3.4.   Jennifer King Chen

My background includes a degree in astrophysics, interest in teaching/education, and in particular, designing and implementing effective astronomy curricula in the classroom.

GEMS & curriculum testing: GEMS is known for its rigorous testing and re-testing of curriculum materials before publication. The goal, as always, has been to develop materials that assist teachers with meeting the many demands they face in the classroom. Similar to the GEMS guides, the *Space Science Sequences* went through various levels of testing. GEMS staff first pilot tested an initial draft of the curriculum in local classrooms. Based on observations and results collected during pilot testing, a national field test draft was sent out to teachers around the country willing to test the curriculum in their classrooms. Collected quantitative and qualitative responses from these teachers and their students were analyzed and incorporated into the final versions of the 3-5 and 6-8 *Sequences*.

Summary of paired pre- and post-unit student questionnaire gains for the Sequences: At the beginning and end of each unit, teachers are guided to give unit questionnaires to their students. The unit questionnaire functions both as an assessment tool for the teacher and as a learning tool for students. Data for the 3-5 *Sequence* was collected from 1401 paired pre- and post-unit student questionnaires. Data for the 6-8 *Sequence* was collected from 400 paired pre- and post-unit student questionnaires.

SSS for Grades 3-5	Mean % Correct Gain	Effect Size
Unit 1: How Big and How Far?	17	0.53
Unit 2: Earth's Shape and Gravity	20	0.61
Unit 3: How Does the Earth Move?	13	0.35
Unit 4: Moon Phases and Eclipses	12	0.24
SSS for Grades 6-8	Mean % Correct Gain	Effect Size
Unit 1: How Does the Sun Affect the Earth?	11	0.36
Unit 2: Why Are There Seasons?	22	0.59
Unit 3: The Solar System	13	0.30
Unit 4: Beyond the Solar System	17	0.36

It should be emphasized that it is difficult to achieve even moderate effect sizes with short-length curricula (such as the Units in the *Sequences*), so the field-test questionnaires data is positive and encouraging.

Meeting state and national standards requirements: As curriculum developers, we know that of particular concern to many teachers is whether or not the material they are using meets state and national standards. With the GEMS-SSS we've made some effort to include space science concepts beyond those in the standards. Unit 4 in the 6-8 *Sequence* is a primary example of this. It's especially important to note that the content and activities in this Unit succeed (as can be seen by the field test data) because they *build off* of the standards themselves. Without first establishing a concept framework within the standards, it would be very difficult to effectively take the curriculum beyond the standards, as Unit 4 has done. Most importantly, whether designing curriculum to or beyond the standards, we care about what will realistically work in the classroom, and the field test feedback from both teachers and students indicates that we have addressed that goal very effectively.

3.5. Traci Wierman

My role in this panel is the implementation end of the pipeline. Having spent 16 years in K - 8 formal education, followed by 9 years designing and directing education programs for an inter-disciplinary informal institution, I now have the opportunity to advocate for and support the use of this material in both formal and informal settings. There is a healthy tension between the two, formal and informal, the world of school and the world beyond its reach.

For those of you charged with designing fresh, new, innovative approaches to engaging audiences of all ages, can you envision the human orrery laid out in some permanent fashion in a gallery or plaza type setting? The marks we stood on at the beginning of our session could be made from bottle glass, tile, or other visually appealing and durable substances. Placing a small sign nearby, with the right graphic included, your visitors could create their own human orrery with their family, friends, or school mates, just one extension of the SSS into your own programming.

As the *Space Science Sequence for Grades 3-5* is a new product for us, we went through our first summer of offering professional development on its contents. With a group of teachers from NASA Explorer Schools, directors of our GEMS Network Sites and Centers, and others, we held a two-day workshop at LHS in July 2007. Those in attendance, regardless of background and prior knowledge, came away having learned new content AND new approaches to delivering "old" ideas. Weightlessness, in particular, is one subject in the 3-5 *Sequence* that seems to be one that us Earth-bound adults often have a difficult time with.

Supporting teachers in advancing their own content knowledge, building their confidence about the ideas they are being asked to teach, and guiding them through effective and engaging delivery is our goal as we embark on the implementation path that the GEMS-SSS offers. Additionally, we are working to support on-going district-wide efforts with this material, as the *Sequences* beg a new approach from GEMS for both delivery and classroom support. Since July, we have been working with Florida State University, Tallahassee on a gold-standard research project that will contribute efficacy data on the SSS. Our publisher, Carolina Curriculum (http://www.carolina.com/carolina_curriculum/), is very encouraged by the initial months of product availability, tripling their revenue estimates, meaning we can triple the number of teachers and ultimately, students, who will benefit from this material.

Finally, I'd like to add another perspective with regard to designing and teaching to the standards and beyond. When I worked at Turtle Bay Exploration Park in Redding, CA, the following is the disclaimer we made to teachers as printed on our school programs brochure: "State content standards are reinforced and supported in the delivery of all programs. We strive to take students beyond the standards, knowing that life far exceeds the reach of these important benchmarks." This seems to be the same spirit that the designers and collaborators of the *Space Science Sequences* have been guided by.

4.   The "Detecting Planet Transits" Activity in Brief

After each workshop presenter gave their brief statements on their roles and perspectives with regard to the GEMS-SSS project, we presented and facilitated a second hands-on activity, this one a transit/planet-finding activity based first on core standards, but also addressing an exciting new area of astronomical discovery that is actually beyond the current science education standards for middle school (i.e. extrasolar planets). This workshop activity was based on one found in the "Beyond the Solar System" Unit 4 of the 6-8 *Space Science Sequence*.

In the workshop and classroom activity, participants/students learn about the search for extrasolar planets using the method of transit detection. Teams are given access to a variety of materials and asked to construct a model that can be used to demonstrate the transit of a planet across the face of a star. Each team exhibits its model to the class and discusses which aspects of a transit the model represents best. By viewing each other's models and observing a star's brightness dim as a planet transits it, students discover yet another way scientists can analyze light to learn about distant objects. Key concepts that are addressed in two transit/planet-finding classroom activities in the 6-8 *Sequence* are: (a) when a planet transits a star, it partially blocks the light of the star; and (b) current planet detection methods, such as transit observation, detect only a small fraction of the planetary systems that exist.

5. Summary of the Input and Feedback from Participants During the Closing Discussion

In the closing interactive discussion, we strived to gather and capture the insights and experiences of participants with regard to designing and teaching to the standards and beyond. We posted on a large sheet at the front of the room a fundamental question, and what follows are the quick responses generated, paraphrased here.

"Why go beyond standards (sometimes)?"

- There is really so much to teach.
- Integration of technology is important.
- Integration of mathematics is important.
- There are both process and content standards to consider (i.e. not just science content standards).
- Some education materials are just too basic, so more depth is needed.
- Sometimes there's "the teachable moment", something that is in the news.
- It's vital to stay fresh as a professional.
- Content relevancy to students is important.
- Sometimes you want to convey to students about being part of something bigger.
- It motivates learning.

We'd especially like to thank the scientists and educators who participated in our workshop. Those who put their names on our sign-in sheet were:

1. Susan Schultz, Stanford Linear Accelerator Center (SLAC)

2. Jim Lochner, NASA Goddard Space Flight Center

3. Deborah L Jensen, Univ. of Texas Medical Branch at Galveston (UTMB)

4. Lora K. Hine, Cornell Univ.

5. Wil van der Veen, New Jersey Astronomy Center for Education (NJACE)

6. Theresa Moody, New Jersey Astronomy Center for Education (NJACE)

7. Sandra Laursen, Univ. of Colorado

8. Terry Kucera, NASA Goddard Space Flight Center

9. Sandra Preston, McDonald Observatory

10. Russ Harding

11. Donald Lubowich, Hofstra Univ.

12. Nancy Schaff, Cornell Univ.

References

NASA, "Implementing the Office of Space Science Education/Public Outreach Strategy: A Critical Evaluation at the Six-Year Mark," A Report by the Education and Public Outreach Task Force of the Space Science Advisory Committee (2003) (http://science.hq.nasa.gov/research/OSS_EPO_Task_Force_Report.pdf)

Nelson, G.D., "An Evolutionary Framework for Instructional Materials," from NSTA Reports, **18**, No. 1, 6-8 (2006)

Wiggins, G. and McTighe, J., Understanding by Design (Association for Supervision and Curriculum Development, Alexandria, VA, 1998)

EPO and a Changing World
ASP Conference Series, Vol. 389, © *2008*
C. Garmany, M. Gibbs, and J. W. Moody

Implications for EPO Design from Cognitive Science and Educational Design Research

Karen Carney

Adler Planetarium & Astronomy Museum 1300 S. Lake Shore Drive; Chicago, IL 60605, USA

Abstract. In the last thirty years, cognitive scientists have come to new understandings of how people remember, develop and use knowledge, as well as what useful knowledge looks like. These new understandings have profound implications for the educational pro-fession in general and open up questions as well as opportunities for the EPO profession. This session will begin with an introduction to what we know about knowledge, memory and reasoning and then talk about learning/instructional opportunities for using the EPO community to address some of these needs. Participants will be encouraged to reflect on the kinds of knowledge involved in their EPO programs and what cognitive science says about what it takes to learn such knowledge. They then will be introduced to general tools from the educational design community that they could use to help learners build appropriate understandings.

1. Introduction

This paper is an attempt to bring a contemporary, theory-informed understanding of knowledge construction to the EPO community and to present some implications for design in the EPO community. This paper is in three sections. The first section overviews current theory about knowledge and knowledge construction. The second outlines implications of this for educational design and presents some approaches for EPO professionals. The third section reflects on the unique opportunities and constraints offered by some EPO work. This paper is intended to introduce some concepts for discussion. I cannot hope to do justice to a rich field of research in three pages, and include references to articles and books that a curious reader can go to in order to learn more.

2. What do scientists understand about knowledge construction?

What is knowledge?

A contemporary definition of knowledge would be something like: Knowledge is a person's mental representation of information in memory that can be retrieved and applied appropriately. I will be discussing two key aspects of this in this paper. First, knowledge is *retrieved* out of memory and is *applied* to some situation. Second knowledge is a *mental representation.*

First, we must discuss how memory works. People can be thought of as having two kinds of memory, both of which are used when we think: short-term, or working memory and long-term, or storage memory. Working memory is where we hold information that we are currently consciously processing. People can typically hold only 7 ± 2 pieces of information in active memory at any given time, about the length of a phone number. An illustration of this is being asked a question when trying to remember a new phone number. Usually that phone number can't be retrieved after the question, because short-term memory cannot hold the phone number and process the question at the same time. Long-term memory, on the other hand, has an almost unlimited storage capacity. We are not conscious of most of what is stored there. When we think about something that we have already learned, we are retrieving knowledge from long-term memory and using it in short-term memory. (For a discussion of memory and research into memory see Bruer 1995).

Long-term memory is not a sponge that absorbs what we learn or experience. Rather every person's memory contains their own *mental representation* of what they have experienced. A mental representation is a memory, but it does not exactly reflect reality. For example, if one pictures a tiger, is it possible to count the number of stripes? For most people, the number of stripes is not part of the mental representation.

But how is knowledge represented and organized? First, not all knowledge is the same. It is useful to differentiate between information, associations and understandings. Information is data. It could be a phone number, a weight, a measure, a person's name. Associations are relationships between information. There are different kinds of associations. A person's name is categorically associated with the organization that he represents, or two people with red hair are superficially associated with each other. Understanding is a unification of other kinds of information in ways that allow one to make predictions or explain behavior. Understanding is information that allows reasoning about cause and effect, sometimes in a complex way.

Studies into how people solve problems show that even when people have knowledge in long-term memory that could solve a problem, they often do not use it (DiSessa 1996, Chi, Feltovish, & Glaser 1981, Gentner, Rattermann, & Forbus 1993). Factual information not associated with other knowledge is not typically retained and used later. To illustrate this think of the difference between recalling a new work associate's position and her phone extension. The position is easier to recall because one understands its function and the results of it being filled. The phone extension is harder to recall since it lacks the mental representations with relevant connections to real life that are more likely to be productively used.

Knowledge Construction

Because knowledge is being actively represented by our minds the knowledge representations that we build in long-term memory depends on the experiences that person has had and what they thought about those experiences as they had them. All of our experiences play a part in how we process information and build a mental representation of any given topic. For example, imagine two children at a sky show at a Planetarium. One lives in the country and has seen stars moving across the sky every night. The other is from the city and has never seen more than a few of the brightest stars. The child with experience with stars will be better able to understand how to identify the new constellation that is demonstrated. The other child might walk away with a more basic, emotional impression of the sky. She might even disbelieve the show altogether. Based on the similarity between the planetarium and a movie theater, she may believe she just saw a made-up story.

When people build an understanding, they also build an understanding of when and how it can be applied or how it is relevant (DiSessa & Sherin 1998). One challenge in schools is that learners build a narrow scope of where a taught concept is to be applied—the test or lab that it is needed for—and never build associations to everyday life. This leads to "inert" knowledge, knowledge that people have but never use. In order to understand this further, we must understand more about how people construct knowledge.

People start to build knowledge through experience. When one has a new experience, one does not know what to expect and so focuses on many details, some of which are important and some of which aren't. The engagement here is intense and usually can only be reached by being immersed in a new situation or deeply engaged in a detailed, realistic story. A mental representation of a specific experience is called a case (Kolodner 1993). They are rich in detail. So for example, when a child goes to a planetarium for the first time, they pay attention to the many things that are new and different about the planetarium. They remember many details about it. Cases are often used as a backbone for other learning. Having built one case, the next time a child encounters a similar situation, he or she calls upon this case as a template and compares the new situation to the template. To continue the planetarium example, when he or she visits an IMAX theater and compares these two experiences, he or she can figure out what is specific to each individual forum and what is true of both. Adult coaching can be helpful at this level, as an alert adult can point out similarities or ask questions about differences, helping children to further develop this more general knowledge. Once the child has gone to two or three comparisons, he or she has built up a more abstracted understanding that helps him or her generate interpretations of and expectations about what will happen and what will be seen. This knowledge is more abstract than the original case and less richly detailed, but it also can be applied to new and different settings more easily.

The same basic process can hold for conceptual understandings, but is more difficult and requires more intervention by experts. A learner starts with experiences of phenomena in the world, say motion, and builds specific cases. With more experiences, detail becomes less important and the general knowledge is formed, along with a notion of when it might be applied. At this point, the learner has an understanding of a class of phenomena, but no expert concepts or vocabulary to inform that understanding. Often this process is unconscious. So for example, very young children fairly effortlessly build a personal understanding of how motion works. Teachers then need to help learner relate expert ideas that are important to a domain (for example $F = ma$) to the understanding that a child has constructed. If this is not done, learners may never relate the taught information about motion to his or her constructed one. In fact, strong physics students can deny that the laws of physics really describe everyday motion (DiSessa 1996). Expert guidance, and exposure to many examples that differ superficially help learners to build an understanding of these concepts that are more likely to be recalled and used appropriately. After an understanding is constructed it continues to be refined. This is done through seeking out or being given additional information or examples. At this point, the learner may be able to reflect on the state of his or her own knowledge. He or she can seek out new experiences or new expert perspectives on his or her understanding. A good overview of how people learn can be found in Bransford, Brown, & Cocking (1999).

Table 1.   Knowledge Construction

Step in Knowledge Construction	Explanation
Building an initial Case	Learners build a rich, detailed representation of a specific experience. It is used as a template when a person encounters something similar later.
Retrieval and use of prior knowledge	Learners encounter a situation that reminds them of a previous case and they retrieve the case. They use the prior case as a guide for reasoning about the new situation.
Comparison and creation of abstractions	Learners consciously or unconsciously compare two or more cases, and pick out what is the same and what is different about them. The similar ideas become part of a more abstract knowledge reprsesentation in memory.
Reinforcement and refinement	Learners are aware that they have an understanding and can consciously compare their understanding with others. They seek out information that fills the remaining gaps in their understandings.

There are additional emotional and personal influences on knowledge construction that may influence whether individuals construct an understanding how they use it in the future. Learners may or may not be motivated to learn any given concept. Motivation also affects how knowledge is represented and retrieved. If a learner learns something in order to get an A on the test and for no other reason, he or she has less of a chance to retrieve it later in life. People also have emotional responses to certain concepts or subject areas. Should they have a strong aversion to any given idea or topic, it may affect the way that they process information and that will affect what is stored in memory. Likewise, a person's self-concept sometimes affects learning. If a learner believes that he or she is "a math person" but not "an art person" this will affect his or her approach to the subject and how and what they remember.

3.   Design of Learning Environments

The above discussion has profound implications for the design of learning environments. Because each individual constructs understandings rather than receives them, then any educational design must work with the individual's knowledge construction. The learner's prior knowledge and perceptions of the topics to be learned should be the starting point for all educational design. This begins with the identification and investigation of the specific audience for EPO efforts. The needs and knowledge of preschoolers will vary considerably from those of their teachers, for example.

Equally important is a thorough understanding of the topics or content to be taught. How do experts understand these ideas? What are the prerequisite building blocks for a thorough understanding? EPO professionals may want to consider what is an appropriate How are these ideas used by experts? After identifying the audience, one must investigate what the intended audience already knows and thinks about the topic at hand. It is important to understand what prior conceptions audience members might have, and what misconceptions are common to this audience learning the target concepts. Guidelines such the state standards or benchmarks as well as national guides such as as the AAAS atlas of science literacy (AAAS 1989) can be an invaluable resource for understanding what concepts act as prerequisites for others and what is age and developmentally appropriate. Driver et al. (1994) presents a good overview of learner misconceptions in many ideas from research. Further investigation can be done through surveys, interviews or literature review. When designing for a professional audience, such as teachers, it is useful to look at their professional requirements such as local standards and performance objectives to see how any proposed design would help meet their goals.

Table 2.   Knowledge Construction

Step	Further Information
Choose and investigate topic	Know how experts understand the topic, how understandings of it are used, and what prerequisites exist for understanding.
Choose and investigate audience	Be specific about the audience, investigate its prior knowledge, possible misconceptions, current state of understanding and development and motivation towards the topic.
Specify a learning goal	This should emphasize some aspect of understanding, not facts or associations. Learners should be able to reason about your topic to predict or describe.
Specify an outcome	Choose a task that cannot be done without an understanding of your learning goal. This can demonstrate learning.
Evaluate	Check performance of learning outcome as well as other goals for the program.

The next step is choosing a specific understanding that you would like your audience to build. The language used to describe the goal here should emphasize the nature of this understanding, and so emphasize some kind of explanation or prediction. If the learning goal is "learn about the solar system" you are probably presenting associations or information. If the learning goal is "explain what would happen to the orbit of Jupiter if it doubled in mass" you are teaching an understanding. Knowledge construction is idiosyncratic and we cannot trust that people will learn everything as we wish they might simply because we presented information. We need to find out if individuals have constructed the understanding we intended. To do this, we specify a specific demonstration of understanding. Wiggins & McTighe (1998) outline a specific template called a "KUD" which helps designers to specify in advance what the learner will know, understand, and do as a result of learning. See table 3 for a sample KUD.

Table 3.   A Sample KUD for a Family Planetary Geology Course.

Part of KUD	Example
Understanding goals	1. Geologic processes shape the surfaces of planets, letting us learn what processes have been at work from the appearance of the surface of a planet
	2. Geologic processes and conditions create rocks of different kinds.
Knowledge supporting understanding	1. Planetary processes shape the surfaces of planets.
	Volcanism – produces volcanoes
	Erosion & deposition – produces canyons and valleys
	Meteors – produce craters
	2. Different kinds of rocks look different from each other Little particles of rock get glued together and form sedimentary rocks. These often form layers or patterns. Igneous rocks can have big crystals that are locked together, or can be smooth Impacts from meteors can make breccia, a rock with jagged pieces welded together.
Demonstration	1. Students will look at a picture of the surface of a planet and infer whether there might have been erosion or plate tectonics there in the past
	2. Students will be able to look at a rock type and make an inference about how it was formed, and what the conditions are like its planet of formation

Finally, programs need to be assessed and evaluated. At Adler our evaluation is of whether they are able to do what we specified above.

4. Examples of Design for Learning in the Informal Environment

EPO has special constraints that need to be considered when designing but also offer unique opportunities. One challenge is the nature of the content. Often the topics are esoteric or complex, and extra care must be taken when structuring their learning for various audiences. Extra care may be necessary to ensure that audience members see the programming as relevant or motivating. Many EPO projects fall in the "informal learning" realm which is a real or virtual venue for learning outside of the normal school experience. An informal learning environment can be a computer interactive, a museum gallery, downloadable video or an after school club. People often, but do not always choose to interact with an informal learning environment of their own free will, according to existing interest or curiosity. There is more of an expectation that the experience be fun or entertaining than there is with a traditional school-based learning environment. In this discussion, I will present examples from the work of my own department at the Adler Planetarium & Astronomy Museum when appropriate.

First, an informal learning environment can help visitors have initial rich, immersive experiences from which to build initial cases. At Adler, we have several venues with which to provide such offerings. In our bringing the heavens to Earth gallery, visitors step behind a screen and are immersed in the sounds and sights of the South Pacific. There they pilot a canoe by a rising star. A sky show gives visitors the opportunity to experience a full night sky or make a virtual visit to an ancient skywatching culture.

The museum environment can also offer the opportunity to compare different cases and build more abstract understandings. Explicit comparisons can be made with signage or other exhibit elements, facilitation or gallery guides. For example, our "tools of exploration" scavenger hunt invites visitors to compare such disparate items as a telescope, the Mars Rovers, and computer visualizations, to learn of the tools that help us understand space better. We emphasize cause and effect reasoning in programming. In our *Exploring Space* Cyberspace Computer Classroom Program we build the idea that the human body has a narrow threshold for survival by letting visitors vary pressure, temperature, and gas levels for a simulated astronaut with and without a spacesuit.

Conceptual refinement happens when visitors seek out new understandings. Many aspects of any museum are well suited for this; visitors spend hours pouring over labels on exhibit elements, reading gallery guides and chatting with docents. Our space flight docent program puts knowledgeable amateurs on the floor with models and other artifacts. We also offer the visitors chances to chat with staff astronomers, both on the floor and through our adult courses.

An informal learning environment also influences some of the human or emotional aspects of learning. At Adler, we want to help our audience to perceive science as fun and doable. Our youngest visitors learn about the presence of the atmosphere by making kites and reflecting on what keeps them in the air. Older children are invited to experience the simulated gravity of the Moon by jumping on a gravity simulation. We also address our visitors' self-concept by emphasizing that space exploration careers include many talents in our programming and exhibits. For example, the new *Shoot for the Moon* exhibit has a ticker tape of possible jobs that are part of space exploration, including uniform designer, nutritionist, farmer, geologist as well as astronaut.

Second, we will consider the understandings that learners must gain through EPO work. EPO by definition exists to help audience members understand the science or other aspects of active scientific investigations and missions. The concepts covered are deep and rich, and often a full understanding and appreciation of them relies on prerequisite knowledge. One challenge is helping audience members be interested or curious about such endeavors, and giving them the tools to understand them. For this reason, it is necessary to use and build on conceptual understandings. Paradoxically, because the knowledge is in many cases abstract and impersonal, it is more important than ever to be learner-centered in the design of EPO.

Finally, it is important to consider that we are constantly learning about how to better help people engage with our EPO projects in fruitful ways. Scientists are still defining all aspects of learning and exploring what kinds of interactivity and immersion and guidance are best for learners. This paper outlines how modern understandings of cognition can inform design in the informal environment, but the opposite could also be true. The informal learning environment also offers itself as a natural learning laboratory. The informal environment offers us an opportunity to experiment with new approaches and new technologies for learning on an ongoing basis.

References

Bruer, J., *Schools for Thought: A Science of Learning in the Classroom* (MIT Press, Cambridge, MA, 1995)

DiSessa, A., "What Do 'Just Plain Folks' Know About Physics?" in The Handbook of Education and Human Development: New Models of Learning, Teaching and Schooling, edited by Olson, D. J. R, and Torrance, N. (Blackwell, Cambridge, MA, 1996), pp. 709-730

Chi, M., Feltovich, P., and Glaser, R. "Categorization and Representation of Physics Problems by Experts and Novices", Cognitive Science, **5**,121-152 (1981)

Gentner, D., Rattermann, M.J., and Forbus, K.D., "The Roles of Similarity in Transfer: Separating Retrievability from Inferential Soundness", Cognitive Psychology **25**, 524-575 (1993)

DiSessa, A. and Sherin, B. "What Changes in Conceptual Change?", International Journal of Science Education, **20**(10) 1155-1191 (1998)

Kolodner, J. *Case-Based Reasoning*, (Morgan Kaufmann, San Mateo, 1993)

Driver, R., Squires, A., Rushworth, P., and Wood-Robinson, V., *Making Sense of Secondary Science, Research into Children's Ideas* (Routledge-Farmer, New York, 1994)

Bransford, J. D., Brown, A. L., and Cocking, R. R. (Eds.), *Expanded Edition of How People Learn: Brain, Mind, Experience, and School*, (National Academy Press, Washington D.C., 1999) pp. 51-78

American Association for the Advancement of Science, *Science for All Americans: A Project 2061 Reports on Literacy Goals in Science, Mathematics, and Technology* (American Association for the Advancement of Science, Washington D.C., 1989)

Wiggins, G., McTighe, J., *Understanding by Design*, (Association for Supervision and Curriculum Development, Alexandria, VA, 1998)

EPO and a Changing World
ASP Conference Series, Vol. 389, © 2008
C. Garmany, M. Gibbs, and J. W. Moody

Portfolio on a Shoestring

Sara E. Mitchell and S. Beth Barbier

*SP Systems, Inc. & NASA Goddard Space Flight Center, Astrophysics
Science Division, Greenbelt, Maryland, 20771, USA*

Anita Krishnamurthi

*CRESST/University of Maryland & NASA Goddard Space Flight
Center, Astrophysics Science Division, Greenbelt, MD 20771, USA*

James C. Lochner

*CRESST/Universities Space Research Association & NASA Goddard
Space Flight Center, Astrophysics Science Division, Greenbelt, MD
20771, USA*

Abstract. Many education and outreach programs face two daunting shortages: time and money. EPO professionals are frequently challenged to develop
quality efforts for a variety of audiences and settings, all on a shoestring budget. How do you create a broad and cohesive education and outreach portfolio
with limited resources? In this session, we discussed several effective strategies
to make the most of your assets, such as adaptation of existing programs and
materials, mutually beneficial partnerships, and innovative (and inexpensive)
dissemination techniques. These approaches can fill in the gaps in your portfolio, increasing the scope and impact of your EPO efforts. There are a variety of
cost-effective tools and techniques that can bring your EPO endeavors to a wide
range of audiences and settings. Turn your program's EPO wish list into reality
through savvy leveraging of existing personnel, funding, and materials... or find
a partner that can help you fill any gaps in your portfolio.

1. Introduction

Whether you are creating a new education and public outreach (EPO) program
or working on an existing one, it is essential to consider the entire range of
activities and materials that you can offer. Through careful planning, you can
enhance the efficiency and impact of your program. The resultant portfolio
presents an organized collection of offerings to your audiences, and allows you to
readily make connections within your own program and with outside programs.

1.1. What is a Portfolio?

A portfolio is a coordinated collection of activities and materials that address a
wide range of audiences. A successful portfolio is not merely a loose assortment
of elements, but a strategically organized ensemble of pieces that both meet
your program goals and work together harmoniously. A portfolio offers the

opportunity for activities to build upon each other, or for individual materials to reach a wider variety of audiences.

Your portfolio will need to address the specific EPO requirements of your particular institution or organization. Your planning should also consider the overall flow of education and outreach within your organization to provide a series of successive offerings for audience members. This offers a lasting range of activities for new participants or those who wish to continue their current involvement.

1.2.   Why Do I Want a Portfolio?

A successful portfolio helps focus an EPO plan to better meet audience needs and maximize impact. Coordination reduces overlapping efforts and allows you to reach a wide range of audiences. By assessing the needs of your specific audiences and aligning your offerings accordingly, you can create an EPO program that addresses both typical audiences and niche audiences that might otherwise be overlooked.

Portfolio planning can greatly improve the cost effectiveness of an EPO program. Finding opportunities to share staff and resources across multiple projects can save money, avoid duplication, and free up time for other efforts or partnerships. For a new EPO program, the time and money saved can allow you to support a larger variety of offerings and get them up and running more quickly. Current efforts in an existing program can be strategically aligned in a portfolio, and the savings can be used to expand the program or increase its impact.

Another benefit of a portfolio is that its development encourages and facilitates partnerships. Partnerships within an organization are very useful for alignment with organizational requirements and goals, and to provide a larger series or range of EPO offerings to each audience. EPO programs from different institutions can share resources cooperatively to maximize impact and avoid duplication of efforts at a higher level. Coordination between groups can be challenging, but the rewards include cost savings, bigger ideas, and greater reach for every involved program

1.3.   Limitations

You would like to provide quality activities and materials, reach every appropriate audience, and create a broad and cohesive portfolio... all on a shoestring budget. So what's stopping you?

Every EPO provider is familiar with the biggest shortages facing their programs: money, people, and time. Regardless of your budget, the size of your staff, or the schedule for your projects, it never seems like enough.

Money: You would like to have a bigger budget, and you feel the pressure of that finite dollar amount in every decision that you make. Proposal opportunities offer the chance to increase your funding, but it takes time to write a successful proposal, awards are not guaranteed, and money from any award is not available immediately. Even then, a winning proposal may not be enough, as many awards are insufficient to accomplish major changes in your program or fund additional staff.

People: Staffing ties directly into funding - it is often difficult to find the manpower to accomplish your portfolio goals. Your existing staff may be small, or too busy to take on new efforts. Experience can be an issue, especially when approaching new opportunities that require unfamiliar skills or knowledge. Partnerships can provide an additional challenge, as you need staff committed to finding outside assistance or keeping an existing connection afloat.

Time: It can take a significant amount of time to properly address a complex project like assembling and carrying out a portfolio of activities. The saying that "time is money" is especially true when considering personnel funding. Can your staff find the time to work on the portfolio, or can you hire additional people to take on the job? Unfortunately, your time constraints may be further tightened by organizational deadlines, funding requirements, or upcoming events.

2. Getting Started

The limitations listed provide a serious challenge to implementing or improving an EPO portfolio. But it is possible to move forward, work with (or around) those obstacles, and reach your goals.

2.1. What Do You Have?

The first step toward a quality EPO portfolio is an assessment of what you already have. One existing resource may be your staff members, who are most likely well-qualified and enthusiastic. Consider what your staff can already do. An inventory of your materials and activities (print, web-based, hands-on, etc.) and current funding is also in order, as well as an assessment of your available space - a cost-saving resource that is frequently overlooked.

It is helpful to consult your current partners and advisors. They may already be resources for information, money, networking, and/or advice. Your partners may have appropriate and perhaps complementary skills, and may be willing and able to assist in portfolio development and support proposed portfolio activities.

2.2. What Do You Need?

Your portfolio needs address any essential requirements that may come from your management or organization, or are tied into your funding. You may be required to reach a particular audience, include specific content, or fit into an existing EPO network. What outside expertise is required to fill any gaps in your plan? These obligations are unique to each EPO program, and it is useful to speak with management and other supervisory or advisory bodies to make sure that you are aware of these needs.

2.3. What Do You Want?

This is where your creativity comes into play - brainstorming a range of ideas for your portfolio. Consider the audiences you would like to reach, materials you would like to create, and methods or technologies that you could integrate into your plans.

During this brainstorming, record and save every idea that is generated. Then sort these possibilities into two categories: practical and wish list items. Some ideas will be accessible and imminently useful in your portfolio. These are the concepts that you can refine and develop in your immediate efforts. Other ideas, which may exceed your current resources, can remain candidates for future portfolio additions. No matter how far-fetched, this wish list provides inspiration and keeps all of your brainstormed ideas on the table. When resources permit, you will already have possible expansions for your portfolio.

2.4.   Moving Forward

Creating a successful portfolio requires effective collaboration and communication. Throughout your planning and execution, keep open lines of communication within your team and with outside advisors and partners. Talk to people to learn about the development of their own portfolios, and ask them who they recommend as advisors - these individuals may also be useful to you.

From time to time, you'll need to take a step back and assess your plans. Outside opinions will help you stay objective, and may reveal shortcomings or ideas that you haven't considered. Your trusted advisors can review your plans and help you identify and implement revisions.

You can avoid frustration by learning from the successes and challenges faced by others. Draw ideas from similar EPO programs, and don't be afraid to pattern your efforts after something that works! Following the advice and best practices of successful EPO providers will help you assemble your plans efficiently and avoid many obstacles during each phase of portfolio development and execution. Imitation isn't just the highest form of flattery - it is also an essential technique for creating an effective and efficient EPO portfolio.

3.   Shoestring Strategies

There are many potential approaches to developing an excellent EPO portfolio with limited resources. We highlighted three proven strategies and explored the opportunities for portfolio development with each technique. This is by no means a comprehensive guide, but these practices should be considered during any portfolio planning.

3.1.   Adaptation of Existing Resources

This strategy could be called "thinking inside the box," because it takes your existing assets and repurposes them for different audiences. Adaptation reduces the duplication of efforts and devises new uses for existing projects instead of inventing entirely new projects, saving time and money while reaching a wider range of audiences.

Take stock of your materials, methods, partnerships, and other resources that could help you meet your portfolio needs. It is often worthwhile to network with others in your content area and see what they have to offer, inside and outside of your own organization. If you locate outside materials of interest, find out if you can use or adapt these resources. You may need permission, and you should include appropriate credit if you use them.

Also consider the amount and type of adaptation needed. Some modifications may be obvious, and others provide a challenge. You may choose to change the level of content, method of usage, or distribution methods. If adaptation seems too difficult, it may not be worthwhile - you shouldn't have to force any activity or material to fit a new audience.

Session Discussion: Workshop attendees offered a variety of ideas on the adaptation of existing EPO resources. Changing the audience is one tactic, modifying formal education activities to fit the needs of an informal setting (such as an after-school or family science program) is another. Some participants suggested a change in packaging, such as assembling activities from a variety of programs into a single thematic kit (like ASP's Family ASTRO or NASA's Beyond Einstein Explorers' Program). Another idea is to turn educator workshops into professional development workshops for a network such as the NASA Solar System Ambassadors, whose members can disseminate your activities to a larger audience.

Attendees also identified limitations to this strategy. Adaptation definitely requires people with the time and skills to make modifications, and not every activity or material will be a good fit for another audience. The suggested adaptations may also require additional resources, such as training and funding for materials. And online distribution poses a specific challenge, with technology limitations and accessibility requirements.

3.2. Networking and Partnerships

Making friends within the EPO community can open doors and save time and money. Networking is valuable for portfolio development and advertising, and meetings offer a connection with potential advisors and partners.

Professional conferences (in EPO, science, or education) provide the opportunity to present your EPO portfolio and see what others are doing. A presentation or poster can communicate what you have to offer, as well as what you need. This is an opportunity to ask for assistance or advice, and to seek collaboration to fill in any staffing or resource gaps. You may also identify potential partners for grant proposals, which will help with staff and financial resources.

It is also important to consider what you can do to help potential partners. A successful partnership is a symbiotic relationship, so you will need to contribute value to it.

Session Discussion: When we challenged session participants to find a potential partner in the room and briefly discuss how they could work together, a lively and productive discussion ensued. Every pair was successful to some extent. Some teams identified opportunities to share information, materials, or curricula between their EPO programs. One pair discovered a mutual involvement with volunteerism - one person needs volunteers, and the other is connected to a network of potential assistance. Pairs also identified the possibility for shared events, such as teacher workshops or informal education programs. There were also several possible connections with community groups or non-profit organizations.

This practice also has many potential obstacles. A partnership needs to be a good fit for all involved, and this cannot be forced. Both parties need to be doing similar or complementary work. It is necessary to set your own priorities first and then find a partner with compatible priorities. Be clear on responsibilities, deadlines, goals, objectives, and outcomes for the partnership. The biggest challenge facing any partnership is sustainability, and it takes time and effort to build a relationship and make it last. This is especially difficult with management turnover and the frequently associated changes in program requirements, and it may take high visibility work that meets those requirements to keep partners happy, thus allowing you to pursue your own goals. One participant suggested having at least three contacts within a partnering organization, in order to maintain the partnership through potential staff changes.

3.3.   Getting It Out There

There are a variety of possible distribution channels for your EPO materials and activities, but your choice should be tailored to match your target audience and resources. While it is tempting to choose the most inexpensive, simple, or innovative channel, it needs to be appropriate for the end user. It is useful to seek advice or consult research to determine the best methods and uncover new possibilities.

There are a few means of narrowing down the seemingly endless options for distribution. It helps to assess what you have tried in the past, and what has worked for others. There are undoubtedly efficient methods that meet your audience needs and don't break the budget. New technology is offering many exciting, cost-efficient, and wide-reaching opportunities.

One interesting possibility for distribution is contributing to a kit or larger package of EPO activities and materials. This might allow you to piggyback on other programs' efforts, or consolidate efforts to reach a specific audience. It is also worthwhile to find out who is already planning a distribution or presentation to your target audience, and ask to contribute to it.

Session Discussion: Each attendee had the opportunity to describe one of their EPO efforts and receive advice from other participants about distribution. This discussion provided a lengthy list of possible methods and resources tailored to specific materials and activities. Suggested techniques included: advertisement of workshops through NASA education networks and NSTA mailing lists, distribution of multimedia to museums and science centers, distribution of curriculum materials through EPO networks or to home school audiences, repackaging of radio content to a podcast or clips for school morning announcements, solicitation of volunteers through Facebook or high schools with community service requirements, and sharing of after-school programs with Boys and Girls Clubs or 4H Clubs.

Distribution is most significantly limited by the needs and restrictions of your target audience. Methods should provide what the audience really needs, and metrics must be collectable to determine the results of distribution. Many of these ideas require significant time, and it takes even more time to develop a new distribution technique if no existing ones fulfill your needs.

4. Conclusions

The advice and strategies discussed can help you meet the needs of a wide range of audiences, creating a coordinated and savvy portfolio that makes the most of your resources.

If you are planning a new EPO portfolio, you are in the perfect position to match up your efforts during the initial planning stages. Considering the "big picture" from the beginning will make it much easier to meet your program goals and avoid gaps or disconnects. Set priorities, find advisors, and design your activities and materials to minimize labor and maximize impact for years to come.

Organizing an existing EPO program into a cohesive portfolio can be tricky, especially if your program has existed for a long time. It is an obstacle and an asset to have so many existing resources! Identify what you have and the biggest gaps in your offerings - filling these should be a priority. Successful development of a portfolio will help you take inventory of your activities and materials, and strategically adjust staff time and money within your program. Portfolio implementation is key to efficient refinement and/or expansion of an existing program.

No matter what your situation, take every opportunity to network and seek advice and information. This session was designed to facilitate collaboration and information sharing among participants. When working on a shoestring budget, communication, collaboration, and coordination will help tie up loose ends, and this interaction is key to every stage of portfolio development and implementation.

Acknowledgments. The authors would like to thank the participants in our session on September 6, 2007. Your ideas and insights were critical to the development of this paper.

EPO and a Changing World
ASP Conference Series, Vol. 389, © 2008
C. Garmany, M. Gibbs, and J. W. Moody

A Graduate-Level Professional Development Program in Science for In-Service Middle and High School Teachers

Bernhard Beck-Winchatz, Lynn Narasimhan, and David Jabon

DePaul University, Interdisciplinary Science and Technology Center, 990 W Fullerton, Suite 4400, Chicago, IL 60614, cnarasim@depaul.edu

Abstract.   Recent research on learning and cognition has produced new insights into designing effective professional development programs for mathematics and science teachers. This research suggests that "teacher learning programs must become more collegial and in-depth, longer in duration, and tailored to the experience levels of the learners, be they novice or expert teachers" (Stiles & Mundrey 2002). Guided by this research, DePaul University in Chicago has developed an interdisciplinary Masters of Science in Science Education (MSSE) degree program for urban middle school and high school teachers. The program has a strong contemporary earth and space science component, including a course in astrobiology. The MSSE program is designed to strengthen the teachers' science content knowledge and skills, improve their classroom practice, and ultimately enhance their students' learning in science. We will share a variety of strategies we have employed in the design, development, and implementation of the program. We will also discuss what we have learned about the professional development needs of Chicago teachers as well as the research tools we have used to assess the effectiveness of our program. An overarching principle of the program is the integration of science content knowledge with classroom practice and with research on how students learn.

1.   Program Features

DePaul's Master of Science in Science Education (MSSE) program evolved out of our work with Chicago teachers in the NASA Space Science Broker/Facilitator program, which began in 1998. Part of our charge as Broker/Facilitators was to help Chicago teachers integrate current space science educational materials developed by NASA into standards-based instruction, and create opportunities for the teachers to learn about NASA resources. Over time we developed a cadre of 10-15 teacher consultants with whom we met on a regular basis to brainstorm ideas for NASA-related professional development, and to plan events such as our annual Chicago Teacher Space Science Symposium. In these meetings with our teacher consultants a consensus emerged that professional development beyond one-day workshops and other short-duration events is needed to have a significant impact on science instruction in Chicago. In 2004 we successfully applied for a grant from the US Department of Education Math and Science Partnerships (MSP) program to help us establish the DePaul University Master's of Science in Science Education program. This grant funded most of the tuition for the first two cohorts, totalling 44 teachers. Additional funding was provided by the Illinois Space Grant Consortium, Commonwealth-Edison, and the Chicago Public Schools.

The 12 courses in the MSSE program are taught by full-time faculty, nine from the College of Liberal Arts and Sciences, two from the School of Education, and one from the School of New Learning. All courses integrate science education research in the course design, in the professional development activities (see §2.), and in the project evaluation (see §3.).

Table 1.   The 12 courses of DePaul's Master's of Science in Science Education program. Courses that are part of the earth and space science strand are in italics.

	Year 1	Year 2	Year 3
Summer	Physical Science 1	Evolution and Ecology	*Environmental*
	Physical Science 2	*Astrobiology*	*Science*
Fall	*Light and Waves*	*Weather and Climate*	Capstone
Winter	Chemistry	*Geology and Planetary Science*	
Spring	Biology	*Astronomy*	

New science content is introduced in the context of the K-12 classroom. It is designed to challenge the teachers as adult learners who are able to understand science concepts at a much deeper level than their students. At the same time these concepts are connected to the curriculum to facilitate the application of new understandings to their classrooms. Instruction is inquiry based and models the practices we want the teachers to apply in their own classrooms. In spite of the apprehensiveness of some of the teachers in our program, MSSE courses do not avoid the use of mathematics, but focus on the importance of mathematical applications to science inquiry, and on connections between the science and math curriculum.

For example, as part of a unit on mechanical and electromagnetic waves in which teachers conduct laboratory experiments related to reflection, refraction, diffraction and interference of slinky, water, sound, and light waves, they conduct an analysis of the "Waves" strand map from the AAAS Atlas of Scientific Literacy (American Association for the Advancement of Science 2001, 2007). This map shows how more basic properties of waves that can be introduced in elementary grades, such as the idea that light acts like a wave in many ways, or that waves can be described in terms of speed of a disturbance and distance between the peaks of the disturbance, ultimately lead to an understanding of the more advanced concepts the teachers investigate in their lab work. It also shows the interrelatedness of wave concepts with other parts of the curriculum and summarizes related science education research about student pre- and misconceptions. The teachers also read and discuss research-based K-12 curriculum related to waves and model related classroom activities, such as the Project ARIES "Exploring Waves" curriculum (Grossman 2001), to gain practical knowledge of how these ideas can be introduced to their students. They use mathematics to analyze and interpret the data from their lab work, and discuss ways in which to connect K-12 science curriculum related to waves to important concepts in geometry and algebra.

In the process of designing a master's program that meets the needs of middle school and high school teachers we have encountered a number of ongoing challenges. Most science faculty at DePaul have little experience with courses for teachers, and some are reluctant to take on this challenge because they are not familiar with state and national science education standards and K-12 curriculum. They know that traditional introductory science courses do not meet the needs of teachers, but they may be uncertain about how to modify their courses so that they are more appropriate for this audience. Teachers come into our programs with a wide range of science content background knowledge and classroom experience. They range, for example, from teachers who have not taken any courses in physical science since high school, to high school physics teachers, and from second-year teachers to teachers who have been in the classroom for over twenty years. Thus, identifying learning goals that are appropriate for a graduate program, and assessing the progress of the teachers toward these goals presents a major challenge.

The 10 faculty members from the science departments and Schools of Education and New Learning who teach in the MSSE program meet once or twice per quarter to discuss these challenges, share ideas, and develop common strategies. Similar to the teachers, MSSE faculty also joined the program with a wide range of backgrounds. Some had years of experience in teacher training and science education research, while others were teaching courses for teachers for the first time. From these meetings a model has emerged that is based on the commitment that the students of the teachers in the MSSE program should ultimately be the beneficiaries of all activities in the program. Unlike traditional courses in which instructors set common learning goals that all students are expected to meet, MSSE faculty and teachers work together to identify individualized and appropriately challenging learning goals for each teacher. Metacognition and reflection are emphasized as a means for teachers to participate in setting their own learning goals and monitor their own progress.

2. Research Base

DePaul's Master of Science in Science Education incorporates science and mathematics education research in several ways:

1. The design and ongoing refinement of the program are informed by current research in mathematics and science teaching and learning.

2. Research-based tools are used in professional development activities for teachers.

3. The evaluation plan is emerging from an increased understanding of education research and provides opportunities to contribute further to the literature in that area.

The program design is grounded in research indicating that all students can and do learn through their engagement with prepared, caring, and dedicated professionals and that providing teachers with innovative professional development and meaningful interactions with other urban educators will have a positive impact on student achievement. (See Mayer, Mullens, & Moore 2000 and Committee on Science and Mathematics Teacher Preparation 2001 for relevant reviews of current thinking in these areas.) In general, effective implementation of the national and local science education standards demands pedagogical knowledge, content knowledge, and pedagogical content knowledge on the part of the teachers (Schulman 1986).

In particular, the design incorporates findings and/or recommendations that relate student achievement with teacher professional development, such as those found in a series of reports from the National Research Council. The first of these reports, *How People Learn: Brain, Mind, Experience, and School* (National Research Council 1999a), lays out three findings that have a solid research base:

- Students come to the classroom with preconceptions about how the world works. These preconceptions shape how new learning is assimilated.

- To develop competence in an area of inquiry, students must: (a) have a deep foundation of factual knowledge, (b) understand facts and ideas in the context of a conceptual framework, and (c) organize knowledge in ways that facilitate retrieval and application.

- A "metacognitive" approach to instruction can help students learn to take control of their own learning by defining learning goals and monitoring their progress in achieving them.

In the companion report, *How People Learn: Bridging Research and Practice* (National Research Council 1999b), the authors argue that these core learning principles have profound implications for the professional development of teachers:

- Teachers must draw out and work with the preexisting understandings that students bring with them.

- Teachers must teach some subject matter in depth, providing many examples in which the same concept is at work and providing a firm foundation of factual knowledge.

- The teaching of metacognitive skills should be integrated into the curriculum in a variety of subject areas.

A third report, *How Students Learn* (National Research Council 2005), contains examples of how educators have applied the concepts from *How People Learn* in nine different contexts. For instance, three chapters give detailed explanations of model curriculum and instruction in science for three grade levels: primary (a unit on light), middle (a unit on gravity), and secondary (a unit on genetics). Finally, *Taking Science to School: Learning and Teaching Science in Grades K-8* (Duschl, Schweingruber, & Shouse 2007) delineates four strands of scientific proficiency and begins to flesh out how teachers can implement the second core principle from *How People Learn* with examples of instructional sequences that weave together the four strands and coordinate conceptual learning. The learning principles for educators embedded in these four reports have served as guides and models for the faculty who developed the MSSE.

Additional resources that focus more directly on professional development include *Designing Professional Development for Teachers of Science and Mathematics* (Loucks-Horsley et al. 2003) and *Learning Science and the Science of Learning* (National Science Teachers Association 2002). These documents provide a framework and useful suggestions for the process of planning professional development. Recommendations that "teacher learning programs must become more collegial and in-depth, longer in duration, and tailored to the experience levels of the learners, be they novice or expert teachers" (Stiles & Mundry 2002) were influential in our decision to create a master's degree for current teachers. A seminal article, *The Frame and Tapestry: Standards-Based Reform and Professional Development* (Thompson & Zeuli 1999), was influential in setting the goal of transformative professional development, as characterized by the following features:

- Create a high level of cognitive dissonance.

- Provide time, contexts, and support for teachers to think.

- Ensure that the dissonance-creating and dissonance-resolving activities are connected to the teacher's own students and context, or something like them.

- Provide a way for teachers to develop a repertoire for practice that is consistent with the new understanding teachers are building.

- Provide continuing help in the cycle of (a) surfacing the new issues and problems that will inevitably arise from actual classroom performance, (b) deriving new understandings from them, (c) translating these new understandings into performance, and (d) recycling.

A third set of resources is helpful both in the design of the program and as means to help teachers in the MSSE program align their own curriculum, instruction, and assessment with state and district standards. The *Atlas of Scientific Literacy* contains clusters of strand maps that show grade-level progressions of, and connections between, relevant AAAS benchmarks. The *Science Curriculum Topic Study* (Keeley 2005) is a study guide arranged by topics intended to "deepen teachers' understanding of how to use standards and research within the context in which they are working" (p. xvi). Both tools help educators relate the content embedded in the science standards to the design of effective strategies that will result in student learning.

3. Program Evaluation

A comprehensive, on-going evaluation of the program is required both by funding agencies and also by universities. While this requirement is fraught with challenges, program evaluation has great value: It provides an opportunity to assess the program more thoroughly than otherwise; it helps to clarify program design; and, it provides an opportunity to contribute to the body of research on the professional development of teachers.

Two challenges immediately present themselves. One is inherent in the nature of the professional development program: we want to improve the learning of the students of the teachers in the MSSE program, but our intervention is restricted to teachers. It is a methodological challenge to attempt to infer causality from the professional development to any changes in the learning and attitudes of the teachers' students. A second challenge is one of experimental design. The Department of Education, especially through it Institute for Education Sciences, is strongly encouraging random controlled experiments, following a medical model. The preferred design is to recruit twice as many teachers for a professional development program and then randomly assign half to receive the professional development while the other half does not. Wait-list control groups, where the control group receives the professional development later, are sometimes used. Recently, certain quasi-experimental designs, especially regression discontinuity quasi-experimental designs, (Shadish, Cook, & Campbell 2001) have been included in the list of preferred designs.

Our evaluation is a multi-level quasi-experimental study of the teachers as well as the students. We use two control groups: (1) A group of teachers with similar teaching assignments as the teachers in our program, along with their students, and (2) a set of schools that are matched to the schools of the teachers in our program on a number of socio-demographic characteristics.

The students are evaluated in three ways. First, we look for any differences in standardized test scores between the students of teachers in the program and students from a matched school. In the state of Illinois, science is included in the state-wide standardized tests only in the fourth and seventh grades, so standardized test scores are only available for a portion of the students. Second, we compare responses on a survey about the classroom environment, called the Constructivist Learning Environment Survey (CLES) (Taylor, Fraser, & Fisher 1997), to students of a matched teacher who is not in the program. The CLES, which has been psychometrically validated (Aldridge et al. 2000) has 36 Likert scale questions that measure the characteristics of the classroom environment: the extent to which the science learned at school is relevant to students' out-of-school lives and work aspirations; the extent to which teachers and students see science as a human activity involving values and assumptions, rather than an impersonal and objective study of the real world; the extent to which students feel able to have a voice in what happens in the classroom and to question the teacher and the discipline; the extent to which students have a sense of agency about their learning, and an active involvement in choosing activities and assessment approaches; the extent to which students are allowed to learn together collaboratively through negotiating and constructing models; and the extent to which students have a positive attitude toward science class. Third, we compare students' responses on a survey on their beliefs about the nature of science and the nature of science as practiced in the school classroom, the Beliefs about Science and School Science Questionnaire (BASSSQ) (Chen 1997, Chen, Taylor, & Aldridge 1998) to control group students' responses. The instrument, which has also been psychometrically validated (Fraser 1997), has 41 Likert scale questions relating to the process of scientific inquiry in general, the process of science inquiry in science classes, certainty of scientific knowledge in general, and certainty of school science knowledge.

The teachers are evaluated in three ways as well. First, they take a locally constructed science content pretest and post-test. This test measures their science content knowledge across physics, chemistry, biology, earth science, astronomy, and environmental science. Questions were drawn from the 2003 Grade 8 Third International Mathematics and Science Study, publicly released Massachusetts Comprehensive Assessment Systems Grade 8, 9, and 10 exams, the Force Concept Inventory (Hestenes, Wells, & Swakhamer 1992), and the Astronomy Diagnostic Test (Hufnagel et al. 2000). Second, they and their matched teachers respond to the teacher version of the Beliefs about Science and School Science Questionnaire described above. Finally, the teachers complete the Survey of Enacted Curriculum (SEC) (Blank, Proter, & Smithson 2001). The SEC, a joint project of the Wisconsin Center for Education Research and the Council of Chief State School Officers, is designed to measure content and cognitive demand of the curriculum that is actually taught in the classroom. This survey has been shown to be a very cost effective proxy for costly classroom observations.

The evaluation work is on going, but some preliminary results for the first two cohorts of teachers in the program show that in the grades when science is tested (4th and 7th in Illinois), the students of teachers participating in the program have higher standardized test scores than the students of matched comparison teachers. The differences are statistically significant (the two exceptions are Cohort 1 in 2007 and Cohort 2 Grade 4 in 2007). In the case of Cohort 2 Grade 4 and Grade 7 there is some indication of a widening gap between the students of MSSE teachers and the comparison students. However, the quasi-experimental design of the study prevents us from inferring any causality.

Results from the Constructivist Learning Survey show statistically significant differences between the responses of MSSE teachers' students and the responses of matched teachers' students. In particular, based on the 2007 survey both cohorts' students have a more positive attitude toward science. However, there was no significant change on the other subscales in the responses of the first cohort's students from 2006 to 2007.

No statistically significant changes from 2006 to 2007 have been observed on any of the teacher and student subscores of the Beliefs about Science and School Science Questionnaire. Nor have we found any significant difference between program teachers and comparison teachers and between their students. Anecdotal evidence suggests that some of those who are filling out the questionnaire are confused by some of the questions. The BASSSQ instrument may not be the appropriate instrument to detect changes in the understanding of the nature of science for our project.

The two greatest challenges of the evaluation work have been experimental design and a paucity of appropriate evaluation instruments, such as normalized and validated science content exams and attitudinal surveys. There are serious practical and ethical issues that make random controlled experiments difficult to put into practice in a teacher professional development program, and our quasi-experimental design does not allow us to infer causality for some of the detected differences between the teachers in the program and their students and control teachers and their students. To address the second issue new validated evaluation instruments are currently being developed at a number of institutions.

4.   Summary and Conclusions

The starting point for DePaul's Master's of Science in Science Education program was the realization that to improve science instruction in Chicago sustained professional development opportunities for teachers are needed that go beyond short term programs such as the ones offered by NASA. Offering a master's program for teachers in which most courses are taught by science faculty presented a number of interesting challenges. These included the lack of experience of many faculty in tailoring their courses to the needs of teachers, and the difficulty of identifying learning goals that are both appropriate for a masters level program and meet the needs of teachers with a wide variety of backgrounds in science content and classroom experiences. Math and science education research resources that we found to be particularly helpful for the design of the MSSE program include "How People Learn," "How Students Learn," "Taking Science to School" and "Adding it Up" (referenced above). While the evaluation required by the funding agencies presents significant challenges, including the difficulty to causally link our work with teachers to the progress of their students and the lack of appropriate evaluation instruments, we also found that it allows us to assess the program more thoroughly, refine the design, and contribute to the literature on teacher professional development. We recently received a planning grant from the US Department of Education MSP program to develop an environmental science masters program for teachers that builds on our experience with the MSSE program, and leverages more short-term professional development opportunities offered by the Peggy Notebaert Nature Museum. Similar opportunities through the MSP program may exist for other organizations interested in partnerships between providers of teacher workshops and other short-term professional development events and universities.

References

Aldridge, J. M., Fraser, B. J., Taylor, P. C., and Chen, C. -C., "Constructivist Learning Environments in a Cross-National Study in Taiwan and Australia," International Journal of Science Education, **22**(1), 37 (2000)

American Association for the Advancement of Science (AAAS), *Atlas of Scientific Literacy*, (AAAS, Washington DC, 2001) Vol. I

American Association for the Advancement of Science (AAAS), *Atlas of Scientific Literacy*, (AAAS, Washington DC, 2007) Vol. II

Blank, R. K., Porter, A. C., and Smithson, J., *New Tools for Analyzing Teaching, Curriculum and Standards in Mathematics & Science: Results from Survey of Enacted Curriculum Project*, (Consortium for Policy Research in Education, Washington, DC, 2001)

National Science Teachers Association, *Learning Science and the Science of Learning* edited by R. Bybee (NSTA Press, Arlington, VA, 2002)

Chen, C. -C., "Development of a Questionnaire for Assessing Teachers' Beliefs about Science and Science Teaching in Taiwan and Australia," Paper presented at the 70th Annual Meeting of the National Association for Research in Science Teaching (1997)

Chen, C. -C., Taylor, P. C., and Aldridge, J. M., "Combining Quantitative and Qualitative Approaches in a Cross-National Study of Teacher Beliefs about Science," Paper presented at the 71st Annual Meeting of the National Association for Research in Science Teaching (1998)

Committee on Science and Mathematics Teacher Preparation, *Educating Teachers of Science, Mathematics, and Technology: New Practices for a New Millennium*, (National Academy Press, Washington DC, 2001)

Duschl, R., Schweingruber, H., and Shouse, A., *Taking Science to School: Learning and Teaching Science in Grades K-8*, (National Academy Press, Washington DC, 2007)

Fraser, B., "Classroom Environment Instruments: Development, Validity, and Applications", Learning Environments Research, **1**, 7 (1998)

Grossman, M. C., *Astronomy Based Physical Science, Exploring Waves: Ripple Tanks, Vibrations, and Sound* (Charlesbridge Publishing, Watertown, MA 2001)

Hestenes, D., Wells, M., and Swackhamer, G., "Force Concept Inventory," The Physics Teacher, **30**, 141 (1992)

Hufnagel, B., Slater, T., Deming, G., Adams, J., Lindell, A. R., Brick, C., and Zeilik, M., "Pre-course Results from the Astronomy Diagnostic Test," Publications of the Astronomical Society of Australia, **17**, 2 (2000)

Keeley, P., *Science Curriculum Topic Study* (Corwin Press, Thousand Oaks, CA, 2005)

Loucks-Horsley, S., Hewson, P., Love, N., Mundry, S., and Stiles, K., *Designing Professional Development for Teachers of Science and Mathematics*, 2nd ed. (Corwin Press, Thousand Oaks, CA, 2003)

Mayer, D., Mullens, J., and Moore, M., *Monitoring School Quality: An Indicator's Report, National Center for Education Statistics #2001030* (NCES, Washington, DC, 2000)

National Research Council, *How People Learn: Brain, Mind, Experience, and School*, edited by J. Bransford, A. Brown, and R. Cocking (National Academy Press, Washington DC, 1999a)

National Research Council, *How People Learn: Bridging Research and Practice*, edited by M. S. Donovan, J. Bransford, J., and J. Pellegrino (National Academy Press, Washington DC, 1999b)

National Research Council, *How Students Learn: History, Mathematics, and Science in the Classroom* edited by M. S. Donovan and J. Bransford (National Academy Press, Washington DC, 2005)

Shadish, W. R., Cook, T. D., and Campbell, D. T., *Experimental and Quasi-Experimental Designs for Generalized Causal Inference* (Houghton-Mifflin, Boston, MA, 2001)

Shulman, L. S., "Those Who Understand: Knowledge Growth in Teaching," Educational Researcher, **15**(2), 4 (1986)

Stiles K. and Mundry, S., "Professional Development and How Teachers Learn: Developing Expert Science Teachers," in Learning Science and the Science of Learning, edited by Bybee, R. (NSTA Press, Arlington VA, 2002)

Thompson, C. and Zeuli, J., "The Frame and the Tapestry: Standards-Based Reform and Professional Development," in The Heart of the Matter: Teaching as the Learning Profession, edited by Sykes, G. (Jossey-Bass, San Francisco, CA, 1999)

Taylor, P. C., Fraser, B. J., and Fisher, D. L., "Monitoring Constructivist Classroom Learning Environments," International Journal of Educational Research, **27**, 293 (1997)

EPO and a Changing World
ASP Conference Series, Vol. 389, © *2008*
C. Garmany, M. Gibbs, and J. W. Moody

A Guide to the Learning Cycle and Exploring Student Ideas in Science

Dr. Wil van der Veen and Theresa Moody

New Jersey Astronomy Center, Raritan Valley Community College P.O. Box 3300, Somerville, NJ 08876

Emilie Drobnes

NASA Goddard Space Flight Center, Code 671, Greenbelt, MD 20771

Abstract.   Over the last few decades our understanding of how students learn best has increased dramatically. Students construct understandings by trying to fit new ideas and concepts into their prior understandings. Unfortunately these best practices are infrequently applied in the classroom or in educational outreach programs. Research indicates that instructional models, such as the BSCS 5-E's, can help students learn fundamental concepts in science. It is crucial that EPO professionals model best practices in their teacher training, and incorporate them in their education outreach or educational products. We will review the three principals of learning and the BSCS 5-E instructional model with emphasis on the crucial first stage of Engagement and list resources that can help EPO professionals and teacher engage students' ideas in science.

1.   Introduction

One of our goals as Education and Public Outreach (EPO) professionals is to help science teachers improve their instructional practices to improve student learning. Because many of us are involved in curriculum development and/or teacher training we should be aware of and apply research findings that can be incorporated in the curriculum materials we develop or teacher trainings we conduct and that will facilitate connections between teachers, the curriculum, and students. In recent years the use of instructional models has gained popularity with science educators. Research reports, such as *How People Learn: Brain, Mind, Experience, and School* (Bransford, Brown, & Cocking 2000) and its companion, *How Students Learn: Science in the Classroom* (Donovan & Bransford 2005), have confirmed that the use of an effective, research-based instructional model can help students learn fundamental concepts in science.

Learning cycles are not new and were originally proposed in the early 1960's by Atkin & Karplus (1962). The learning cycle was initially proposed as a 3-stage model (Exploration, Concept Development, and Application). Two additional stages were subsequently added: an Evaluation stage at the end, and an Engagement stage at the beginning. In this paper we highlight the 5-E instructional model or learning cycle developed by Biological Science Curriculum Study (BSCS) and we propose it as an effective model to be used by EPO professionals for both curriculum development as well as teacher training. For a full report of the origins, effectiveness, and applications of the BSCS 5-E instructional model (see Bybee *et al.* 2006).

2.   The Three Principles of Learning

How Students Learn: Science in the Classroom focuses on three principles of learning that are particularly important for us as EPO professionals to understand and incorporate in our work:

1. "Students come to the classroom with preconceptions about how the world works. If their initial understanding is not engaged, they may fail to grasp the new concepts and information, or they may learn them for purposes of a test but revert to their preconceptions outside the classroom."

2. "To develop competence in an area of inquiry, students must (a) have a deep foundation of factual knowledge, (b) understand facts and ideas in the context of a conceptual framework, and (c) organize knowledge in appropriate ways."

3. "A "metacognitive" approach to instruction can help students learn to take control of their own learning by defining learning goals and monitoring their progress in achieving them." The first principal should ring true for many of us who are familiar with the *Private Universe* and *Minds of Our Own* videos (Schneps & Sadler 1988). Unfortunately these important principles are infrequently applied by the majority of teachers and many EPO professionals who develop curriculum materials and/or conduct teacher trainings. Instructional models, such as the BSCS 5-Es, can help apply the above principles of learning.

3.   The BSCS 5-E Instructional Model

The BSCS 5-E Instructional Model, or the 5-Es, consists of the following phases: Engagement, Exploration, Explanation, Elaboration, and Evaluation. Each phase has a specific function and contributes to the teacher's coherent instruction and to the learners' formulation of a better understanding of science. When teachers or EPO professionals "plan lessons around the 5 stages of the learning cycle, students move from concrete experiences to the development of understanding, to the application of principles" Llewellyn (2002). The following is a brief description of each of the five phases in the BSCS 5-E instructional model

3.1.   Engagement

"The first phase engages students in the learning task. The students mentally focus on an object, problem, situation, or event. The activities of this phase make connections to past experiences and expose students' misconceptions; they should serve to mitigate cognitive disequilibrium.

Asking a question, defining a problem, showing a discrepant event, and acting out a problematic situation are all ways to engage the students and focus them on the instructional task. The role of the teacher is to present the situation and identify the instructional task. The teacher also sets the rules and procedures for establishing the task.

Successful engagement results in students being puzzled by, and actively motivated in, the learning activity. Here, the word "activity" refers to both mental and physical activity." (Bybee *et al.* 2006)

3.2. Exploration

"Once the activities have engaged the students, the students have a psychological need for time to explore the ideas. Exploration activities are designed so that the students in the class have common, concrete experiences upon which they continue formulating concepts, processes, and skills. Engagement brings about disequilibrium; exploration initiates the process of equilibration. This phase should be concrete and hands on. Educational software can be used in the phase, but it should be carefully designed to assist the initial process of formulating adequate and scientifically accurate concepts.

The aim of exploration activities is to establish experiences that teachers and students can use later to formally introduce and discuss concepts, processes, or skills. During the activity, the students have time in which they can explore objects, events, or situations. As a result of their mental and physical involvement in the activity, the students establish relationships, observe patterns, identify variables, and question events.

The teacher's role in the exploration phase is that of facilitator or coach. The teacher initiates the activity and allows the students time and opportunity to investigate objects, materials, and situations based on each student's own ideas of the phenomena. If called upon, the teacher may coach or guide students as they begin reconstructing their explanations. Use of tangible materials and concrete experiences is essential" (Bybee *et al.* 2006).

3.3. Explanation

"The word "explanation" means the act or process in which concepts, processes, or skills become plain, comprehensible, and clear. The process of explanation provides the students and the teacher with a common use of terms relative to the learning task. In this phase, the teacher directs students' attention to specific aspects of the engagement and exploration experiences. First, the teacher asks the students to give their explanations. Second, the teacher introduces scientific or technological explanations in a direct, explicit, and formal manner. Explanations are ways of ordering the exploratory experiences. The teacher should base the initial part of this phase on the students' explanations and clearly connect the explanations to experiences in the engagement and exploration phases of the instructional model. The key to this phase is to present concepts, processes, or skills briefly, simply, clearly, and directly and to move on to the next phase.

Teachers have a variety of techniques and strategies at their disposal to elicit and develop student explanations. Educators commonly use verbal explanations; but, there are numerous other strategies, such as videos, films, and educational courseware. This phase continues the process of mental ordering and provides terms for explanations. In the end, students should be able to explain exploratory experiences and experiences that have engaged them by using common terms. Students will not immediately express and apply the explanations-learning takes time." (Bybee *et al.* 2006).

3.4. Elaboration

"Once the students have an explanation and terms for their learning tasks, it is important to involve the students in further experiences that extend, or elaborate, the concepts, processes, or skills. This phase facilitates the transfer of concepts to closely related but new situations. In some cases, students may still have misconceptions, or they may only understand a concept in terms of the exploratory experience. Elaboration activities provide further time and experiences that contribute to learning.

During the elaboration phase, students engage in discussions and information-seeking activities. The group's goal is to identify and execute a small number of promising approaches to the task. During the group discussion, students present and defend their approaches to the instructional task. This discussion results in better definition of the task as well as the identification and gathering of information that is necessary for successful completion of the task. The teaching cycle is not closed to information from the outside. Students get information from each other, the teacher, printed materials, experts, electronic databases, and experiments that they conduct. This is called the information base. As a result of participation in the group's discussion, individual students are able to elaborate upon the conception of the tasks, information bases, and possible strategies for its [the task's] completion.

Note the use of interactions within student groups as a part of the elaboration process. Group discussions and cooperative learning situations provide opportunities for students to express their understanding of the subject and receive feedback from others who are very close to their own level of understanding.

This phase is also an opportunity to involve students in new situations and problems that require the transfer of identical or similar explanations. Generalization of concepts, processes, and skills is the primary goal" (Bybee *et al.* 2006).

3.5. Evaluation

"This is the important opportunity for students to use the skills they have acquired and evaluate their understanding. In addition, the students should receive feedback on the adequacy of their explanations. Informal evaluation can occur at the beginning and throughout the 5-E sequence. The teacher can complete a formal evaluation after the elaboration phase. As a practical educational matter, teachers must assess educational outcomes. This is the phase in which teachers administer assessments to determine each student's level of understanding" (Bybee *et al.* 2006).

4. The Engagement Phase

For the purpose of this paper, we want to focus on the first and very important phase in the learning cycle: the Engagement phase. This phase relates to the first principle of learning which notes that for learning to take place students' initial ideas must be engaged. However, engaging student ideas is easier said then done. To effectively engage students' ideas we first need to know what those ideas might be. A large body of research exists on student ideas in science and is summarized in an excellent book: *Making Sense of Secondary Science: Research into Children's Ideas* (Driver *et al.* 1994). This book had almost gone out of print till it was rediscovered as part of the Curriculum Topic Study project (Keeley 2005).

But even when we know what students' ideas might be, it is not an easy task to get students, especially when they are in middle or high school, to talk about them. Unless students can feel 'safe' and are no longer faulted for 'incorrect' answers, they may open up and share what they think. This process is crucial, both for the teachers as well as the learner. The teachers need to know what students are thinking, whereas the student needs to become aware of their own thinking before further learning can take place. All of the above applies when EPO professionals conduct trainings for teachers. Teachers come to trainings to increase their content knowledge and get ideas for how to teach it effectively. For learning to take place their initial ideas must be engaged. For some it is quite uncomfortable to admit to serious misconceptions on topics they have taught for many years. At our own workshops we have had teachers admit to teaching their students that the Sun goes around the Earth and that the Earth's shadow is causing the phases of the moon. From our experiences conducting hundreds of teacher trainings we have found that such misconceptions are not limited to astronomy, but are present in all science content areas and among teachers of all grade levels, including high school teachers.

Over the years some excellent probes have been developed to uncover student ideas and recently two books were published on this topic: *Uncovering Student Ideas in Science, Vol. 1* (National Science Teacher Association Number 1 best seller in 2007, Keeley, Eberle, & Farrin 2005) and *Uncovering Student Ideas in Science, Vol. 2* (Keeley, Eberle, & Tugel 2007). These probes are not limited to astronomy, but cover all areas of science. Books with probes for specific science content areas (such as astronomy) will be forthcoming (Keeley, private communication).

5.   Examples of Probes in Astronomy

Within astronomy there are misconceptions on almost any topic (Comins 2001, Plait 2002). The most common areas of misconception deal with Moon Phases, Seasons, Gravity, and Size and Scale. But even on seemingly easy topics, such as the day and night cycle, we have found that misconceptions exist even among middle school students. Examples of excellent probes in astronomy are listed below.

1. **Day & Night:** Common misconceptions about the day and night cycle range from the sun going behind the moon at night to the Earth going around the Sun in a day. (Darkness at Night - From: *Uncovering Student Ideas in Science - Vol. 2*, Keeley, Eberle, & Tugel 2007)

2. **Seasons:** A common misconception about seasons is that the changing distance between the Earth and the Sun is responsible for the seasons. (Sun-Earth Survey - From: *The Real Reasons for Seasons - Sun-Earth Connections*, Gould, Willard, & Pompea 2000)

3. **Moon Phases:** A common misconception about moon phases is that they are caused by the Earth's shadow. (Predicting Phases & Features - From: *Universe at Your Fingertips* - Activity A-1 (Fraknoi 1995). Going through a Phase - From: *Uncovering Student Ideas in Science - Vol. 1* (Keeley, Eberle, & Farrin 2005).

4. **Gravity:** A common misconception about gravity is that there is no gravity in space. (The Earth's Shape & Gravity - From: *Universe at Your Fingertips* - Activity C-1, Fraknoi 1995).

5. **Size & Scale:** The vastness of the universe or even our own Solar System is difficult to grasp for anyone since it goes far beyond our daily experiences. (Cosmic Survey - From: *NASA's Structure and Evolution of the Universe Education Forum* http://cfa.www.harvard.edu/seuforum; Emmy's Moons and Stars - From: *Uncovering Student Ideas in Science - Vol. 2,* Keeley, Eberle, & Tugel 2007).

6. Survey of Session Participants

Our session was attended by 34 participants, 21 of which returned a brief Astronomy Education Survey. The survey was designed to find out how familiar participants were with some of the national resources in science education, the principles of learn-ing, and instructional models. Participants rated their familiarity with the following resources on a scale of 1 (never heard of it) to 6 (actively incorporate it): *AAAS Atlas for Science Literacy, AAS Benchmarks for Science Literacy, National Science Education Standards, How People Learn, How Students Learn, Private Universe video, Making Sense of Secondary Science.* Participants were most unfamiliar with *Making Sense of Secondary Science* (70% never heard of it), followed by the *AAAS Atlas for Science Literacy* (45% never heard of it), and *How Students Learn* (30% never heard of it). Participants were most familiar with the *National Science Education Standards* with only 5% that never heard of it. The resource most often used in their work was the *Private Universe* video (60%) and the *National Science Education Standards* (45%). All other resources were used by less than 25% of the participants. Only 20% of the participants were able to name the principles of learning and 30% were able to list an instructional model and describe how they would use it in their work.

References

Atkin, J.M., and Karplus, R., "Discovery of Invention?" Science Teacher **29**(5) 45 (1962)

Bransford, J.D., Brown, A.L., and Cocking, R.R., How People Learn - Brain, Mind, Experience, and School, National Research Council (National Academy Press, Washington, D.C., 2000)

Bybee, R. W., *et al.* (2006) http://www.bscs.org/pdf/bscs5efullreport2006.pdf

Comins, N., *Heavenly Errors* (Columbia University Press, New York, 2001)

Donovan, M.S. and Bransford, J.D 2005, "How Students Learn - Science in the Classroom," National Research Council (National Academy Press, Wawshington D.C., 2005)

Driver, R., Squires, A., Rushworth, P., Wood-Robinson, V., "Making Sense of Secondary Science - Research Into Children's Ideas" (Routledge, London, UK, 1994)

Fraknoi, A., *The Universe at Your Fingertips* (Astronomical Society of the Pacific, San Fransisco, 1995)

Gould, A., Willard, C., and Pompea, S., "The Real Reasons for Seasons - Sun-Earth Connections" (Lawrence Hall of Science, Berkeley, CA, 2000)

Keeley, P., Science Curriculum Topic Study (Corwin Press, Thousand Oaks, CA, 2005)

Keeley, P., Eberle, F., and Farrin, L., "Uncovering Student Ideas in Science, Vol. 1 (NSTA Press, Arlington, VA, 2005)

Keeley, P., Eberle, F., and Tugel, J., "Uncovering Student Ideas in Science, Vol. 2 (NSTA Press, Arlington, VA, 2007)

Llewellyn, D., "Inquiry Within - Implementing Inquiry-Based Science Standards" (Corwin Press, Thousand Oaks, CA, 2002)

Plait, P., *Bad Astronomy* (John Wiley & Sons, New York, 2002)

Schneps, M. H. and Sadler, P. M., A Private Universe (Annenberg/CPB, New York, 1988)

EPO and a Changing World
ASP Conference Series, Vol. 389, © *2008*
C. Garmany, M. Gibbs, and J. W. Moody

Drive-By Professional Development is NOT the Answer

Marsha Bednarski

Physics - Earth Sciences Department, Central Connecticut State University, New Britain, CT 06053, USA

Abstract. Relevant professional development along with teacher and program support must be provided over time. A "One-Shot" teacher professional development experience, or what I like to call Drive-By PD, is not effective in almost any significant way to improve teaching practice (Loucks-Horsley *et al.* 1998). This workshop focused on identifying and discussing factors to consider when planning EPO.

1. Introduction

Teachers learn from their own practice (National Research Council, 2000) so providing opportunities for teachers to implement activities learned in PD is crucial. While implementing new activities, teachers need to gather student data, make observations of their own teaching and the teaching of others, and interact with other teachers to improve their own teaching practices (NRC 2000). To this end it is imperative that professional development activities be well though out and aligned with content and teaching standards. Lessons learned from Project S.C.I.E.N.C.E. (Science Communities Involve Everyone in Collaborative Endeavors), a twice funded grant program from the Connecticut Department of Higher Education for teachers in grades 3-5, provide the framework for the development of this session.

The session participants worked in groups to brainstorm and share how to plan effective EPO. They brought with them a vast array of experience. Included were university faculty, museum staff, grant writers, and public school curriculum experts. The brainstorming sessions were organized around three phases of developing an outreach plan for K-12 teachers: planning, implementing, and evaluating. Participants recorded one and two word factors to consider for each phase and shared them with the group. At the conclusion of this brainstorming and sharing session, their suggestions were compared to the steps followed in Project S.C.I.E.N.C.E., hereby referred to PS.

2. Planning an Effective Professional Development Program/Partnership

The key to planning effective professional development opportunities for teachers is to bring together key constituents who can bring ideas and needs to the table. These include, but are not limited to, district administrators, higher education partners, teachers, parents, and students working together to plan, implement, evaluate, and revise PD opportunities. It was exciting to have such a variety of backgrounds in the participant group.

2.1.   Factors to Consider in the Planning Stage

Participants in this workshop offered the following factors to consider in the planning stage (among others): research based, know your audience, needs assessment, standards/content, set goals, relevance, consider experience, implementation, expert speakers, networking, collegiality, active engagement, modeling appropriate methods, support, and best practices. It was interesting to note that many of the factors offered by the workshop participants - research, standards, goals, relevance, and support - were addressed in the initial planning session of PS with district administrators and university faculty.

PS looked at the needs assessment in three ways; needs of the district, needs of the teachers, and needs of the students. Workshop participants felt that the needs of the teachers were most important. District data was gathered from local and state exams. Often times, districts have administrators who collect and analyze this data. But it is important to not forget the teachers. They are directly involved with the administration of these exams and can also identify areas of need. At individual schools, conversations around exam data can yield a vast amount of data.

Teacher data can be gathered formally through needs assessments. One way is to use the state and/or national content and teaching standards as a framework to create a Likert scale instrument giving all teachers the opportunity to have input. Teachers involved in PS were emailed a needs assessment that was directly aligned with the Connecticut science standards for grades 3-5. Surveys were returned and content areas identified as weakness areas were given high priority in planning the PD activities. Other priority areas were identified by administrators from the other sources of data. We did cover all of the science content standards for those grade levels but focused on the need areas and only reviewed the non-priority areas.

In addition to standardized exams, student data can be gathered from a variety of sources. These sources include in-class written and verbal assessments. Again, the teacher is the key to gathering this data. Student achievement became a focus during many PS activities.

2.2.   Factors to Consider in the Implementation Phase

The workshop participants offered the following factors to consider in the implementation stage: recruitment, number of participants, location, room temperature, time, schedule/agenda, focus on learning goals, effective use of technology, intro with impact, presenters who model active learning, "I'm here to HELP attitude", flexible, KISS, differentiation (for teachers and student planning), vary strategies, modalities, techniques, fun, how and what to evaluate, assessments, and support.

Discussion around these factors brought many ideas into play. PS found recruitment to be crucial and extremely difficult. Initial contact was done through district administrators. Follow-up was done via email and posted flyers. Success demanded that the project director keep on top of recruitment. Logistics was also a concern. Time, comfort, accessibility, and availability of technology and resources were all addressed by holding PD at the university where these issues were successfully addressed. Also, the teachers liked the accessibility of the labs and resources.

Addressing learning modalities, differentiation, and varying strategies, as suggested by the workshop participants, was done in PS through an inquiry learning environment/community. The NRC (2000) suggests that inquiry is an important means for knowledge acquisition. Teachers need to understand inquiry, learn science concepts through inquiry, and know how to teach through inquiry. PS began the year-long program with an intensive one week summer institute. The first day immersed teachers in science process skills through interactive inquiry activities. The activities included the very basic observation skills to the more complicated experimental skills. (For specific activities refer to the PS web site www.physics.ccsu.edu/projectscience.) This initial set of activities provided teachers with the opportunity to experience and discuss inquiry and its implications for them and their teaching.

The remaining days of the PS institute were filled with inquiries around earth, life, and physical science content in line with the state standards. Teachers were given problems, materials, and activities which allowed them to investigate content at their level. PS included teachers and content for grade 3-5 teachers. As a planning committee we felt that teachers should become knowledgeable in content area for the entire grade range, not just for a particular grade level. In that way, teachers who may change grade levels would be accommodated and those who would stay at their grade level would have knowledge of what the students should know when they enter a grade and what they will be learning when they go on to the next. We also felt it was a good idea to expose as much science as we could to provide science background information for teachers who would serve as science coaches in their buildings or districts.

An important element to the institute activities was the opportunity teachers had to work together in inquiry, to engage in discourse, to learn, and become comfortable with the content they were responsible to teach to their students. Lecturing from higher education faculty was nonexistent. Interactive discussions during and after the activities provided the information the teachers needed. Another important part of the institute was the inclusion of specific inquiry activities teachers could use with their students along with the supporting materials. For each content area, teachers engaged in their own inquiry then explored how the information could be introduced in their own classrooms. Similarly, workshop participants offered discourse, along with the availability of activities and materials, as key to learning.

As discussed in the workshop, six additional Saturday and Friday evening sessions were offered. Topics included a field trip to Hammonasset State Park in CT, Astronomy, Integrating Science and Language Arts, Embedded Tasks, Performance Assessment and Rubric Development, and Examining Student Work. These follow-up activities were extremely important as they provided an opportunity to have discussions with the other teachers in the project and evaluate the classroom implementation and student achievement of the standards presented during the summer institute.

On-going support was provided by university faculty to work with teachers in the classroom. Some of the participants in this project were training to be the science coaches in their schools and/or districts. These teachers provided other teachers from their schools and from their district who were not part of the project with standards based PD activities.

The final meeting of the year was evaluating student work. Teachers brought samples and pictures of student work and discussed their instructional and assessment strategies with the group. This was a powerful meeting. At this point in the project, the teachers were comfortable with each other and a truly informative discussion ensued. As the workshop participants suggested, true partnerships between teachers and university faculty involve an open dialogue where all involved act as experts bringing to the table the wealth of their own experience.

2.3.   Factors to Consider in the Evaluation Phase

Participants in the workshop offered the following factors to be considered in the evaluation stage: pre/post tests, immediate feedback, online survey, reflection, written surveys, long answer questions, Likert scale, follow-up data collection, establish a network, immediate impressions, teacher/student learning, "gots and nots", number of returning teachers, number who recommend the workshop, performance assessment tasks (teachers produce usable product). It is interesting to note that there was a variety of evaluation strategies offered by the workshop participants, from very formal structured evaluations to more informal means of evaluation. As discussed in the workshop as an example, PS used a variety of these strategies.

For the summer institute of PS a pre/post self reported rating scale (1=poor, 10=excellent) for the conceptual understanding of the specific CT Science Frameworks (listed as 3.1 etc.) addressed in the institute was administered (see Table 1) as well as an end of the institute content assessment.

Table 1.   Pre/post test - self-reported conceptual understanding of CT Science Standards. 1=poor; 10= excellent.

Self reported rating scale	Pre average score	Post average score
Physical Science (3.1, 4.1, 5.1) Properties of Matter, Forces and Motion, Energy Transfer and Transformation	4.6	7.2
Life Science (3.2, 4.2, 5.2) Heredity and Evolution, Matter and Energy in Ecosystems, Structure and Function	5.6	7.2
Earth Science (3.3, 4.3, 5.3) The Changing Earth, Energy in the Earth's Systems, Earth in the Solar System	4.2	7.2
Science, Technology, Society (3.4, 4.4, 5.4) Resources, Electrical and Magnetic Energy, Instruments to Enhance the Quality of Life (camera, eye glasses, magnifiers, periscopes, telescopes, human eye)	4.2	7.2

These data suggests that the teachers had an increased comfort ability with the science content areas included in the CT Science Frameworks. This was important because many of the PS participants were novice teachers who had a poor science background. Other teachers were veteran teachers who had never taught science before. They expressed their appreciation for the project and the support over the year. In addition to the needs assessment, a written test asking for explanations and examples of the content from the Ct Science Frameworks was administered at the conclusion of the institute. The average score on the content test by the participants was 81% (n=29.)

The following written comments were also included:

- "All hands-on activities, little teacher oriented and student exploration a majority of focus. Individual hypothesis tested, explored and results determined based on explained results and variable change. The best 5 days of PD I have ever attended. This model should be used for all workshops. It involves the multiple intelligences in our learning."

- "I found this course very useful and extremely fun. I feel more confident teaching the topics to my class. The instructors presented the material in an enjoyable and informative way. I would sign up again and recommend this workshop to others! Thank you!"

- "This has been the most informative, useful, and FUN workshop I have ever attended. Thank you so much for all of your efforts in providing this for us."

- "Even though I don't feel I answered the questions on the test to my best ability, I feel I learned so much more to help me teach science. I thought the week flew by and I loved all the hands-on activities which I can definitely use in my classroom. This has by far been The Best workshop I've ever taken in my 25 years of teaching!! The food was great too! I look forward to the rest of the classes!"

No formal assessment was administered at the end of the project. Through discussions in follow-up sessions, it was clear that the activities and resources were used during the school year to teach science. Teachers reported much student success with the concepts and a deep appreciation for the materials provided by the grant to use in their classrooms.

3. Conclusion

Many of the factors offered by the participants during the session paralleled those which went into the planning, implementation, and evaluation phases of PS. The varied backgrounds of the workshop participants brought many perspectives to the table. As a result, some great suggestions and strategies were shared during the workshop, and participants investigated PS as a concrete example of how these factors could be used in practice.

Overall, successful K-12/university partnerships should revolve around the needs of the teachers, not what university faculty believe should be going on in the classroom (Tomanek 2005). Once needs are identified, the NRC (2000) states that successful standards-based reform needs to include long-term, comprehensive, inquiry PD for teachers. Learning outcomes for teachers in a successful PD program must include learning science concepts through inquiry and learning how to teach their students through inquiry.

A very important partnership developed as a result of Project S.C.I.E.N.C.E. Higher education faculty, district administrators, and teachers continue to work together to plan for PD opportunities. Some of the teachers have enrolled in our graduate program. University faculty continue to work with each other and with administrators and teachers in the schools. Planning for future grant projects and opportunities for additional grade level teachers is ongoing. Other districts are inquiring as to how they can get involved. And finally, inquiry pedagogy is expanding among higher education faculty for use in their own coursework and is now part of department goals used for program evaluations. Workshop participants at the Astronomical Society of the Pacific meeting have increased tools and motivation to develop such a program at their own home institution.

References

S. Loucks-Horsley, P. Hewson, N. Love, S. Mundry, and K. Stiles, *Designing Professional Development for Teachers of Science and Mathematics*, 2nd ed. (Corwin Press, Thousand Oaks, CA, 2003)

National Research Council, *Inquiry and the National Science Education Standards: A Guide for Teaching and Learning* (National Academy Press, Washington D.C., 2000)

D. Tomanek, Cell Biology Educator, **4**, 2809 (2000)

EPO and a Changing World
ASP Conference Series, Vol. 389, © 2008
C. Garmany, M. Gibbs, and J. W. Moody

The Collection of Data for the Research Component of the Internet-Based, "Doctor of Astronomy" Professional Degree Program at James Cook University

William Millar,[1,2] Graeme L. White,[1] Miroslav Filipović[3] and Alex Hons[1]

Abstract. We discuss the means by which students collect, analyze and use original data to fulfill the research component of the Internet-based, professional "Doctor of Astronomy" degree, at the James Cook University Centre for Astronomy. We give an example of such data obtained with the 1.9 meter telescope at the South African Astronomical Observatory. We also discuss the use of such data in an introductory level astronomy class at a community college.

1. Introduction

James Cook University in Townsville, Australia offers a professional doctorate program in astrophysics, astronomy history and astronomy education, delivered fully over the Internet. The program contains both lecture material and research. Two-thirds of the program is original research examined by thesis-portfolio.

1.1. Subjects (course work)

The courses are: *Modern Astrophysics (AS5011)* – Introduces students to the basics of the universe, *Astronomy Instrumentation (AS5012)* – Introduces students to the basics of astronomical instrumentation, *Doctoral Astronomy Literature Review (AS6011)* – Substantive and detailed review of the literature for a designated research topic, *Doctoral Pilot Research Project (AS6012)* – Pilot research project, and *Professional Doctorate Research Thesis (Astronomy) (PD7605)* – The thesis-portfolio.

2. Examination of the Doctor of Astronomy Portfolio

Examination of the student's work covers graded course-work components and the thesis-portfolio. There are three examiners. The work presented must be principally the student's, at a Doctoral/Ph.D. standard. It must have approximately 50,000 words adjusted appropriately for the content of the work. The work should be equivalent to at least three refereed papers. If the Ph.D. option is taken, the thesis must be at least 100,000 words.

3. Internet-Based Learning

Learning through the Internet allows students to participate in programs too specialized to be offered locally. Internet delivery allows the university the econ-

---

[1]Centre for Astronomy, James Cook University, Townsville, QLD 4811, Australia.

[2]Grand Rapids Community College, Grand Rapids, Michigan, 49502.

[3]University of Western Sydney, Penrith South, DC, NSW 1797, Australia.

omy of scale, providing a larger student participation than campus classes alone. It also allows student scheduling flexibility. The programs grant fully qualified specialist degrees from an accredited national university.

4.   The Collection of Data

The portfolio-thesis is the major portion of the degree work and must be based on original data.

4.1.   Collecting Data for an Astrophysical Thesis

International travel is essentially required (Australia, South Africa, South America) to use professional observatories. We apply for telescope time as the project warrants (the student needs enough data for at least three papers). Figure 1 shows example data for an astrophysical thesis-portfolio.

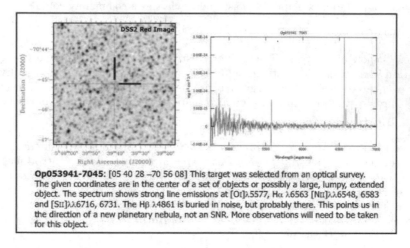

Figure 1.   Observation of a candidate SNR.

5.   Publication and Use of the Data

These data are published in a refereed journal and/or through a professional conference. These published papers are included as chapters in the thesis-portfolio.

5.1.   Use in an Introductory Level Astronomy Class

These data have been used in an introductory astronomy course at a community college, to show each step of the process of data gathering, reduction and analysis. This is done via a Power Point type presentation.

   Acknowledgments.   We wish to thank the South African Astronomical Observatory for the use of their facilities. We acknowledge the use of the Image Reduction and Analysis Facility (IRAF) of the National Optical Astronomy Observatories (NOAO), of the Figaro, Starlink and PNDR software packages. We also wish the thank the Australian Government for an International Facilities Use Grant for our travel to the South African Astronomical Observatory.

EPO and a Changing World
ASP Conference Series, Vol. 389, © *2008*
C. Garmany, M. Gibbs, and J. W. Moody

Project S.C.I.E.N.C.E. (Science Communities Involve Everyone in Collaborative Endeavors)

Marsha Bednarski

*Physics-Earth Sciences Department, Central Connecticut State
University, New Britain, CT 06050, USA*

Abstract. This poster describes Project S.C.I.E.N.C.E, a professional development program for in-service teachers in grades 3, 4, and 5 which aligns inquiry with the NRC National Science Education Content Standards.

1. Introduction

In an effort to improve science education, an increasing number of grant opportunities are available at the national, state, and local levels which seek to involve scientists and university-level science educators in the enrichment of in-service teachers. Project S.C.I.E.N.C.E. is an example of a successful (twice-funded) state-level consortium project which focused on space/earth science and physical science professional development (PD) for elementary teachers in grades 3, 4, and 5 in the form of a summer institute and follow-up sessions throughout the school year. Funding was made possible by the Connecticut Department of Higher Education as part of the teacher Quality Partnership Grant Program.

2. The Program

2.1. Goals

The main goal of this program was to provide elementary teachers with the necessary tools (science content and pedagogy) to be able to implement inquiry-based science instruction and assessment strategies to teach for understanding of content outlined in the new CT Science Frameworks, for all learners. Since individual state science frameworks are aligned with the National Science Education Standards, the lessons learned are applicable to many science professional development projects as the activities can be tailored to any state's standards or frameworks.

2.2. Getting Started

Paramount to any successful PD program is planning. The planning team for Project S.C.I.E.N.C.E. consisted of faculty from across the university (from the Schools of Arts and Sciences, and Education and Professional Programs), public school administrators, and public school teachers. Data from state standardized tests, teacher surveys, district PD and curriculum needs, and administrator input were all part of identifying the needs of the teachers. It was found that there was a great weakness in the science backgrounds of elementary teachers and their ability to conceptualize and teach through inquiry. In light of the new CT Science assessment tests, it was deter-mined that grades 3,4, and 5 teachers were in the greatest need of science PD.

2.3. The Program Begins

Once identified, participating teachers were emailed a content needs survey to complete before the initial summer institute. In this way, we were able to develop instruction and activities focusing on the teachers' weakest content knowledge areas. It was no surprise that their greatest weaknesses were in space/earth science and physical science.

The five day summer institute began with a full day of inquiry activities. It is important for teachers to understand inquiry, learn science concepts through inquiry, and be able to teach using inquiry (National Research Council 2000). The remaining days of the institute were devoted to engaging teachers in learning space/earth science and physical science content through inquiry. In addition, teachers participated in science inquiry activities aligned with the CT Science Frameworks that they could use in their own classrooms.

Follow-up PD days during the year offered teachers additional content activities as well as curriculum and instructional design and performance assessment and rubric development. The best way to assess understanding of the standards taught through inquiry us to use a variety of assessment strategies. These strategies can range from simple observations and discussions for the more straightforward inquiry skills, such as using data and developing descriptions, to more open-ended projects or products that demand that students produce evidence of their understanding, such as performance tasks and portfolios (National Research Council 2000).

The culminating PD activity at the end of the year was having teachers use student work generated from teacher developed inquiry lessons and assessments. Sharing and discussing what student understanding looks like in relation to the standards is how teachers can begin to judge the effectiveness of their instructional planning, implementation, and assessment practices.

Conclusion

As a result of this project, teachers reported increased confidence in their abilities to teach space/earth science and physical science. Their knowledge in the identified initial weak content areas tested out at an average of 82 percent mastery. The PD activities of the project were rated among the best teachers had ever participated in. Finally, student work demonstrated the effectiveness of teacher-developed science inquiry instruction and assessment of science standards.

References

National Research Council, *Inquiry and the National Education Standards*, (National Academy Press, Washington, D.C., 2000)

EPO and a Changing World
ASP Conference Series, Vol. 389, © 2008
C. Garmany, M. Gibbs, and J. W. Moody

Understanding the Regulations and Ethical Considerations of Astronomy Education Research

Sanlyn R. Buxner, Erik Brogt, Erin F. C. Dokter, and Jessie C. Antonellis

The University of Arizona, PO Box 210069, Tucson, AZ 85721

Abstract. We present regulations and ethical considerations of conducting and participating in astronomy education research.

1. Astronomy Education Research on Humans

The emerging field of astronomy education research presents new challenges to astronomy researchers because the research involves human participants and is regulated by federal law. Institutions that receive federal funding for research on humans must comply with federal regulations for all research that involves human subjects. Institutions that fall under these guidelines must have an institutional review board (IRB) that regulates research activities that involve humans. Its role is to ensure that research conducted under its auspices does not impose unnecessary risk to participants, that the research is ethical and that participants' rights are protected. When conducting research with humans at an institution with an IRB, permission or exemption must be granted *prior to* the initiation of the project including recruitment of participants. Institutions may have additional policies and governing boards to oversee research done at the institution and/or by employees. The following rules apply to those doing research at institutions with formal IRBs. Research at institutions without specific research policies should consider following the same basic guidelines as a matter of professional ethics.

1.1. Recruitment and Consent of Participants

In most cases, participants must be given the choice of participating in a study or not. It is the IRB, not the researcher, that determines the level of risk and if consent is required. Instructors doing research on their own classes must be particularly careful to avoid coercion for participation. Children (participants under the age of 18) are a specially protected population because of their increased vulnerability to coercion. Formal consent to participate is usually done in writing.

1.2. Data Collection and Confidentiality

Under IRB regulation, only the researchers are entitled to know who is participating in the study and which data belongs to a given participant. Students' IDs, names, and any other information identifying them may never be published for research regard-less of their consent. Data collected for purposes of tracking students with identifiable information must be de-identified and recoded. The data must be kept confidential and secure. Data must be kept under lock and key, on a password protected computer, and participants' identities cannot be discussed with non-researchers. Data collected for one research project cannot be used for another without separate IRB approval and possibly participant consent. In addition, the Family Educational Rights and Privacy Act of 1974 (FERPA) prohibits the public use of personally identifiable student data.

1.3.   Participant Rights and Benefits

Participants have the right to not participate or withdraw from the study at any time, without adverse consequences. For example, you may require all students to complete the final but you cannot penalize them if they decline the use of their final exam data in a research study. You cannot withhold access to materials or benefits that are part of the regular education or intervention setting. Participants may be given small incentive to participate such as small amounts of money or food. Participants that decline participation cannot be put in a control group because those in a control group are still a part of the study.

IRB requires that you are upfront with participants about possible risks and any benefits that may result from participation in the study. Risks are usually low in astronomy education research; however psychological risk can be present if participants feel uncomfortable or threatened by any aspect of the study, for instance if they believe their answers will be used to make judgments about them or as a formal assessment. IRB may require that by the conclusion of the study, those in the control group to receive comparable benefit to those that received the intervention.

1.4.   Publication

Intent to publish your results makes your data research data by definition and as such requires IRB approval, and possibly participant consent, regardless of whether you consider your work to be evaluation or research. Both evaluation and research involve systematic investigations involving humans and both must be conducted with consideration of the laws, participants' rights and ethical conduct.

For a copy of the poster or decision tree, please contact sbuxner@as.arizona.edu.

References

Brogt, E., Dokter, E., and Antonellis, J., Astronomy Education Review, **6** (2007)
National Commission for the Protection of Human Subjects of Biomedical and Behavioral Research, *The Belmont Report: Ethical Principles and Guidelines for the Protection of Human Subjects of Research* (1979).
    http://www.hhs.gov/ohrp/humansubjects/guidance/belmont.htm.
U.S. Department of Education, *Family Educational Rights and Privacy Act* (1974)
    http://www.ed.gov/policy/gen/guid/fpco/ferpa/index.html.
U.S. Department of Health & Human Services, *Code of Federal Regulations, Title 45: Public Welfare, Part 46: Protection of Human Subjects* (2005)
    http://www.hhs.gov/ohrp/humansubjects/guidance/45cfr46.htm.

EPO and a Changing World
ASP Conference Series, Vol. 389, © 2008
C. Garmany, M. Gibbs, and J. W. Moody

Building a Data Education Community Online

Carol A. Christian

Space Telescope Science Institute, 3700 San Martin Dr., Baltimore, MD 21218, USA

Jordan Raddick

Department of Physics and Astronomy, Johns Hopkins University, 3400 N. Charles St., Baltimore, MD 21218, USA

Kirk Borne

College of Science, George Mason University, 4400 University Dr. MS 6A2, Fair-fax, VA 22030, USA

Abstract. In the astronomy education community, many of us use research data from large astronomical projects as part of the materials that we design. These large datasets can have many advantages for educators. Large datasets allow students to explore a broad range of astronomical questions, and teachers and students can be excited to know that they are looking at the same data that professional astronomers look at. However, the effectiveness of data on student understanding and motivation has not been well-studied, and the community is new enough that best practices are still evolving. As we continue to develop and evaluate EPO materials based on large datasets, it is important to communicate the products and insights that we develop. However, regular communication can be difficult because of our geographic dispersion and busy schedules. To help improve communication around the topic of large professional datasets in EPO, we have started a public "Data in Education" blog. The purpose of the group blog is for people to talk to each other to develop new ideas and collaborations. New posts appear every Tuesday and Friday on many topics, and we encourage comments and discussions on any topic. The address of the blog site is http://dataineducation.blogspot.com.

1. Why a blog?

In the past few years, new telescope and camera technology has allowed astronomers to make detailed surveys and measurements of the sky. Those data and results are coming into physics and astronomy classrooms through web-based tools. These tools allow students to work with the same data that professional astronomers work with. The challenge now is to turn the data into activities that are scientifically accurate, include educational best practices, and are aware of the realities of classroom life.

Many scientists, instructional developers, and teachers, including us, are working on such educational products. But many of us work in isolation, making it difficult to brainstorm new ideas and share lessons learned. Furthermore, many instructional developers have only infrequent contact with the teachers and students who are the final audience for our activities. Clearly, we need some means to interact with other developers, teachers, and students in a more regular way.

A blog (short for web log) is a web site where authors post new content regularly, and readers comment on that content. Many Internet users use blogs as journals or opinion pages, but blogs can also be used for collaborative work - one person can post ideas, and others can extend and develop those ideas in the comments. We intend our blog to be collaborative, and we want comments from as many different people as possible!

Blog-based collaboration has many advantages over collaboration by E-mail: blog entries are archived on a server, so they do not need to be sorted into folders in an E-mail client; they can be tagged by content for easier searching; and they can link to other blogs, extending the online community of practice.

2. Our blog

We have created a new blog at http://datalineducation.blogspot.com. We use Blogger, a commercial provider, to allow readers to comment using an interface they are familiar with. We post a new entry every Tuesday and Friday.

If you would like to help with the blog, the best thing you can do is read and comment. A blog can't exist without a community, and a community can't exist without readers, so we need you! We are especially interested in hearing from teachers, since we are designing activities intended for you and your students. We hope to provide interesting ideas and questions for you every Tuesday and Friday.

EPO and a Changing World
ASP Conference Series, Vol. 389, © 2008
C. Garmany, M. Gibbs, and J. W. Moody

Lessons Learned Beyond the Solar System

Mary Dussault, Erika Reinfeld, and Roy Gould

Harvard-Smithsonian Center for Astrophysics, 60 Garden Street, Mail Stop 71, Cambridge, MA 02138

Abstract. The Beyond the Solar System Professional Development Project (BtSS) aims to increase the prevalence and quality of space science teaching about the origin and evolution of the universe. It was designed to meet specific audience needs and has developed an ongoing network of nearly 1,000 space science educators, including a core Leadership Team whose members provide professional development across the country. The project's cornerstone resource is a professional development DVD, "Beyond the Solar System: Expanding the Universe in the Classroom," available at the project web site: http://www.universeforum.org/btss/

1. Audience Needs Assessment

In 2004, educators at the Harvard-Smithsonian Center for Astrophysics conducted a national survey of space science educators to find out what factors influenced the teaching of Big Bang cosmology in the classroom. Of the nearly 600 educators surveyed, 38% did not teach the subject. The top three factors influencing this decision were: "I would need more content knowledge," "Not enough time," and "No adequate text or material to teach these topics."

When asked to rate the usefulness of various resources for teaching about Big Bang cosmology in the classroom, a strong majority of respondents deemed graphic visualizations of cosmology concepts, explanations of the science of Big Bang cosmology, and inquiry-based classroom materials and activities to be "essential" or "very useful." The graphic visualizations deemed most "essential" for teaching about cosmology were the Big Bang, the structure of the universe, and the formation of stars and galaxies. "Illustrations of common student questions and misconceptions" and "scenes of other teachers teaching these topics" were not rated as highly, but research has shown these factors to be important elements in successful professional development programs. The Beyond the Solar System program has been specifically designed to meet these needs.

2. Professional Development

The BtSS Professional Development Project has reached thousands of educators from 45 states, D.C., Puerto Rico, and more than two dozen different countries. Approximately 1,000 of these educators have registered to become ongoing participants in the project's continued outreach program. The majority of these educators teach middle or high school science.

2.1.   Expanding the Universe in the Classroom

The professional development DVD "Beyond the Solar System: Expanding the Universe in the Classroom" contains 135 minutes of video and 30 PDF resources, organized in two core strands: a science content strand, and a teaching and learning strand. The modular format of the DVD allows teachers and professional development providers to adapt the materials to a variety of settings.

Since its release in 2006, space science educators have used this resource in classrooms, workshops, summer institutes, teacher education courses, museums, planetariums, and other community organizations. The DVD has been distributed to more than 4,500 educators, more than two thirds of whom received these DVDs from teacher-educators as part of targeted professional development workshops for middle and high school teachers.

2.2.   Leadership Initiative

In August 2006, a national team of 24 experienced astronomy professional development providers participated in a BtSS Summer Leadership Institute at the Center for Astrophysics. These NASA educators, pre-service faculty members, informal educators, and master teachers deeply explored the pedagogical and science content of the BtSS DVD. Team members now incorporate BtSS resources into their ongoing professional development offerings.

As a result of this experience, members of the leadership team showed measurable gains in understanding targeted concepts of origin and evolution of the universe (e.g. universal gravity and the origin of elements), as measured by the MOSART Astronomy Concept Inventory (see section 2.3).

2.3.   Assessment Tools

The Beyond the Solar System project has also supported the dissemination of current education research about student and teacher learning, such as those materials developed by the Misconception Oriented Standards-Based Assessment Resources for Teachers (MOSART) project at the Center for Astrophysics. BtSS-supported astronomy and space science assessment tools are now publicly available to educators who complete the MOSART online tutorials. These tutorials can be accessed at MOSART project web site which is located at http://www.cfa.harvard.edu/smgphp/mosart/about_mosart.html.

Acknowledgments.   BtSS and the development of the Astronomy/Space Science assessment items were supported by NASA's Science Mission Directorate, via the Universe Education Forum. The MOSART project is supported by NSF.

EPO and a Changing World
ASP Conference Series, Vol. 389, © *2008*
C. Garmany, M. Gibbs, and J. W. Moody

Adapting Formal Education Materials for Out-of-School Settings

Heather Gibbons

Pacific Science Center, 200 2nd Avenue N, Seattle, WA, 98109, USA

Denise A. Smith

Space Telescope Science Institute, 3700 San Martin Drive, Baltimore, MD 21218, USA

Abstract. How can we work effectively with out-of-school time programs to engage youth in science and technology? What types of materials can be easily integrated into out-of-school learning experiences? Can existing formal education materials be adapted for use in out-of-school settings? To address these questions, the Origins Education Forum and the Pacific Science Center have partnered to identify best practices for integrating NASA space science content into out-of school learning opportunities. Lessons learned are applicable to a wide range of education and public outreach efforts.

1. Introduction

NASA's space science missions have created a variety of formal education materials to inspire, engage, and educate students in key topics associated with NASA's scientific explorations of the universe. Recognizing the potential that these materials hold for conveying current science to youth in out-of-school-time (OST) settings, we provided fourteen OST groups and three science centers with a selection of existing NASA materials. We have identified best practices for adapting formal education materials for use in OST settings from follow-up discussions and focus groups with these organizations, as well as a survey of existing web sites and literature.

2. Elements of Successful Programs

OST programs that successfully incorporate space science materials exhibit several characteristics. They involve scientists, educators, and community members in pro-gram development. Focus groups participants stressed the importance of recognizing the diverse needs of OST programs. These include the need to demonstrate relevance to participants, to acknowledge the roles of both large and small institutions, to show long-term commitment, and to provide adequate resources. Providing professional development, mentoring, recognition, and on-going evaluation are also important ingredients to success.

3. The Out-of-School-Time Environment

OST settings emphasize free-choice learning along with inspiring deeper interest and a desire to learn more. They focus attention on demonstrating the personal relevance of their topics, and regularly use art, music and physical activity to connect with participants. Successful activities focus on science as inquiry, and allow for free exploration and discussion. Implications for adapting materials for OST settings include a need to identify the "hook" or "wow" factor that will engage the learner, and to point towards resources for further learning. Activities also need to show science as an ongoing process where concepts are related to each other and to participants' daily lives. "Make and Take" type activities or other personal reminders can be powerful ways to allow learners to develop ownership. Creative ways of integrating science with aspects of art, music, and physical activity make products and programs more useful and relevant in the OST environment. Since educators working in OST settings increasingly need to link to education reform efforts, materials should include connections to literacy, mathematics, and appropriate education standards.

4. Operational Factors and Successful Solutions

Educators in OST settings work within a suite of operational factors that must be considered when providing products or programs. OST activities are often of shorter duration than formal classroom activities. OST educators also face a high amount of turnover in program participants. Effective materials therefore focus on a single concept, and are brief and modular so that they can stand on their own. OST programs also involve participants from multiple age groups, and do so with staff with varying backgrounds and high turnover. In addition, planning time, space, and funds are frequently limited. Successful activities and materials, therefore, provide opportunities for older participants to guide younger ones, and encourage teamwork. For ease of staff use, OST materials should show science as approachable, highlight the specific inquiry strategies that are being targeted, include suggestions for presenting concepts, and provide all the necessary science background, including common misconceptions. Any supplies should be easy to use, easy to find, low cost, and require minimal storage space.

5. Closing Thoughts

By working together to meet the needs of the OST community, scientists and educators can expand the reach of their programs to reach a diverse audience of youth and families. Adapting existing formal education materials for use in OST settings allows developers to leverage content that has already been researched and vetted for educational use. This strategy allows existing programs to mine their current resources for the gems that also work outside of the classroom, while supporting learning that is going on within.

Acknowledgments. The Origins Education Forum coordinates the EPO efforts of NASA space science missions seeking to understand the origins of galaxies, stars, planets, and life. The Space Telescope Science Institute operates the Origins Education Forum on behalf of NASA's Science Mission Directorate.

EPO and a Changing World
ASP Conference Series, Vol. 389, © 2008
C. Garmany, M. Gibbs, and J. W. Moody

Astro 001: Interactive, Online, and with a Sci-Fi Storyline

Kimberly A. Herrmann, Christopher Palma, Jane C. Charlton, and
Anand Narayanan

*Department of Astronomy & Astrophysics, Pennsylvania State
University, 525 Davey Lab, University Park, PA 16802, USA*

Abstract.   We present a new, fully on-line astronomy course for undergraduate non-science majors at Penn State that was offered for the first time in Spring 2007 with an enrollment of 422 students. The entire course content is conveyed through an interactive story, capitalizing on the many multimedia astronomy resources publicly available on the Internet. The four units of the course (Basic Astronomy and the Nighttime Sky, Our Solar System, Stars and the Milky Way Galaxy, and Extragalactic Astronomy and Cosmology) deliver the same content as a traditional Astro 001 course. Each unit follows the educational adventure of a different fictional Astro 001 student who has been "abducted" by aliens. The four units are united by a character, the Riddler, who poses riddles about various aspects of astronomy, and whose identity and purpose is revealed gradually as a reward for completion of various subtopics. This initial offering of the course was entirely web-based except for traditional evening in-class exams. Our first offering was very successful: it was very popular with the students, the exam grades were about 10 percent higher than usual, and we expect an even higher enrollment in our second offering in Fall of 2007. This Spring we used the Astronomy Diagnostic Test (ADT), but plan in the Fall to use a different pre- and post-assessment that will benchmark each of the four content units. Our future plans include adapting the course into a shorter form to be delivered in middle schools. We gratefully acknowledge funding from STScI IDEAS grant HST-ED-90284-01-A and a Zaccheus Daniel travel grant.

1.   The Four Units

In Unit 1, Basic Astronomy & the Nighttime Sky, Nate, a PSU student just starting an Astro 001 class, gets abducted by aliens so they can test him to determine the capabilities of the human race. Nate meets a "Riddler" who helps Nate prepare for his tests after solving each riddle that reveals the topic of the next test. Nate learns about seasons; eclipses and the phases of the Moon; the constellations; the physics of light; spectroscopy; telescopes; and gravity.

In Unit 2, Our Solar System, Avani, another Astro 001 student, is transported into a future in which every major body in the Solar System has a Great Museum installed in its orbit. She and her companion, another "Riddler," begin at Earth and proceed upon a guided tour of these Great Museums. Unit 2 presents formation of the Solar System; detailed information on each planet; Kepler's Laws; tectonics and volcanism; planetary atmospheres; magnetic fields and aurorae; ring systems and satellites; asteroids and comets; and the conditions for the development of life.

In Unit 3, Stars and the Milky Way Galaxy, Satoshi, another Astro 001 student, is distressed that the Sun is fated to engulf Earth. While taken aback by this horror, he is whisked away by two aliens, the helpful "Professor" and a trickster "Riddler," initially in search of sun-like stars, but then on a Milky Way tour. The trio explore the Sun as an example star; the nearest stars and some related topics; the brightest stars and more stellar topics; the interstellar medium and stellar birth; stellar clusters and evolution; stellar deaths and remnants; and the Milky Way Galaxy's general structure.

In Unit 4, Extragalactic Astronomy and Cosmology, a fourth unwitting PSU Astro 001 student visits ten alien races, each with its own point of view on existence and what is most important. Thomasin learns about recent developments in astrophysics, coupled with interpretations meant to inform students' responses to "What should Thomasin declare as her major field of study?" Unit 4 reveals galaxy classification and interactions; the distant universe; the significance of the Hubble Deep Field; quasars and gamma ray bursts; subatomic particles; the Big Bang; the universe's evolution and fate; dark matter and dark energy; and the possibility of multiple universes.

2. Goals and Our Status in Reaching Them

We had many goals in designing this course. Firstly, we hoped to excite students about astronomy by immersing them in a story. This appears to be working well based on many positive student comments. Secondly, we hoped to engage students (they answer 300 multiple choice questions woven through the story) so they will achieve a greater understanding of the concepts. There was a 15.6post-ADT. Because the ADT stresses Unit 1 material, we plan to supplement it with a few extra questions in the future. Thirdly, our course has helped to increase enrollment in PSU astronomy courses by helping to set an all-time record for spring enrollment in our first offering. Lastly, three grad students have already enjoyed the unique EPO experience by helping design the course and more are planning to help in the improvement stage.

3. Future Plans

We hope to (1) enhance the course with more animations to resemble modern video games, (2) develop more uniform activities to decrease our reliance on external web-sites, and (3) expand to a high school, middle school, and/or public audience.

Acknowledgments. We gratefully acknowledge the help of Brett Bixler of Penn State's Education Technology Services, Jin Sung An of Academic Services and Emerging Technologies, John and Denise Wagner of Information and Technology Services, Rosemary Schwegel, and Johnny Johnson. We would also like to thank the conference organizers.

EPO and a Changing World
ASP Conference Series, Vol. 389, © 2008
C. Garmany, M. Gibbs, and J. W. Moody

LSST EPO: Understanding by Design

Suzanne H. Jacoby, Julia K. Olsen

LSST Corporation, 4703 E Camp Lowell Dr, Suite 253, Tucson AZ 85712

Michelle M. Nichols

Adler Planetarium, 1300 S Lake Shore Dr, Chicago IL, 60605

Abstract. The potential for education and public outreach with the Large Synoptic Survey Telescope (LSST) is as far reaching as the telescope itself. LSST data will be available to the public, giving anyone with a web browser a movie-like window on the Universe. Our goal is to provide access to the LSST database in an appropriate and usable format suited to broad audiences including the general public, formal education programs, informal learning centers, and citizen-scientists wishing to make a contribution to scientific research. Using the principles of Backward Design, described in Understanding by Design (Wiggins & McTighe 2005) we have begun to assess audience needs and conceptualize our Education and Public Outreach (EPO) program. By sharing our process and progress to date, the LSST EPO development team endeavors to demonstrate a structured approach from which other EPO programs can benefit.

1. Introduction

Scheduled to begin operations in 2014, the 8.4-meter LSST will survey the entire visible sky deeply in multiple colors every week with its three-billion pixel digital camera. As LSST provides an overall new view of the sky, the LSST EPO program provides the instruments for the public, museum visitors, and students to properly examine, understand and participate in this achievement. In doing so LSST EPO rein-forces public trust in science, confidence in the transparency of its methods, and excitement about its discoveries. The LSST EPO program therefore provides a test-bed for best practices in the rapid educational diffusion of new information, an opportunity to test new educational practices utilizing data, and an understanding of the educational data diffusion networks and how they should be managed for maximal data flow to students and the public at large. The challenge is to select which ideas should go forward, coordinate various individual efforts, and build an integrated EPO pro-gram as ambitious as the telescope itself.

2. Our EPO Process

EPO team members involved in designing and developing LSST EPO programs at each of the partner institutions include experts in the fields of formal and informal education, program evaluation, public outreach program development, museum exhibit and planetarium show development, inquiry-based education materials design, and web-based activities development. The LSST Understanding by Design (UbD) team is distributed across the U.S. and in regular communication via email, scheduled teleconferences and face to face meetings when possible.

To meet the needs of formal and informal educators, the LSST collaboration is constructing an EPO program based on the principles of Backward Design to be used as a model for other EPO providers. The Backward Design principles provide a conceptual framework, design process, and template to promote participants' understanding of the key ideas of any educational outreach program. The essential component of this process is to explicitly state the key ideas or goals while simultaneously identify-ing the desired outcomes of the program, then determining what constitutes accept-able evidence of program success. Using the key ideas, desired outcomes, and acceptable evidence, the planning team designs the learning experiences. When developing learning experiences it is important to use a variety of instructional strategies, to think about the intended audience, to consider the participants' prior knowledge, and to scaffold the sequence of learning to help participants advance from their cur-rent knowledge and skill level to successfully achieve program goals. The unique dimension of this design process is that it requires planning teams to consistently integrate all the components and to examine the impact one decision might have on the other components of the planning process.

3. Results So Far

We have largely completed identification of desired results; we have articulated our overarching EPO goals, have developed the overall desired understandings and essential questions, and have determined key knowledge and skills which are fundamental to the project. Our assessments reflect all of our EPO goals. We are making significant progress in determining acceptable evidence for assessing our institutional effectiveness in all EPO areas including the evidence for positive attitudes towards scientific research, progress in basic skills, conceptual development and content knowledge. Finally, we are planning learning experiences with our partner institutions, who are formulating their materials and outreach based on this plan. We envision our current work to be the overarching plan for the EPO programs and materials which utilize LSST data, and that our partner sites will themselves repeat this process throughout their various LSST-based projects. More information can be obtained at http://www.lsst.org/Education_Outreach/lsst_epo.shtml.

References

Wiggins, G., and McTighe, J., *Understanding By Design, Expanded 2nd edition*, (Association for Supervision and Curriculum Development, Alexandria, VA, 2005)

EPO and a Changing World
ASP Conference Series, Vol. 389, © *2008*
C. Garmany, M. Gibbs, and J. W. Moody

Lessons From Breezy Hill: Thirteen Years of Children's Activities at Stellafane

Kristine Larsen

Physics Earth Sciences Department, Central Connecticut State University, New Britain, CT 06053, USA

Abstract. This poster describes the challenges and constraints encountered in thirteen years of providing astronomical children's activities at the annual Stellafane Convention of Amateur Astronomers.

1. Introduction

One of the most important institutions in amateur astronomy is the annual Stellafane Convention (http://www.stellafane.org). Surveys of Stellafane attendees conducted in 1993 and 1994 by this author found that the convention was unwittingly ignoring the needs of its youngest attendees. In response, the author began offering a program of hands-on educational astronomy activities at each convention in order to actively engage children.

2. Challenges and Constraints

Over the past thirteen years, the author has identified and overcome a number of challenges and constraints. First and foremost, it is important to effectively use the limited available space and resources. Twenty-four children can be comfortably accommodated in the library of the McGregor Observatory. Since the room has multiple uses, all materials need to be easily stored between workshops. All materials used in the activities must be brought in by the author (including water, if needed).

It is also important to KICS (Keep it cheap stupid). There is no budget for these activities so all materials are either donated or purchased by the author. Club members collect coffee cans, paper towel tubes, or other common household items for use in the workshops. Annual outlay for the workshops has been successfully kept to under $50.00.

One cannot predict the number of participants or their ages. Sufficient materials must be held in reserve for unexpectedly large crowds. Although the activities are advertised for children ages 5-12, children much younger may attend. With parental help, very young children can participate in cutting and writing, but astronomy-based coloring pages, puzzles and crayons are a valuable alternative. Activities should be selected for their ability to be extended for older children and simplified for younger children.

Some children will attend all workshops in a given year and also attend year after year. As a result, activities should not be repeated any sooner than every three years.

Time is also a valuable commodity so one must KIBS (Keep it brief stupid). Each session is allotted one hour and is composed of two short activities. This allows latecomers to do at least one whole activity. It is also advisable to have on hand astronomy games (such as solar system bingo) to fill time as needed.

Finally, it is important to ensure the relevance and educational value of the workshops. Activities are selected which are aligned with national science standards (National Research Council 1996) and utilize a number of varied skills. The relevance of the workshops to the convention is achieved by tying the theme of the workshops to that of the keynote speaker.

3.   Walking the Walk: The 2007 Convention

The 2007 keynote talk discussed Mars landing sites. A general theme of planets was, therefore, chosen for the workshops. The National Science Education Standards (National Research Council 1996) selected to frame the activities were: observable properties of objects (K-4); changes in the shape of the moon (K-4); the structure of the solar system (5-8); and the causes of the phases of the moon and eclipses (5-8).

The six activities comprising the three workshops were as follows: Models of Saturn and its rings using a 2.5" styrofoam ball and an uncoated CD; Mars-Earth comparison flashcards ; Scale model of the Earth-Moon system using 3" and 3/4" styrofoam balls attached with a precut 90" string; Moon phase flipbook; Construction paper for scale sizes of the eight planets, which the children used to compare and contrast their sizes; Adding machine tape and scale model of the solar system. Attendance varied from 8 to 16 children per workshop, ages 3 to 10. Parents were as enthusiastically engaged in the activities as the children, and a number of elementary school teachers and scout leaders took additional materials home to utilize the activities themselves.

4.   Conclusion

The children's activities program at Stellafane has enjoyed thirteen years of success. Individual children have attended for five years or longer, and have even come back as "helpers" once they became too old to take part in the activities. Despite the practical constraints and challenges to developing such a program, the Stellafane experience has demonstrated that success can be achieved with limited resources and limitless potential.

References

National Research Council, *National Science Education Standards*, (National Academy Press, Washington D.C., 1996)

Template available at http://www.physics.ccsu.edu/larsen/earthmars.html

EPO and a Changing World
ASP Conference Series, Vol. 389, © 2008
C. Garmany, M. Gibbs, and J. W. Moody

Education And Public Outreach for NASA's WISE Mission

Bryan J. H. Méndez

Space Sciences Laboratory, University of California at Berkeley, 7 Gauss Way Berkeley, CA 94720-7450

Abstract. The WISE (Wide-field Infrared Survey Explorer) mission is a NASA MIDEX mission that will map the entire sky in infrared light, searching for the nearest and coolest stars, the origins of stellar and planetary systems, and the most luminous galaxies in the Universe. The ultimate product of WISE will be an all-sky image atlas in 4 infrared wave bands, and a catalogue of over 300 million sources. The Education and Public Outreach (EPO) Program for WISE will bring together a veritable who's who of professionals in formal and informal astronomy education from around the nation to engage students, teachers, and the public in this exciting mission and its science. We designed our EPO plan to train WISE Educator Ambassadors in authentic infrared astronomy research, create standard-based curriculum on exciting topics in infrared astronomy, engage students and the public in asteroid research, develop programming for museums and science centers, and engage the public in WISE science.

1. Introduction

The Wide-field Infrared Survey Explorer (WISE) is a NASA MIDEX mission, set to launch in Fall 2009. WISE will map the entire sky in infrared light, searching for the nearest and coolest stars, the origins of stellar and planetary systems, and the most luminous galaxies in the Universe. The ultimate product of WISE will be an all-sky image atlas in 4 infrared wave bands, and a catalogue of over 300 million sources. The Education and Public Outreach (EPO) Program for WISE will bring together many partners from around the nation to engage students, teachers, and the public in this exciting mission and its science.

2. WISE Education and Public Outreach

In the classroom: WISE EPO will work with NOAO, the Spitzer Science Center, and WISE scientists to train a group of master teachers in infrared astronomy research. These teachers will become WISE Educator Ambassadors and will take their research knowledge into the classroom, creating lesson plans, involving their students in authentic research, and teaching other teachers how to do the same. We will also partner with the Hands-On Universe project to train teachers in a project for their students to use WISE data to discover new Asteroids. We will develop several lesson guides for teachers in English and Spanish about WISE science based on national science education standards. We will conduct teacher professional development workshops on the WISE educator guides and other exemplary lessons from our partner infrared missions.

Outside the classroom: we will partner with Space Dynamics Laboratory in Utah (who is building the WISE cryogenic instrument) to conduct workshops about WISE science and technology for Native American students, teachers, and families in the surrounding area. Ball Aerospace will also visit Hispanic and inner city students in after-school programs, such as MESA, to present technological lessons and activities related to WISE. Through the internet we can allow average citizens to aid in the search for dangerous near Earth asteroids, in a possible project called Aster-oids@home. We will work with the Astronomical Society of the Pacific, SOFIA and Spitzer EPO to create infrared astronomy outreach kits to be used by amateur astronomy clubs across the country. We will work with the Space Science Institute to incorporate WISE information into their Alien Earths traveling exhibit, educator workshops, and website. At the Hayden Planetarium in New York City, WISE data will be incorporated into their Digital Universe Atlas and the story of the WISE mission will be told in short AstroBulletins. WISE image data and science content will also be disseminated in a show for the ViewSpace program about infrared astronomy, featuring information about infrared space telescopes like WISE, SOFIA, Spitzer, and JWST.

For the General Public: WISE maintains a public website that contains back-ground information about the WISE mission, its science, and its team. It also will contain educational resources for students and teachers including images, simulations, and movies. WISE EPO will produce a number of print materials that feature beautiful imagery of the infrared sky. Among other places, these products will be distributed at a WISE exhibition booth at professional meetings and the JPL Open House. Finally, WISE scientists will regularly give lectures for public audiences about the intriguing science behind the WISE mission.

These programs will also be monitored and evaluated by an independent professional evaluator, Cornerstone Evaluation Associates. They will insure that the WISE EPO program effectively communicates the exciting science and technology behind the WISE mission to inspire, engage, and educate their audiences.

2.   Conclusion

The WISE EPO Program is a multifaceted enterprise bringing together a veritable who's who of professionals in formal and informal astronomy education. We are guided by the philosophy that the excitement and wonder of space science discoveries should be shared with everyone, and that it is the responsibility of space scientists to give back to the general community that supports their inspiring work. The WISE mission will provide the professional astronomical community with a map of the sky leading to new discoveries for years to come. It is our intention that the WISE EPO program will inspire students, teachers, and the public at large to appreciate, understand, and take part in those great discoveries.

EPO and a Changing World
ASP Conference Series, Vol. 389, © 2008
C. Garmany, M. Gibbs, and J. W. Moody

The Evolution of the Penn State University Astronomy Outreach Program

Christopher Palma and Jane C. Charlton

Penn State University, 601 Davey Lab, University Park, PA 16802

Abstract. The Penn State Dept. of Astronomy & Astrophysics has a long tradition of outreach. Faculty, students, and staff all participate as volunteers to create and deliver a variety of outreach programming to diverse audiences, including for example K-12 students, K-12 teachers, and senior citizens, in addition to open events that invite all members of the general public to attend.

In the past four years, the University and the Department have provided institutional support for science outreach efforts. Many of our programs also receive financial support through NASA Education and Public outreach awards and through NSF awards to PSU Astronomy faculty. We actively collaborate with the NASA Pennsylvania Space Grant Consortium, the Penn State Center for Science and the Schools, four local school districts, and our colleagues from other science disciplines at the University. With this set of partners we are able to continue to innovate and offer new outreach programming annually.

In this poster, we present an overview of the variety of outreach programs offered recently and those in the development stages. We describe how each program fits into the Department and University structure. In this way we provide a case study of a large, dynamic, university-based astronomy outreach venture.

1. Introduction and History

The faculty and students in the Department of Astronomy & Astrophysics at Penn State have a long history of participating in a variety of outreach programs. Our signature programs include:

1. **The Penn State In-Service Workshops in Astronomy**: A professional development workshop program for teachers created by Professors Eric Feigelson and Dan Weedman in 1996.

2. **AstroFest**: A four night festival of astronomy, held concurrently with the Central Pennsylvania Festival of the Arts, created by Professor Jane Charlton and her Students Nahks Tr'Ehnl, Jane Rigby, and Karen Knierman in 1999.

3. **Planetarium Program**: Using a small (15 foot diameter) planetarium, graduate and undergraduate students have presented night sky tours to visiting K-12 classes for many years.

These and other outreach programs have been maintained by faculty and students who have for the most part volunteered their time. In 2003, however, the Dean of the Eberly College of Science at Penn State created a new full-time faculty position to support the Department and College's outreach efforts. Since 2003, the outreach efforts in Astronomy have been expanded, and new partnerships have been formed.

2.   Evolution of Astronomy Outreach at Penn State

All of our signature programs have been expanded. For example, we have offered new types of professional development programs for teachers (Saturday morning programs and sessions at the PA Science Teachers Association) and created new curricula for our traditional week long programs with more of an emphasis on inquiry-based activities. We have installed an "AstroWall" 3D visualization system, and incorporated a "3D Tour of the Universe" and "3D Tour of Mars" into both AstroFest and the Planetarium program.

We have created entirely new programs to reach additional audiences. In 2007, we taught an Elderhostel course in astronomy for senior citizens for the first time. Since 2004, we have participated in the College's "Action Potential Science Experience" summer camps, creating and offering three new camps; "Star Voyagers" for K-3 grade students, and "Mission to Mars" and "Searching for Life on Other Planets" for 4-8 grade students.

The University outreach community has begun to collaborate more extensively. We are working with the PA Space Grant Consortium and faculty from other disciplines (science education, geosciences, engineering) and the Bald Eagle, Bellefonte, and Penns Valley school districts on a new initiative to improve STEM education in these three rural school districts. We have been collaborating with Penn State's "Center for Science and the Schools". This organization was just awarded the NASA Aerospace Education Service Project contract, and we expect to collaborate on their nationwide program for teacher professional development.

3.   The Future

Given the faculty and student dedication to outreach and the University commitment to outreach in the form of a College "Outreach Office", we expect to continue to expand the programs we can provide to a variety of audiences. Among many new initiatives, we will be distributing thousands of diffraction grating masks at the 4th Fest fireworks program in 2008 and 2009 in order to introduce the audience to the concept of spectroscopy, we are planning family science nights in the three Space Alliance school districts listed above, and we intend to create a new professional development workshop on black holes for 2008.

The faculty and students continue to innovate as we plan these new outreach programs. We hope to continue to involve many faculty and students in the delivery of these new programs and to expand our audience to new communities.

Acknowledgments.   We gratefully acknowledge NASA and NSF for supporting many of the programs cited in this paper.

EPO and a Changing World
ASP Conference Series, Vol. 389, © *2008*
C. Garmany, M. Gibbs, and J. W. Moody

Searching for New Earths: Teaching Children How We Seek Distant Planets

Christine Pulliam

Harvard-Smithsonian Center for Astrophysics, 60 Garden Street, Cambridge, MA 02138

Abstract.   Teaching science to children ages 8-13 can be a great challenge, especially if you lack the resources for a full-blown audio/visual presentation. How do you hold their attention and get them involved? One method is to teach a topic no one else covers at this educational level: something exciting and up-to-the-minute, at the cutting edge of science. We developed an interactive 45-minute presentation to convey the two basic techniques used to locate planets orbiting other stars. Activities allowed children to hunt for their own planets in simulated data sets. We also stimulated their imagination by giving each child a take-home, multicolored marble "planet" and asking them to discuss their planet's characteristics. The resulting presentation "Searching for New Earths" could be adapted to a variety of educational settings.

1.   The "Wobble" Method: Radial Velocity

Most of the 200 plus known extra-solar planets have been discovered by radial velocity searches. Essentially, astronomers look for stars that "wobble" back and forth along our line of sight (radially) due to the gravitational tug of an unseen world. A Jupiter-sized planet can induce a velocity shift of tens of meters per second. That velocity shift shows up in the star's spectrum. Extremely high-precision measurements are needed to detect these spectral shifts.

The details of spectral measurements would be difficult, if not impossible, to explain to our target age group, especially in the time allotted to this activity. Therefore, we focused much of this section on wobbles visible in the plane of the sky: the astrometric technique. Both our demonstrations and handout activities used position wobbles, rather than line-of-sight wobbles, to indicate the presence of planets. This compromise allowed us to introduce the basic idea of wobbling without overcomplicating the presentation by adding technical concepts like spectra and the Doppler shift. In this activity, we also conveyed the idea that larger (more massive) planets cause larger wobbles and smaller (less massive) planets cause smaller wobbles, which allows us to determine a key characteristic of the planet.

2.   The "Dimming" Method: Transits

Recently, transit searches have proved highly successful at detecting planets. In a transit search, astronomers look for a planet that crosses in front of (transits) its parent star once per orbit. When the planet blocks a fraction of the star's light in a "mini-eclipse," the star dims. That dimming can be measured through precision photometry.

This technique offers several advantages. Transit searches can examine thousands of stars at once, and can detect smaller planets than radial velocity searches. A transit also allows you to measure the physical size of the planet relative to the star. Disadvantages include a bias toward planets with tight, short-period orbits and an abundance of false events due to grazing binary-star eclipses. Also, a transit will not be seen unless the Earth, distant star, and planet line up very precisely.

The transit technique proved easier to convey to a young audience. The concepts are intuitive: light from a star is blocked, so the star dims, and a bigger planet blocks more light than a smaller planet. We also introduced the idea that transit timing tells astronomers the size of the planet's orbit. (Such calculations also can be made for radial velocity measurements, but we did not cover that mathematically-intense notion in the previous section.)

3.   Appealing to the Imagination

After the technical aspects of planet searching had been covered, we offered a chance for the children in our audience to let their imaginations run wild! Every child was given a multicolored marble and asked to tell us what sort of planet it represented. We guided their speculations with focus questions: Is your planet hot or cold? Is it close to its star or far away? Does it have air (an atmosphere)? Does it have life? What kind of life?

The responses were as varied as the audience. As a memento of the event, everyone got to take their marble home with them.

4.   Summary

Textbooks, by their nature, are behind the times when it comes to rapidly evolving fields like the hunt for extrasolar planets. In an effort to convey the excitement and wonder of this new realm of astronomical research, we developed a 45-minute presentation for children ages 8-13, complete with audience participation, three guided activities, and a PowerPoint presentation filled with images and animations.

Response to this program was overwhelmingly positive. As with similar CfA out-reach programs for children, we required that parents make reservations in advance and mailed out free tickets to confirmed participants. Ticket requests exceeded available seats by a factor of four. This program could prove equally popular in other settings, such as individual schools or museums.

Acknowledgments.   This outreach program was developed and taught with the aid of former CfA public affairs staff assistant Ruth Bazinet, under the guidance of CfA public affairs director David Aguilar.

Honoring Susan Deustua

Noreen Grice - Klumpke-Roberts Award Winner

Part V

International Year of
Astronomy 2009

EPO and a Changing World
ASP Conference Series, Vol. 389, © *2008*
C. Garmany, M. Gibbs, and J. W. Moody

Dark Skies as a Universal Resource, Citizen-Scientists, and the International Year of Astronomy

Constance E. Walker, Stephen M. Pompea, and Robert T. Sparks

National Optical Astronomy Observatory, 950 N. Cherry Ave., Tucson, AZ 85719

Chuck Bueter

www.nightwise.org, 15893 Ashville Ln., Granger, IN 46530

Abstract.   The ongoing loss of a dark night sky as a natural resource for much of the world's population is a growing, serious issue that not only impacts astronomical research, but also human health, ecology, safety, security, economics and energy conservation. This workshop was designed to train educators who will become local leaders in light pollution education. During the workshop, we provided the "know-how" and the means for workshop attendees to become participants or community leaders in promoting the GLOBE at Night 2008 program, toward a quantitative global effort in 2009 as one of the major US programs in the planned International Year of Astronomy.

1.   Introduction

The ongoing loss of a dark night sky as a natural resource for much of the world's population is a growing, serious issue that impacts not only astronomical research, but also human health, ecosystems, safety and security, and energy conservation. Dark-skies education efforts are most effective when they get people involved in making measurements locally and when they develop a heightened awareness of light pollution as a global problem with a local solution.

The Dark Skies workshop at the 2007 Astronomical Society of the Pacific conference in Chicago was designed to train educators who will become local leaders in light pollution education. Over the last two years, NOAO and the GLOBE project have conducted the GLOBE at Night program to enable "citizen-scientists" around the world to contribute measurements on sky-brightness to a growing global database in two ways: simple unaided-eye observations that anyone can do (with some basic guidance) and quantitative digital measurements through a handheld, well-calibrated sky brightness meter.

During the workshop, we provided the "know-how" and the means for workshop attendees to become participants or community leaders in promoting the GLOBE at Night 2008 program, toward a quantitative global effort in 2009 as one of the major US programs in the planned International Year of Astronomy. Workshop attendees committing to the program were given sky-brightness meters as well as a kit with teaching materials on preserving dark skies. Participants learned how to use the meters, use the activities in the kit to model best practices on teaching about light pollution and organize a meaningful campaign in their community. In addition to the Sky Quality Meter, the kit contained an activity on shielding, the "Saving the Night" DVD and "Our Globe at Night" posters among other items.

2.   What is Light Pollution? How can it be Minimized?

The workshop opened with a demonstration on the main effects of light pollution, namely glare, light trespass and sky glow, and how with proper shielding these effects can be minimized. The demonstration was conducted in a very dark room without a high ceiling. Along with a simple toy floor mat of city streets and different business buildings big enough for matchbox cars, we used a "mini-light" as a street-light by taking off the reflector (i,e, "candle mode"). These mini-lights are similar to mini-maglights but 28% of the cost. Also to add to the ambiance, we had a 2-inch tall toy figurine of a person and Bob Crelin's illustrations in his book *There Once was a Sky Full of Stars* as the backdrop. To make a mini-planetarium, we took a 4-inch paper cube with holes for stars on one side and an opening for a second mini-light on the opposite side. With the room lights off, we first turned on the mini-light in candle mode for the planetarium and placed it barely inside the cube, allowing stars to be projected onto the ceiling. By turning on the "streetlight", participants noticed instances of glare, sky glow and light trespass into people's homes. To minimize these effects we demonstrated how a simple shield, in this case a PVC cap, could help by covering the top of the "streetlight". A discussion ensued about the differences noticed with and without the shield.

3.   Why Should We Care about Light Pollution?

The demonstration illustrated some reasons and steps to take to minimize light pollution. But since light pollution affects various aspects of life and our environment, a question for discussion was posed, "Why in general should we care about light pollution?" By taking action, the participants said, we can:

- save money and energy

- improve safety for motorists and pedestrians

- increase security and the sense of well-being

- benefit animal habitats

- preserve the starry night

- improve our health and the quality of life

- lessen greenhouse gas emissions that contribute to global warming.

4. What can we do about Light Pollution?

A lack of awareness, rather than specific resistance, is generally the biggest problem in controlling light pollution. -Kohei Narisada & Duco Schreuder

"Star hunts" or "star counts" provide citizen-scientists a fun, fast and no-frills way to acquire heightened awareness about light pollution through firsthand observations of the night sky. Past programs have come from Greece, Austria, Canada, the International Dark-Sky Association and a pilot program between NOAO-North in Tucson and NOAO-South in La Serena, Chile, among others. GLOBE at Night has built upon these programs to become an international citizen-science event to observe the nighttime sky and learn more about light pollution around the world. GLOBE at Night brings together parents, students, and their communities for an engaging and fun science event.

In March 2006, the National Optical Astronomy Observatory (NOAO) and the GLOBE project first conducted the GLOBE at Night program to enable "citizen-scientists" around the world to contribute simple unaided-eye observations on sky-brightness to a growing global database. Citizen-scientists recorded the brightness of the night sky by matching its appearance toward the constellation Orion with one of seven stellar maps of different limiting magnitude. Observations and their exact locations were submitted on-line. More than 18,000 people contributed 4600 observations from 96 countries.

The GLOBE at Night 2007 program has built upon the success of the inaugural campaign in 2006. The international star-hunting event returned March 8-21 in two flavors: the classic GLOBE at Night activity incorporating unaided-eye observations toward Orion, and a new effort to obtain precise measurements of urban dark skies toward zenith using digital sky brightness meters. Both flavors of the program were designed to heighten awareness about the impact of artificial lighting on local environments, and the ongoing loss of a dark night sky as a natural resource for much of the world population. Participation increased to 8500 observations from 60 countries in the last event. In 2008, the dates for GLOBE at Night are February 25-March 8.

5. How do we take the measurements?

To get ready to take observations, participants can look up background information on light pollution, the mythology of Orion, latitude and longitude and magnitudes of stars among other topics on-line at http://www.globe.gov/globeatnight/learn.html.

5.1. Five Fun, Fast, and no-Frills Steps to the Classic GLOBE at Night Program

Participants were introduced to the five steps to the classic GLOBE at Night Program that involve unaided eye observations toward Orion and the comparison of those observations to charts of limiting magnitudes. Those steps are featured on the GLOBE at Night website (http://www.globe.gov/globeatnight/observe.html) as:

1. **Find your latitude and longitude.** There are tentative plans to build this feature into the GLOBE at Night webpages by IYA 2009. Until then sources for acquiring latitude and longitude include Global Positioning Services (GPS), inputting your address at http://www.maporama.com, zooming in to your location with Google Earth maps, or using topological maps. Go to http://www.globe.gov/globeatnight/observe_latlong.html for more information.

2. **Find Orion in the night sky.** There are various ways given on the GLOBE at Night website to find Orion. For examples of these go to http://www.globe.gov/globeatnight/learn_findorion.html. You can also practice locating Orion by latitude though using the interactive facility at http://www.globe.gov/globeatnight/observe_finder.html. What you see can be limited by light pollution. To illustrate this, an interactive slider allow adjustment of both latitude and limiting magnitude. This allows the user to get an idea of the orientation of Orion and the number of stars visible toward it. (See http://www.globe.gov/globeatnight/learn_orionsky.html)

   For the little citizen-scientists there is an activity with fluorescent puffy paints, overhead transparencies and the outline of the constellation of Orion. The outline of Orion is traced onto the transparency with the puffy paints, and allowed to dry and soak up 45 minutes worth of light. A child can then take it outside, aim it toward Orion at arms length and sight in the stars by matching them up with the holes on the transparency. (See http://www.globe.gov/globeatnight/GaN2007OrionAtFingertips.pdf)

   Find Orion by going outside an hour after sunset (approximately between 7-10pm local time). Determine the darkest area by moving to where most stars are visible in the sky toward Orion. If you have outside lights, be sure to turn them off. Wait 10 minutes for your eyes to adapt to the dark. Locate Orion in the sky using the tools in the paragraphs above.

3. **Match the night sky to a magnitude chart.** These are found in either the teacher packets or family packets or are available on-line at http://www.globe.gov/globeatnight/observe_magni-tude.html. Estimate the cloud coverage. Fill out the observation sheet.

4. **Report your observations on-line.** Observations can be reported at http://www.globe.gov/globeatnight/report.html anytime between February 25 and March 20, 2008. Try another set of observations from a different location!

5. **Compare your observations.** You can compare with thousands of observations at http://www.globe.gov/globeatnight/analyze.html which are from all around the world. Explore, zoom in and examine your data with the GLOBE at Night Map Viewer! As in its first year, GLOBE at Night is work-ing on providing data comparisons to other datasets such as population density and nighttime satellite imagery by IYA 2009.

6. How to Expand the Citizen-Scientist Experience

Participants were asked how to expand the citizen-scientist experience, how to make the approach more scientific and the measurements more precise, how to quantitatively and objectively measure changes over time, and how to map a whole city in detail to identify oases.

As a solution we introduced the advantages of a portable sky-brightness meter to take the campaign to another level.

6.1. The Digital GLOBE at Night Program 2007

To make possible the digital GLOBE at Night program, the NSF funded the purchase and distribution of 135 low-cost, handheld, well-calibrated sky quality meters manufactured by Unihedron and called "SQMs". Repeatability of the device's readings is ±0.1 magnitude/square arcsec according to Dr. Patrick Seitzer of U. Michigan. Along with light pollution teaching kits developed by NOAO, the meters were distributed to citizen-scientists in 21 U.S. states plus Washington DC, and in 5 countries, including Chile, where NOAO has major observatories. About 1000 measurements were made. Initial results from 2007 show very good consistency, with obvious gradients in brightness from city center to known dark areas. There were lots of creativity in the way measurements were made, such as via a Moon roof and with the car's a GPS unit. The prototype SQM shows great promise.

The citizen-scientists were teachers, their students, astronomers at local and national observatories, International Dark-Sky Association (IDA) members, and staff from 19 science centers, members of advocacy groups and staff at the National Parks.

At many of the sites where the SQMs were delivered, a local coordinator promoted dark-sky education using the educational kits and trained a number of teachers and amateur astronomers on using the meters. For each meter, citizen-scientists were asked to make measurements from different locations in their region and record on-line their measurements with their latitude and longitude at each location, using either a GPS unit or GIS-related website.

As an illustration of the results, the SQM data for Tucson is plotted against population density in Figure 1 and against the intensity of nighttime lights in Figure 2. There is high correlation between the values of the SQM measurements and those for population density and the intensity of nighttime lights. The higher the population density or intensity of nighttime lights, the brighter the SQM reading. See http://www.noao.edu/outreach/press/pr07/pr0707.html for more premilinary results.

6.2. Characteristics of the SQM

As shown in the Figure 3, the original Sky Quality Meter (SQM) has an angular field-of-view response of ±40 degrees (80 degrees total) for a full cutoff at ±60 degrees (120 degrees total).

6.3. The Easy to Use SQM

The meter readings are somewhat temperature dependent. It is a good idea to leave the meter outside 20 minutes before taking reliable measurements, de-

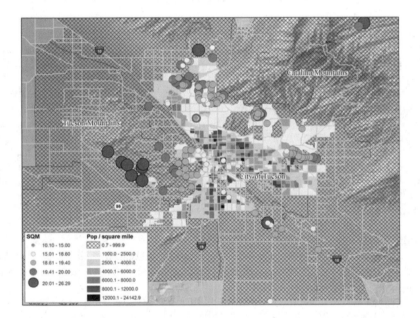

Figure 1.   Sky Quality Meter (SQM) measurements compared with the population density of Tucson. The values for SQM data are in units of magnitudes per square arcsecond. The grey scale progresses from white (brighter skies) to black (darker skies). The points also increase in size, making the darker sites more prominent. The population density is in terms of the number of people per square mile, using the 2005 population values for each census block group. The color scale progresses from white (1000-2500 people/mile^2) to black (12,000 to over 24,000 people/mile^2).

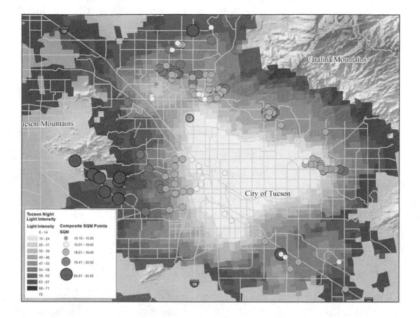

Figure 2.   SQM measurements compared with the nighttime lights for Tucson. The nighttime lights data were collected in 1996 and 1997 as part of the Defense Meteorological Satellite Program (DMSP). The values are a measure of the intensity of nighttime lights in the grid cell. Light intensity is described by a range of values, where smaller values represent higher intensity, and larger values represent lower intensity. The range goes from 0 at minimum value to 72 at maximum value.

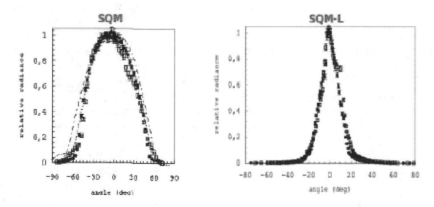

Figure 3.   SQM angular field-of-view response (From A. Tekatch of Unihedron.)

pending on the temperature differential. Once you are ready, point the SQM directly above at the zenith. (The original model of the SQM has the sensor on the same side as the display. In the SQM-L model, the display is on the side and therefore easier to read.) The SQM should be held above head level so that shadows or reflections from your body do not interfere with the reading. Avoid using the SQM in areas that are shaded by trees or buildings. Be at least as far away from a structure as it is high. Pressing and holding the button a second time will display the outside temperature in °C and then °F. Subsequently the model and serial numbers are displayed.

6.4.   The Advantages of Digital Data

Some of the advantages of using the SQM are that you get accuracy to 2 decimal places. There is no aging eye to influence results. The measurements complement the unaided-eye observations. They allow for consistency checks. They provide the start of a baseline of measurements that can be used to track changes over time. They can be compared as "ground truth" with satellite measurements of dark skies or population density studies. They can search for safe urban "dark-sky oases"!

6.5.   Data Input

The data input sought for the meters is its serial number, the date and local time, your latitude and longitude and the meter readings. It would also be prudent to include the unaided eye observations toward Orion during the GLOBE at Night campaign. Optional input includes your name, outside temperature, what percentage of cloud coverage and illuminated Moon you have, and any comments on whether you are near a light, building tree; sky conditions, etc.

7.   Plans for 2008

We will continue to build on the existing infrastructure of local coordinators and participants in GLOBE at Night to create a similar but expanded U.S.-based classic and digital program. We will expand our collaboration with the International Dark-Sky Association (http://www.darksky.org) and a local SQM citizen-science program called Night Vision (http://www.nightwise.org/nightvision.htm).

This effort will support ongoing student-teacher teams, as well as new participants, and build a more formal network of GLOBE at Night sites and coordinators. As in the workshop here, people who commit to the program will have access to sky-brightness meters as well as a kit with teaching materials on preserving dark skies. Participants learn how to do the classic observations, use the meters, organize a meaningful campaign in their community, and teach with the kit. Interested participants will be offered the opportunity to continue SQM measurements year-round.

NOAO and GLOBE are considering plans for web pages linked to the http://www.globe.gov/globeatnight website that will include information about SQMs, allow one to compare classic observations and digital measurements (discussing the importance of both) and instruct on how to make an SQM measurement with the template provided. It will also provide a selection of different types of SQM measurement programs-from grid surveys of one's town on one night (repeatable every month), to seasonal surveys, to surveys every hour over a night at one or more location, to surveys of 8 cardinal directions along one's horizon (concurrent with regular SQM measurements). Information on how to report an SQM measurement will also be provided.

Analysis of the maps will include a comparison with other data sets such as last year's SQM data set, the limiting-magnitude unaided-eye observations, population density, regional environmental concerns (e.g., sea turtles in Florida), and satellite data on nighttime lights (top view looking down versus the SQM's bottom view looking up).

8. Plans for 2009

Through workshops and a website, the program will provide the "know-how" and the means for people to become participants or community leaders in promoting the GLOBE at Night 2008 program. The outcome of the 2008 campaign will provide the basis for a quantitative global effort in 2009 as one of the major US programs in the planned International Year of Astronomy.

Dark skies awareness has also become a cornerstone project for international efforts toward IYA. To facilitate the preservation and protection of the world's cultural and natural heritage of dark night skies in places such as urban oases, national parks and astronomical sites, IAU will be collaborating with NOAO, IDA and other national and international partners in dark-sky and environmental education on several related themes. The themes include worldwide measurements of local dark skies by thousands of citizen-scientists using both unaided eyes and digital sky-quality meters as in the GLOBE at Night program, as well as star parties, new lighting technologies, arts and storytelling, and health and ecosystems.

9. Summary

GLOBE at Night 2007 is a major step in our plans for the International Year of Astronomy in 2009. A central goal is to make digital data collection on light pollution levels into a worldwide activity.

GLOBE at Night has been a collaboration between the National Optical Astronomy Observatory (NOAO), the Global Learning and Observations to Benefit the Environment (GLOBE), the International Dark-Skies Association (IDA), the Centro de Apoyo a la Didáctica de la Astronomía (CADIAS) and Windows to the Universe. NOAO is operated by the Association of Universities for Research in Astronomy (AURA), Inc. under cooperative agreement with the National Science Foundation. The work described in this poster was supported by a grant to NOAO by the NSF AST Division. More information on GLOBE at Night can be found at http://www.globe.gov/globeatnight/.

EPO includes partnering with the local press

Dana Backman educated us on the EPO of SOFIA

EPO and a Changing World
ASP Conference Series, Vol. 389, © *2008*
C. Garmany, M. Gibbs, and J. W. Moody

IYA Tabloid in Your Community

Janice Harvey

Gemini Observatory, 670 A'ohoku Place, Hilo, Hawaii 96720 USA

Abstract.   Gemini PIO would like to offer suggestions on how to approach your local newspaper with the possibility of a tabloid for your community being published during IYA 2009. Local government support, astronomer's articles, advertisers, and someone within your organization to manage the content will be discussed. We will explain the timeline required, number of personnel hours required, developmental stages and income your local newspaper would have to generate in order to produce a quality, table-top tabloid.

1.   General Introduction

In 2003 "Stars Over Mauna Kea", a special supplement/tabloid was produced and distributed in the local newspapers in Hilo, Hawaii with over 30,000 copies printed and distributed. The publication, 48 pages in total, featured profiles of observatories on Mauna Kea, stories about the geology and legends of Mauna Kea, and historical information about the evolution of astronomy in Hawaii. In addition the publication included a series of essays titled "In their own words". These were articles written by key members of the astronomy community.

In 2005 60,000 copies of "Stars Over Mauna Kea II" were printed as a follow-up to the first edition. An article on 'Imiloa Astronomy Education Center, explanations of what types of telescopes sit atop Mauna Kea, and columns written by scientists about the fascinating and significant discoveries being made were featured. Personal stories about careers in astronomy were also highlighted.

In Chile, a similar tabloid, 8 pages in length was published and 5,000 copies were distributed throughout the country. The 2005 tabloid featured Gemini, CTIO and SOAR telescopes.

(Representative figures follow)

Figure 1.   Stars over Mauna Kea

Figure 2.   Stars over Mauna Kea II

Figure 3.   The Chilean Tabloid "Observatorio Aura"

EPO and a Changing World
ASP Conference Series, Vol. 389, © *2008*
C. Garmany, M. Gibbs, and J. W. Moody

The International Year of Astronomy 2009: U.S. Goals, Themes and Plans

Douglas Isbell

National Optical Astronomy Observatory; co-chair, US Program Committee for IYA 2009 and US Single-Point-of-Contact [SPOC] for IYA, 950 N. Cherry Ave., Tucson, AZ 85719, USA

Susana Duestua

American Astronomical Society; co-chair, US Program Committee for IYA 2009, and member of the US Development Committee, 2000 Florida Ave, NW, Suite 400, Washington DC 20009, USA

1. General Introduction

The International Year of Astronomy (IYA 2009) will be a global celebration of astronomy and its contributions to society and culture, highlighted by the 400th anniversary of the first use of an astronomical telescope by Galileo Galilei. Led by the International Astronomical Union (IAU) and endorsed by UNESCO, IYA 2009 aims to stimulate worldwide interest in astronomy and science— especially among young people—under the central theme *"The Universe, Yours to Discover."* IYA2009 events and activities will promote a greater appreciation of the inspirational aspects of astronomy that embody an invaluable shared resource for all nations. Each member country of the IAU has an IYA 2009 Single Point of Contact (SPOC), as do the large astronomy organizations such as ESO and NASA. The U.S. SPOC is Doug Isbell. The NASA SPOC is Hashima Hasan.

1.1. International Objectives of IYA 2009

1. Increase scientific awareness.

2. Promote widespread access to new knowledge and observing experiences.

3. Empower astronomical communities in developing countries.

4. Support and improve formal and informal science education.

5. Provide a modern image of science and scientists.

6. Facilitate new networks and strengthen existing ones.

7. Improve the gender-balanced representation of scientists at all levels and promote greater involvement of underrepresented groups in scientific and engineering careers.

8. Facilitate the preservation and protection of the world's natural heritage of dark skies and cultural heritage of historical astronomical sites.

As the US representative to the IAU, the American Astronomical Society (AAS) established two committees to plan for the U.S. IYA 2009 effort: a Program Committee to develop the ideas for key programs and activities, and a Development Committee to seek funding for the best ideas.

The Program Committee's members cover the spectrum of astronomy outreach in the country, including representatives from NASA (National Aeronautics and Space Administration) the Astronomical Society of the Pacific, the National Radio Astronomy Observatory (NRAO), the National Optical Astronomy Observatory (NOAO), the astronomy media, the planetarium community, and representatives from Mexico and Canada. Development Committee members are drawn from industry, observatories and the private sector.

U.S. Program Committee Members

Doug Isbell (NOAO) co-chair disbell@noao.edu

Susana Deustua (AAS) co-chair deustua@aas.org

Doris Daou (NASA Headquarters) Doris.Daou-1@nasa.gov

Craig Deforest (SWRI and AAS Solar Physics Division press officer) deforest@boulder.swri.edu

Chris De Pree (Agnes Scott College) cdepree@agnesscott.edu

Mary Dussault (Harvard-Smithsonian CfA) mdussault@cfa.harvard.edu

Jon Elvert (International Planetarium Society) jelvert@lasm.org

Rick Fienberg (Sky & Telescope) rfienberg@skyandtelescope.com

Dave Finley (National Radio Astronomy Observatory) dfinley@nrao.edu

Andrew Fraknoi (Foothill College), Secretary, fraknoi.andrew@fhda.edu

Hashima Hasan (NASA Headquarters) hhasan@nasa.gov

Jim Hesser (Canada representative) James.Hesser@nrc-cnrc.gc.ca

Omar Lopez-Cruz (Mexico representative) omarlx@inaoep.mx

Terry Mann (Astronomical League) starsrus@infinet.com

Jim Manning (Astronomical Society of the Pacific) jmanning@astrosociety.org

Aaron Price (American Association of Variable Star Observers) aaronp@aavso.org

Denise Smith (Space Telescope Science Institute) dsmith@stsci.edu

U.S. IYA 2009 Development Committee

Chair - Peter Stockman (Space Telescope Science Institute) stockman@stsci.edu

Mark Adams (NRAO) mtadams@nrao.edu

Kelly Beatty (Sky and Telescope) beatty@skyandtelescope.com

Rolf Danner (Northrup Grumman) rolf.danner@ngc.com

Susana Deustua (AAS) deustua@aas.org

Jay Frogel (Association of Universities for Research in Astronomy)
jfrogel@aura-astronomy.org

Michael G. Gibbs (Astronomical Society of the Pacific) mgibbs@astrosociety.org

Terry Mann (Astronomical League) starsrus@infinet.com

Domenick Tenerelli (Lockheed Martin) domenick.tenerelli@lmco.com

U.S. Program Committee Co-chairs Isbell and Deustua were appointed in mid-February 2007. Upon review of existing material and consultation with the Program Committee, a central new U.S. GOAL for IYA 2009 was presented at a March 2007 meeting of the IYA SPOCs in Garching, Germany, and since modified to include nurturing existing relationships:

> "To offer an engaging astronomy experience to every person in the country, nurture existing partnerships and build new connections to sustain public interest."

To achieve this goal, seven major US themes have been established:

- Looking Through a Telescope (star parties and sidewalk astronomy)

- Dark Skies Are a Universal Resource (citizen-science campaign and related educational activities)

- Astronomy in Arts, Entertainment & Storytelling (ideas include a Rose Parade float and "Astronomy Goes to the Movies" at the 2009 Oscar Awards, cultural astronomy)

- Research Experience for Students, Teachers, and Citizen-Scientists (observations of variable star Epsilon Aurigae and more)

- Telescope Kits & Optics (hands-on activities tied to new inexpensive telescope kits)

- Sharing the Universe Through New Technology (blogs, podcasts, Webcasts, social networking sites. . .)

- The Universe for Classrooms and Families (a booklet of follow-on activities for children, teachers and families, supported by a Galileo Club Card and related Web site).

Each theme is supported by at least one working group, Each theme is also responsible for reaching out to specific underserved audiences, and for building in an evaluation function for their proposed activities. Altogether, the themes now involve more than 70 astronomy outreach professionals, amateur astronomers, educators and volunteers.

U.S. IYA 2009 US Working Group Chairs

Rick Fienberg (Sky & Telescope, rfienberg@skyandtelescope.com) – Looking Through a Telescope

Andrew Fraknoi (Foothill College/ASP, fraknoiandrew@fhda.edu)– Class-rooms and Families

Pamela Gay (SIUE/AstronomyCast, pgay@siue.edu) – New Media

E.C. Krupp (Griffith Observatory, eckrupp@earthlink.net) – Arts & Entertainment

Dennis Lamenti (Indiana University, dlamenti@astro.indiana.edu) – Storytelling and Cultural Astronomy

Peter Michaud (Gemini Observatory, pmichaud@gemini.edu) – Science Centers, Observatory Visitor Centers and Planetaria

Stephen Pompea (NOAO, spompea@noao.edu) – Telescope Kit and Optics Challenges

Aaron Price (AAVSO, aaronp@aavso.org) – Research Experiences for Students, Teachers and Citizen-Scientists

Connie Walker (NOAO, cwalker@noao.edu) – Dark Skies Are a Universal Resource

NASA is developing a set of IYA program ideas that is aligned with this architecture, including early seed funding for the podcast "Are We Alone?" and a multi-wavelength image release from the Hubble/Spitzer/Chandra space telescopes. Major NASA-related events in 2009 include the outcome of the HST Servicing Mission-4, the launch of the Kepler exoplanet-hunting spacecraft, the impact of a probe released by the Lunar Reconnaissance Orbiter, first light for the SOFIA airborne infrared observatory, and the 40th anniversary of the Apollo 11 moon landing on July 20.

Ideas that were suggested and discussed by the 70-person audience in the open session on U.S. plans for IYA 2009 at the ASP meeting in Chicago include astronomy outreach to often-forgotten audiences such as the elderly and people in prison or juvenile detentions centers; developing musical events with symphony orchestras; coordinating with potentially aligned public outreach groups such as the Boy and Girl Scouts; use of Halloween as a chance for telescope viewing and other nighttime activities; and, working with local governments, newspapers, and school superintendents to prime the local educational "system" and perhaps have newspaper inserts or proclamations issued about IYA.

The U.S. effort was commended at the session by fellow presenter Lars Lindberg Christensen of the IAU IYA 2009 Executive Working Group as having "done more than any other nation" to prepare for IYA.

A promotional campaign will begin at the January 2008 AAS meeting in Austin, Texas, to be followed by regular press releases and publicity efforts such as a possible newspaper insert adapted for local markets. A master calendar of astronomical events in 2009 (including a total solar eclipse across Asia in July), prime telescope-viewing targets, and major anniversaries is being prepared.

The United States has taken a leadership role in three of the major cornerstone projects envisioned at the world level by the IAU IYA 2009 Executive Working Group:

The Galieleoscope: an inexpensive (less than $4 per copy) kit-based telescope of sufficient quality to view craters on the Moon and the moons of Jupiter, capable of being mass-produced by the millions (with a commercial sponsor) and distributed in a controlled fashion, primarily through established outreach networks and programs, workshops and public events. [International Task Group Leader: Rick Fienberg].

Dark-Skies Awareness: a multifaceted program of public education and citizen-science activities, including observations (GLOBE at Night [classic and digital] and the Great World Wide Star Count), small exhibits, new media, connections to star party activities, and urban "lights out" events. [International Task Group Leader: Connie Walker].

Image Exhibition: "The Universe from Earth" concept would assemble 100 of the best astronomical images produced by observatories, spacecraft and amateurs from around the world, and create a public display at one of three levels, depending on funding support - platinum level (outdoor, weatherproof), gold level (indoor), or silver level (downloads in standard format for local do-it-yourself). Candidate images are being collected via an ftp site at the Chandra Science Center [International Task Group Leaders: Kim Kowal Arcand and Megan Watzke].

The U.S. IYA 2009 Web site (http://www.astronomy2009.us) has more information on all of the themes and working groups, along with forums for public input and discussion, and related US talks, presentations and materials. The general email address for ideas and comments is US2009yearofastronomy@gmail.com.

A MySpace page for the US program has been established at http://www. myspace.com/2009yearofastronomy and a Facebook site ("I'll be celebrating the International Year of Astronomy in 2009") has been created.

The US Program Committee will submit a proposal to the US National Science Foundation division of astronomical sciences in late 2007. Private fundraising efforts are also underway, led by the Development Committee. It is hoped that these efforts will lead to a small grants program whereby public groups in the US will be able to submit proposals (less than $1,000) for a moderate amount of funding support to hold events and distribute materails.

As part of the summer AAS Meeting in St. Louis, Missouri, 1-5 June 2008, the AAS and the ASP are sponsoring a symposium focused on the International Year of Astronomy. This symposium will serve primarily as the major organizing conference and training workshop for national and regional (North American) efforts related to IYA 2009.

Some key challenges remain:

- Establishing and Staffing a National Program Office
- Obtaining Funding for the Key Projects
- Increasing Community Involvement
- Spreading the Word!!!

EPO and a Changing World
ASP Conference Series, Vol. 389, © *2008*
C. Garmany, M. Gibbs, and J. W. Moody

Using the *Hands-On Optics* "Terrific Telescopes" Kit in the International Year of Astronomy

Stephen M. Pompea, Connie E. Walker, and Robert T. Sparks

National Optical Astronomy Observatory, 950 N. Cherry Ave., Tucson, Arizona 85719, USA

Abstract. *Hands-On Optics* (HOO) is a collaborative four-year program to create and sustain a unique, national, informal science education program to excite students about science by actively engaging them in optics activities. The standards based activities and demonstrations have been successfully used in a variety of settings including formal classrooms, after school clubs, and science centers. One of the themes for the International Year of Astronomy (IYA) is "Looking Through a Telescope". We intend to use HOO activities in conjunction with the IYA to reinforce this important area.

In this workshop, participants completed a series of activities involving refraction, lenses, telescopes, and ultraviolet light and took home a kit containing all the materials required to do the activities with a small group of students. Participants explored the basic properties of positive lenses to create images through the use of hands-on activities, exciting experiments, and educator-lead demonstrations, culminating with the building of a small refracting telescope. Several prototype telescopes were examined in the workshop for use in the International Year of Astronomy.

1. Introduction

Hands-On Optics (HOO) is a National Science Foundation program designed to bring optics education to traditionally underserved students in informal settings (Pompea *et al.* 2005). The activities have been designed for use in settings such as after-school science clubs and in science center education programs. The activities are playful and exploratory, designed to appeal to the non-science student, and rely upon students working together in small, collaborative groups.

We have developed six modules focusing on fundamentally important topics in optics. The topics include simple reflections, multiple reflections, lenses and image formation, polarization, infrared and ultraviolet light, and optical communication. Each module contains enough instructional materials for a classroom of students to do all the activities in the module. The modules are science and math standards-based, have been thoroughly evaluated in a variety of educational settings, and may provide a model for similar instructional materials for this age-level (Pompea *et al.* 2008, Walker, Sparks, & Pompea 2007)

In NOAO's partnership with the Astronomical Society of the Pacific's *Astronomy From the Ground Up* (AFGU) program (funded by NSF ISE), we developed a smaller version of HOO's Module 3, which concentrates on how lenses work and form images. We call this mini-kit *Terrific Telescopes. Terrific Telescopes* has a small number of lenses, screens, and telescopes suitable for demonstrations at small science and nature centers, the target audience of AFGU. We are interested in using *Terrific Telescopes* as part of the International Year of Astronomy (IYA) in 2009 since it provides a well-tested teaching unit on telescopes.

The workshop in at the Astronomical Society of the Pacific meeting in Chicago trained attendees in how to use the *Terrific Telescopes* kit in outreach events. This workshop is our first workshop to prepare for the IYA and explore the best ways to run mini-workshops on using the kits. Our goal is to train a large cadre of science educators across the country to do outreach events in the IYA and in post-IYA years.

We are also in the process of testing various designs for small telescopes that can be mass-produced inexpensively for use in IYA activities. Participants compared several small telescopes we purchased from various companies and qualitatively evaluated their performance. This exercise has informed our efforts to design a small telescope that can be used in IYA.

2.   *Terrific Telescopes* Activities

Terrific Telescopes contains a variety of materials that can be used to illustrate the concepts of refraction, the focal point of a lens, focal length, image formation, how to build a small refracting telescope, and how to estimate the resolution of a telescope. In the *Terrific Telescope* kit we also include an ultraviolet light and some ultraviolet sensitive beads. These, along with the fluorescent ink on the kit bags are used to teach about other parts of the electromagnetic spectrum. This reinforces the concept that telescopes are used to examine different parts of the electromagnetic spectrum. A summary of the activities follows.

Light Through an Acrylic Block:
A Demonstration Starting with a laser shining at normal incidence to an acrylic block, the teacher slowly increases the incident angle. The students observe that the path of the light changes as the incident angle increases.

Light Passing Through a Convex Lens:
A Demonstration When parallel light beams encounter an object such as a lens, the shape of the lens can cause different light rays to bend by different amounts. Students predict the path of the rays through an acrylic block and through a lens, then determine if they are correct by using a water mister or chalk dust to expose the laser beams.

Finding the Focal Length Using a Distant Object:
When looking at a brightly colored lamp on one side of the room, students measure the focal length of a lens by forming an image of the light on a screen and measuring the distance between the lens and the screen. Since the object distance is large, this gives a good measure of the focal length of the lens.

Simple Magnifiers:
In this activity, students explore the magnifying properties of the lenses and notice the connection between how much the lens is curved and its ability to

magnify (magnification). The students can also see how a juice bottle filled with water can be used as a magnifier as well.

Build a Refracting Telescope I:
This is the first of several activities relating to refracting telescopes. Students first determine how to arrange two lenses so that when they look though them they will see a magnified image of a distant object.

Build a Refracting Telescope II:
Using the configuration of lenses that they found previously, students create a magnified image of a distant object. By placing the velum screen in varying locations, stu-dents determine the function of each lens in a basic refracting telescope.

Build a Refracting Telescope III:
The students in groups of two or three build the refracting telescope from the kit. They then look through the telescope at distant objects, making notes about their observations.

A Measure of Resolution:
Using the telescopes from the previous activity, students make and graph measurements to compare the telescope's resolution with that of their eye. Additional options include the comparison of the telescope's measured resolution to its theoretical resolution.

Build a Three-Lens Refracting Telescope:
An Activity for Student Assessment What happens to a telescope's image when a third lens is added to the system? Students find that a third lens creates an upright image. Students then draw the optical layout of the system.

Ultraviolet Light:
An Avon *DermaSpec Skin Imager* and some ultraviolet-sensitive beads are also in the kit. The *DermaSpec Skin Imager* is a long wavelength UV light (near 375 nanometers). The ultraviolet-sensitive beads change color in the presence of UV light. The beads allow you to do experiments such as testing the protective effects of sunscreen lotions. The beads also allow for exploration of questions such as "Can you get a sunburn on a cloudy day?"

3. *Terrific Telescopes* and the International Year of Astronomy

The International Year of Astronomy (IYA) 2009 celebrates the 400th anniversary of the first use of an astronomical telescope by Galileo Galilei. Events are being planned all over the world to help people gain a better appreciation of our place in the universe and how the telescope has transformed our world-view.

One of the themes of the US IYA is entitled "Telescope Building and Optics Challenges with author SMP as working group chair. We are in the process of designing a small telescope that would be roughly equivalent to the telescope Galileo used 400 years ago. The telescope will have similar aperture and magnification and should be able to be mass-produced inexpensively. The telescope will require a small amount of assembly in order to educate people about the optical elements that go into a telescope. Our goal is to distribute this small telescope to schools and science centers for use in public outreach events. We are also exploring whether current telescope kits are feasible for this IYA educational use.

A slightly more ambitious effort is to design a *Saturn Scope*. The *Saturn Scope* would have slightly better quality optics, adequate to see the rings of Saturn. Seeing the rings of Saturn for the first time through a telescope is a very memorable experience that we would like to make available to people during IYA and the years after. These telescope kits are described further in Pompea *et al.* (2008).

The *Terrific Telescopes* kits and the professional development component to use them effectively are only one component of our IYA efforts. We will also embed the kits within the educational context of the complete Hands-On Optics project where possible, in order to extend the learning experience. The larger HOO kits are better suited for teaching optics with a larger class, since they have more materials in each kit. Our goal is to have an extended learning experience about telescopes at each site, wherever possible. Our program will be designed to encourage students to spend more "time on task" with lens and telescopes using the entire collection of HOO materials.

We are also designing optics and telescope-related competitions that can provide more open-ended exploration by students. We had previously designed several of these activities in conjunction with the *Hands-On Optics* project (Pompea, Walker, & Peruta 2005). These designs for the IYA are in the early stage, but we anticipate national competitions that allow students to pursue in-depth out-of-school explorations. Our experience with these competitions, held in conjunction with the Arizona MESA program, is that well-deigned competitions encourage creativity and long-term investigations in optics.

4.   Conclusion

The *Terrific Telescopes* kit fits in well with the IYA themes involving telescopes and optics competitions. Over the next two years, we will build a nationwide network of outreach professionals trained in the use of the *Terrific Telescopes* kit in preparation for IYA 2009. We will also hold workshops at various venues around the country such as the Astronomical Society of the Pacific annual meetings and the American Astronomical Society meetings in order to train astronomy EPO professionals on our kits. We will also continue to train science museum educations through the *Astronomy From the Ground Up* workshops which are held throughout the country and via distance learning. These approaches are designed to create a network of well-trained educators who can effectively utilize any kits and materials provided through the IYA educational infrastructure.

Acknowledgments.   The *Hands-On Optics* Project is funded by the National Science Foundation ISE program. Project PI: Anthony Johnson, Director of the Center for Advanced Studies in Photonics Research at the University of Maryland, Baltimore County (UMBC). Project Co-I are Eugene Arthurs, Executive Director of SPIE-The International Society for Optical Engineering and Stephen Pompea (Manager of Science Education, NOAO) who also serves as Project Director. NOAO is operated by the Association of Universities for Research in Astronomy (AURA), Inc. under cooperative agreement with the National Science Foundation. The *Astronomy from the Ground Up* project is supported by the Informal Education Division of the National Science Foundation.

References

Pompea, S.M, Fienberg, R.T., Deustua, S., and Isbell, D., "Telescope Kits and Optics Challenges for the International Year of Astronomy", Astronomical Society of the Pacific Conference Series, this volume, 2008)

Pompea, S.M. and Hawkins, I., "Increasing Science Literacy in Optics and Photonics through Science Centers, Museums, and Web-based Exhibits", Pro. SPIE: Education and Training in Optics and Photonics, 4588 (2004)

Pompea, S.M., Johnson, A., Arthurs E. and Walker, C.E, "Hands-On Optics: An Educational Initiative for Exploring Light and Color in After-School Programs, Museums, and Hands-On Science Centers", Proc. Ninth International Topical Meeting on Education and Training in Optics and Photonics, Marseille, France (2005)

Pompea, S.M., Walker, C.E., and Peruta, C., "Design and Evaluation of Optics Student Competitions and Contests for Maximal Educational Value", Proceedings Ninth International Topical Meeting on Education and Training in Optics and Photonics, Marseille, France (2005)

Pompea, S.M., Walker, C.E., and Sparks, R.T., "Knowledge and Wonder: Engagements with Light and Color in the Hands-On Optics Project", Exemplary Science in Informal Education Settings: Standards-Based Success Stories, R. Yager and J. Falk eds., NSTA Press, pp. 47-70 (2008)

Walker, C.E., Sparks, R., and Pompea, S.M., "Optics Education in the International Year of Astronomy", Education and Training in Optics and Photonics 2007, Ottawa, Canada, (June 3-5, 2007)

There were many excellent presentations on the International Year of
Astronomy

EPO and a Changing World
ASP Conference Series, Vol. 389, © *2008*
C. Garmany, M. Gibbs, and J. W. Moody

Using New Media to Reach Broad Audiences

Pamela L. Gay[1,2,3] and The IYA New Media Working Group[3]

Abstract. The International Year of Astronomy New Media Working Group (IYA NMWG) has a singular mission: To flood the Internet with ways to learn about astronomy, interact with astronomers and astronomy content, and socially network with astronomy. Within each of these areas, we seek to build lasting programs and partnerships that will continue beyond 2009. Our weapon of choice is New Media. It is often easiest to define New Media by what it is not. Television, radio, print and their online redistribution of content are not New Media. Many forms of New Media start as user provided content and content infrastructures that answer that individual's creative whim in a way that is adopted by a broader audience. Classic examples include Blogs and Podcasts. This media is typically distributed through content specific websites and RSS feeds, which allow syndication. RSS aggregators (iTunes has audio and video aggregation abilities) allow subscribers to have content delivered to their computers automatically when they connect to the Internet. RSS technology is also being used in such creative ways as allowing automatically updating Google-maps that show the location of someone with an intelligent GPS system, and in sharing 100 word microblogs from anyone (Twitters) through a single feed. In this poster, we outline how the IYA NMWG plans to use New Media to reach target primary audiences of astronomy enthusiasts, image lovers, and amateur astronomers, as well as secondary audiences, including: science fiction fans, online gamers, and skeptics.

1. Our Mission and Audience

The International Year of Astronomy New Media Working Group seeks to flood the Internet with ways to learn about astronomy and increase interaction among professionals, amateurs, and laypeople. Amateur astronomers, astronomy and space enthusiasts, and image lovers are our primary audiences, but secondary audiences include science fiction fans, online gamers, and skeptics. We aim to build lasting programs and partnerships that will continue beyond 2009.

At this time, proposed activities explicitly provide mainstream astronomy content in areas related to New Media. While there are many good online formal-educational programs and projects, we have chosen not to incorporate them in our planning, but instead to focus reaching public in media they consume for

[1] Astronomy Cast, http://www.astronomycast.com

[2] Southern Illinois University Edwardsville, Department of Physics, Campus Box 1654, Edwardsville, IL, 62026-1654

[3] International Year of Astronomy, http://www.astronomy2009.us

entertainment. Essentially, we are looking to create programs that invite people to experience and learn about astronomy for the pleasure of the experience.

2.   Strategies

New Media differ from traditional media (such as television, radio, and print) in their informality. Many forms of New Media start as user-provided content. New Media content-building infrastructures answer the content provider's creative whims, and New-Media content can be commented upon, shared, borrowed, adopted, edited, and re-posted by a broad audience. Classic examples of New Media include blogs and podcasts. This media is typically distributed through content-specific websites and RSS feeds, which allow individual Internet users to select preferred streams of media (including text, audio, and video) to be delivered to them automatically. IYA plans to take advantage of these new, content-rich means of communication through a number of programs. The three we are most excited about are podcast provisionally titled "365 Days of Astronomy," guest blogs, and AstroTwitter.

New Media also includes areas such as social networking sites (e.g. MySpace, Facebook), social sharing sites (e.g. YouTube, Flickr), and social linking sites (e.g. Digg, SlashDot). On all of these sites, individuals create online profiles and link from their profiles to content, personal blogs, personal media, and/or opinions and ranking of other content. At this time, IYA has a MySpace profile (developed by the this committee), a MySpace group (by Raquel Shida), and a Facebook group (developed by this committee). We are personifying IYA as a 20-something female from Pisa, Italy (Galileo's home town) who is living in America and just looking to make friends and looking for fun ways to share her knowledge and love of astronomy. These initial, online homes have already attracted attention and positive feedback. As of August 29, 2007, IYA had 106 MySpace friends and our Facebook group has 104 members.

Online communities fall into two broad areas: forums/discussion boards and virtual worlds. IYA currently plans to interact with forums in two ways: by monitoring existing forums for IYA related discussions we can participate in and by creating our on forums at http://www.astronomy2009.us/forums.

On the boundary of New Media are the virtual realities of gamers and Second Life. In many high-speed Internet-based subcultures, individuals spend the majority of their leisure time and leisure money in virtual realities. The gaming worlds of EverQuest, World of War Craft, and EveOnline each have their own economies (money can both be earned on line and converted via real-world to virtual-world money changers), and stores for buying and selling goods. Second Life is also a virtual reality with an economy, but it is unique in not being centered on any game or theme; it is a virtual world focused on the users being social. Within Second Life, users can learn about and purchase real-world goods in virtual stores, and visit virtual museums that are annexes of brick and mortar facilities. We are still exploring possible virtual programs. If you wish to chat with us and pose suggestions, IM IYA Infinity or IYA Dragonash in Second Life.

EPO and a Changing World
ASP Conference Series, Vol. 389, © 2008
C. Garmany, M. Gibbs, and J. W. Moody

GLOBE at Night 2.0: On the Road Toward IYA 2009

Constance E. Walker, Stephen M. Pompea and Douglas Isbell

National Optical Astronomy Observatory, 950 N. Cherry Ave., Tucson, AZ 85719, USA

Abstract. The outcome of the 2008 GLOBE at Night campaign will provide the basis for a quantitative global effort in 2009 as one of the major U.S.-led programs in the planned International Year of Astronomy (IYA). A worldwide dark-skies awareness campaign is a cornerstone activity of IYA 2009.

1. Introduction

In March 2006, the National Optical Astronomy Observatory (NOAO) and the GLOBE project conducted the GLOBE at Night program to enable "citizen-scientists" around the world to contribute simple unaided-eye observations on sky-brightness to a growing global database. Citizen-scientists recorded the brightness of the night sky by matching its appearance toward the constellation Orion with 1 of 7 stellar maps of different limiting magnitude. Observations and their exact locations were submitted on-line. More than 18,000 people contributed 4,600 observations from 96 countries.

With further funding from the National Science Foundation, the GLOBE at Night 2007 program built upon the success of the inaugural campaign in 2006. The international star-hunting event returned March 8-21 in two flavors: the classic GLOBE at Night activity incorporating unaided-eye observations toward Orion, and a new effort to obtain precise measurements of urban dark skies toward zenith using digital sky-brightness meters. Participation increased to 8,500 observations from 60 countries in the last event.

2. The Digital GLOBE at Night Program 2007

To make possible the digital GLOBE at Night program, the NSF funded the purchase and distribution of 135 low-cost, handheld, well-calibrated sky-quality meters (manufactured by Unihedron), or "SQMs". Along with related educational materials developed by NOAO (including a hands-on demonstration of lighting using a flashlight and mask), the meters were distributed to citizen-scientists in 21 U.S. states plus Washington DC, and in 5 countries, including Chile, where NOAO has a major observatory. About 1000 measurements were reported by a variety of citizen-scientists including teachers, their students, astronomers at observatories, International Dark-Sky Association (IDA) members, and staff from 19 science centers.

At many of the sites where the SQMs were delivered, a local coordinator promoted dark-sky education using the educational kits, and trained a number of teachers and amateur astronomers on using the meter. For each meter, citizen-scientists were asked to make measurements from different locations in their region and record on-line their measurements with their latitude and longitude at each location, using either a GPS unit or GIS-related website.

As an illustration of the results, the SQM data for Tucson is plotted against population density in Figure 1. Other preliminary results can be found at http://www.noao.edu/outreach/press/pr07/pr0707.htm.

3.   Plans for 2008

Building upon the existing infrastructure of local coordinators and participants in GLOBE at Night, a similar but expanded U.S.-based SQM program will be implemented in 2008 with additional collaboration from the International Dark-Sky Association (http://www.darksky.org) and a SQM citizen-science program called Night Vision (http://www.nightwise.org/nightvision.htm).

With funding for the 2008 campaign, this effort will support ongoing student-teacher teams, as well as new participants, and build a more formal network of GLOBE at Night sites and coordinators. People who commit to the program will have access to sky-brightness meters as well as an updated teaching kit. Participants will learn how to use the meters, how to organize a meaningful campaign in their community, and how to teach with the kit. Interested participants will be offered the opportunity to continue measurements year-round.

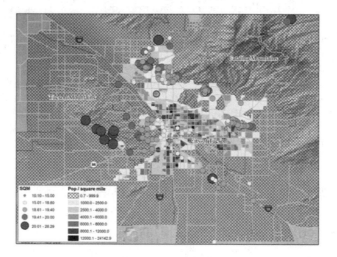

Figure 1.   SQM measurements of Tucson

4.   Summary

The 2008 campaign will provide the basis for a quantitative global effort in 2009 as a major U.S. program in the planned International Year of Astronomy.

GLOBE at Night has been a collaboration between NOAO, the GLOBE program, the IDA, CADIAS and Windows to the Universe. NOAO is operated by the Association of Universities for Research in Astronomy (AURA), Inc. under cooperative agreement with the National Science Foundation. This work was supported by a grant to NOAO by the NSF AST Division.

EPO and a Changing World
ASP Conference Series, Vol. 389, © *2008*
C. Garmany, M. Gibbs, and J. W. Moody

Looking Through a Telescope During the International Year of Astronomy 2009

Richard Tresch Fienberg

Sky & Telescope, New Track Media LLC, 90 Sherman St., Cambridge, MA 02140

Douglas Isbell

National Optical Astronomy Observatory, 950 N. Cherry Ave., Tucson, AZ 85719

Susana E. Deustua

American Astronomical Society, 2000 Florida Ave., NW, #400, Washington, DC 20009

Abstract.   The main goal of the U.S. IYA 2009 effort is to offer an engaging astronomy experience to every person in the country. Since the IYA is a celebration of the 400th anniversary of Galileo's introduction of the telescope to astronomy, the key engaging experience we'll offer is the opportunity to look through a small telescope at the celestial targets Galileo looked at. Another goal of the U.S. IYA effort is to cultivate sustainable partnerships. In addition to their own programs, local amateur astronomers will set up their scopes at events held by professional organizations, including NASA, universities, observatories, planetariums, and museums of science. The relationships forged during this large-scale collaboration for public outreach in astronomy will continue beyond 2009. Our "telescope amnesty" program will invite people to bring their little-used telescopes to IYA 2009 events, where astronomers will teach them how to use them and offer advice on repairs, improvements, and/or replacements, encouraging more people to stay involved in the hobby.

1.   International Year of Astronomy 2009

The main goal of the U.S. IYA 2009 effort, led by the American Astronomical Society, is to offer an engaging astronomy experience to every person in the country. Since the IYA is a celebration of the 400th anniversary of Galileo's introduction of the telescope to astronomy, one of the key engaging experiences we'll offer is to give as many people as possible the opportunity to look through a telescope.

Accordingly, the AAS has established the "Looking Through a Telescope" Working Group, chaired by Rick Fienberg (Editor in Chief, *Sky & Telescope*). Naturally, we'll focus on the celestial targets that Galileo himself looked at, most of which are visible even from light-polluted cities: The Moon, Venus, Mars, Jupiter, Saturn, the Pleiades, Praesepe, the Trapezium, Mizar/Alcor, the Milky Way, and the Sun. We want to offer more than a "gee whiz" experience.

We want people (especially kids) to experience firsthand how observations lead to an understanding of the natural world.

Another major goal of the U.S. IYA effort is to cultivate sustainable partnerships. "Sidewalk astronomy" is an ideal vehicle for astronomy clubs and individual amateur astronomers to participate in IYA 2009. In addition to their own programs, local amateurs will be encouraged to set up their scopes at events held by professional organizations, including NASA, universities, observatories, planetariums, and museums of science or natural history. The relationships forged during this large-scale collaboration for public outreach in astronomy will continue beyond 2009.

We aim to give 10 million people a good look through a telescope in 2009. This is achievable if, for example, 100,000 amateur observers each show the sky to 100 people. We plan to set up an area on the U.S. IYA 2009 website where people can comment on their telescopic observations especially their reactions to "first looks." We hope to collect the comments on a disc or chip and launch them into orbit on a NASA space telescope.

2.   Telescope Amnesty Program

Millions of small telescopes are sold every year, but anecdotal evidence suggests that most are rarely used for astronomy, if at all.

Our "telescope amnesty" program will invite people to bring their little-used telescopes to IYA 2009 events, where astronomers will teach them how to use them and offer advice on repairs, improvements, and/or replacements, turning bad astronomical experiences into good ones and encouraging more people to stay involved in the hobby.

3.   Observing Calendar

Since the most impressive telescopic object is the Moon, and since the Moon figured prominently in Galileo's work, the ideal time to hold monthly sidewalk-astronomy events is on Friday and/or Saturday evenings near first-quarter Moon, which occurs on the following dates in 2009: Sunday, January 4; Monday, February 2; Wednesday, March 4; Thursday, April 2; Friday, May 1; Sun., May 31; Monday, June 29; Tuesday, July 28; Thursday, August 27; Saturday, Sept. 26; Monday, October 26; Tuesday, November 24; Thursday, December 24.

Mercury's best evening apparition for the U.S. is on Sunday evening, April 26, when the planet sits just below the thin waxing crescent Moon (making it easy to find).

Venus is at greatest elongation in the evening sky in mid-January 2009. The main attraction of Venus is its full cycle of phases, which showed Galileo that it orbits the Sun, not the Earth.

Unfortunately, Mars doesn't reach opposition till January 29, 2010, and it'll then be only 14 arcsec in diameter, so it's not a very good evening target in 2009. Still, Mars will be in the news during IYA 2009, thanks to ongoing exploration by current missions and the launch of Mars Science Laboratory in the fall.

Jupiter and its Galilean satellites come to opposition on Friday-Saturday, August 14-15. Note that Neptune reaches opposition on August 17, and that the two planets are just 3° apart that week. This offers a wonderful opportunity to tell people how Galileo missed the chance to discover Neptune when, in December 1612 and January 1613, he observed it near Jupiter and mistook it for a star. Most people, of course, have never seen Neptune (let alone Jupiter) in a telescope. Here's a chance to see two planets at once! Bonus: Jupiter and Neptune will be less than 1° apart and will fit together in a low-power eyepiece on three occasions in 2009: late May (morning sky), early July (late evening, early morning sky), and late December (evening sky).

Saturn's opposition is March 8, but note that Saturn's rings are nearly edge-on, with a ring-plane crossing on Sept. 4, when the planet is only 11° from the Sun. Saturn won't look as "telegenic" as usual, but this does offer a chance to talk about how the changing aspect of the rings made it impossible for Galileo to figure out what was going on there.

The year's best meteor showers in 2009 are the Leonids in mid-November and the Geminids in mid-December (unfortunately the Perseids in mid-August, when the nights are warmer, will be drowned out by moonlight).

The total solar eclipse on July 22 is the longest of the 21st century, lasting 6m 39s at greatest eclipse in the Pacific Ocean. The centerline goes right through Shanghai, China, where totality lasts 5m 56s. Thousands of astronomy enthusiasts will travel to China or the Pacific to see this eclipse, but millions (billions?) more can watch online during the Mother of All Webcasts.

The Moon will just nick the northern edge of Earth's umbral shadow on the last night of the year, Sun., December 31. This partial lunar eclipse isn't visible in most of the Western Hemisphere, but we include it here as icing on the cake of IYA 2009 for observers in the East.

4.   Opportunity for "Citizen Science"

Third-magnitude Epsilon Aurigae is an eclipsing binary star with the longest orbital period known (27.1 years). The next eclipse of this unique object begins in summer 2009. Eps Aur's eclipses last 714 days (nearly 2 years). This indicates that the eclipsing body is of gigantic proportions, on the order of 2,000 solar radii. During the last eclipse, in 1982-84, amateur and professional astronomers around the world acquired photometry, polarimetry, and spectroscopy. Despite the strong effort, many questions remain. The 2009-11 eclipse will be the first to occur during the Digital Age. It offers ideal opportunities to showcase the value of pro-am collaborations and the relationship between advancing technology and advancing science. Partial eclipse begins August 6; totality begins December 21; totality ends March 12, 2011; partial eclipse ends May 15, 2011; see http://www.du.edu/~rstencel/epsaur.htm.

5.   A Telescope in Every Pot

We hope to give thousands (millions?) of kids and adults a chance to build a simple refractor similar to the ones Galileo used. Especially for people who can't afford to buy even a department-store telescope, a do-it-yourself Galileo-scope could be the key to pursuing an interest in astronomy beyond IYA 2009. There are several cardboard-and-plastic refractor kits on the market today, but none are particularly good. Our working group is collaborating with the AAS "Telescope Kits & Optics Challenges" working group, led by Stephen Pompea (NOAO), to develop a better one. For more information, see the AAS International Year of Astronomy 2009 web-site at http://www.astronomy2009.us.

EPO and a Changing World
ASP Conference Series, Vol. 389, © 2008
C. Garmany, M. Gibbs, and J. W. Moody

Telescope Kits and Optics Challenges for the International Year of Astronomy 2009

Stephen M. Pompea and Douglas Isbell

Astronomical National Optical Astronomy Observatory, 950 N. Cherry Ave., Tucson AZ, 85719, USA

Richard T. Fienberg

Sky & Telescope Magazine, 90 Sherman St., Cambridge, MA 02140-3264, USA

Susana Deustua

American Astronomical Society, 2000 Florida Ave, NW Ste. 400, Washington, DC 20009, USA

1. Introduction

We are developing programs that use educational telescope kits to increase science literacy (Pompea & Hawkins 2004) for the International Year of Astronomy 2009. This program builds on our experiences in the NSF-funded informally-oriented *Hands-On Optics* (HOO) project (Walker et al. 2007), a collaboration among SPIE, OSA, and NOAO. Module 3 of the HOO project is devoted to image formation using lens and mirrors. As a culminating activity participants build a small refracting telescope using the Learning Technologies Inc. (LTI) telescope kit. LTI builds and distributes the HOO kits, which were designed at NOAO. NOAO has also developed an abbreviated telescope education kit for the NSF-funded *Astronomy from the Ground Up Project*, with the Astronomical Society of the Pacific and the Association of Science-Technology Centers. This "Terrific Telescopes" mini-kit has been used in a number of workshops for science center educators with considerable success. Our telescope kit project goals are to: 1. Provide designs for educationally effective telescope kits; 2. Provide a means of manufacturing and distributing these kits as needed; 3. Provide basic inquiry-based educational materials on image formation and telescopes for more extended education programs; and 4. Identify and reinforce a dissemination network for these kits and their associated educational programs.

2. Approaches to Telescope Kits

Given the success of the LTI telescope kits, why do we need new ones? The LTI telescope kits are easy to assemble and have great educational value. However, they produce an upside-down image, have no mount to stabilize the view, and suffer from chromatic and other aberrations, which limits their astronomical use. Also, the technique of their construction by students can lead to degraded optical performance due to misplacement or tilting of the eyepiece lens. In general though, we want to build on the many positive aspects of these Project STAR telescopes while improving their optical performance as much as possible.

For the IYA we envision that two telescope kits may be necessary! One kit, the *Galileoscope* would be optimized for looking at the Moon and would give a lower magnification. In this scope, the low-cost of the telescope may determine many design aspects. The *Galileoscope* would have low magnification (15-20 power) and cost. A second telescope, termed, a "Saturnscope" would give higher magnification and be more expensive. The *Saturnscope* would be designed to give a view of Saturn's rings. If produced in bulk, we believe that both telescopes can be reasonably priced and give excellent value for money.

The *Galileoscope* kit must be easy to assemble by students, have moderate image quality, a magnification of 15-20 power, and a field of view the size of the Moon, if possible, and have the ability to be attached to a stable mount. An image that is right side up is desirable. For the *Saturnscope*, it needs a magnification of about 25-50 power and the ability to resolve the disk and rings of Saturn (20-30 arcseconds in size), even if Saturn is becoming edge-on (as it will in the International Year of Astronomy). A steady mount is essential, as is very good image quality. We are investigating a number of new approaches for these kits, including the use of aspheric surfaces, glass and plastic injection molded objectives, various eyepiece designs, novel mounts, and simple methods of stray light control (Pompea 1995). Our optical analysis partners are the Tucson companies Raytheon, Breault Research Organization, and Photon Engineering. Other key members of the working group include a retired optical engineer from Lockheed Martin and a person with experience in telescope systems and manufacturability.

In conclusion, great progress is being made in the design, optical analysis and testing of the kits. The next step is to obtain a better understanding of the manufacturing and production issues and to further develop the dissemination plan.

Acknowledgments.   *Hands-On Optics and Astronomy from the Ground Up* projects are funded by the NSF ISE program. NOAO is operated by the Association of Universities for Research in Astronomy (AURA), Inc. under cooperative agreement with the NSF.

References

Pompea, S. M., "The Management of Stray Radiation Issues in Space Optical Systems", Space Science Rev., **74**, 181-193 (1995)
Pompea, S.M. and Hawkins, I., Pro. SPIE: *Education and Training in Optics and Photonics*, 4588 (2004)
Walker, C.E., Sparks, R., and Pompea, S.M., "Optics Education in the International Year of Astronomy", Education and Training in Optics and Photonics 2007, Ottawa, Canada, (June 3-5, 2007)

EPO and a Changing World
ASP Conference Series, Vol. 389, © 2008
C. Garmany, M. Gibbs, and J. W. Moody

The International Year of Astronomy 2009: NASA Science Mission Directorate Contributions

Denise A. Smith

Space Telescope Science Institute, 3700 San Martin Drive, Baltimore, MD 21218, USA

Mary Dussault

Harvard-Smithsonian Center for Astrophysics, 60 Garden Street, Cambridge, MA 02138, USA

Leslie Lowes

Jet Propulsion Laboratory, 4800 Oak Grove Drive, Pasadena, CA 91109, USA

Hashima Hasan, Doris Daou, and Marilyn Lindstrom

NASA Headquarters, 300 E Street S.W., Washington, DC 20546, USA

Abstract. The International Astronomical Union has proclaimed 2009 as the International Year of Astronomy, citing the 400th anniversary of Galileo's first astronomical use of the telescope as an opportunity to help citizens rediscover their place in the universe and to stimulate worldwide interest in astronomy. This paper summarizes emerging plans for NASA Science Mission Directorate participation in the International Year of Astronomy, based on community meetings with education and public outreach (EPO) professionals affiliated with NASA's space science missions. The resulting framework has broad applicability and potential for collaboration across and beyond NASA.

1. Introduction

Global, national, and local activities held during the 2009 International Year of Astronomy will celebrate astronomy's contributions to society and culture, and encourage citizens of all ages and backgrounds to discover the universe for themselves. The commemoration of Galileo's legacy of observation and discovery also provides a unique opportunity for education and public outreach (EPO) programs to strengthen existing interest in products and programs, engage new audiences and partners, and increase the connectivity and impact of individual products and programs. With this in mind, the NASA Science Mission Directorate (SMD) space science EPO community has begun preliminary planning of a coordinated EPO effort for the International Year of Astronomy.

2. Emerging Plans

Spectacular imagery, fundamental scientific discoveries, and technological breakthroughs associated with NASA's space science missions and research programs can inspire learners of all ages. EPO professionals affiliated with these programs will couple events such as the *Hubble Space Telescope Servicing Mission 4*, the launch of the *Kepler* mission, and the *Lunar Crater Observation and Sensing Satellite*'s (LCROSS) impact with the Moon with proven space science EPO programs to support US and international goals for the International Year of Astronomy. Strategies include:

- *Coordinated professional development for educators.* NASA SMD-funded EPO programs provide a variety of professional development experiences for educators each year, ranging from short duration workshops to multiday symposia to full online courses. We will coordinate these offerings to provide educators working in both formal and informal science education settings with the tools they need to engage their audiences in the International Year of Astronomy.

- *Resources for the informal science education community* The SMD EPO community has an established track record of working collaboratively with informal science educators to provide NASA space science resources that meet audience needs. *ViewSpace* multimedia presentations, image unveilings from the Great Observatories, and planetarium shows from LCROSS and *Kepler* are among the resources that will inspire and engage audiences nationwide in 2009.

- *Authentic science experiences for students, educators, and the public.* Recognizing the role that personal experience plays in learning, the NASA SMD EPO community provides a number of opportunities for the public to make their own observations of celestial objects and to explore NASA data. Opportunities for 2009 will include events hosted by Night Sky Network amateur astronomy clubs and coordinated access to MicroObservatory online telescopes.

Acknowledgments. NASA Science Mission Directorate plans stem from Astrophysics, Planetary Science, and Heliophysics EPO community meetings held in 2006 and 2007. We gratefully acknowledge the contributions of all involved in defining a community-based effort for the International Year of Astronomy. Visit http://www.astronomy2009.org to learn how to participate or to plan your own activities under the international theme: "The Universe: Yours to Discover."

EPO and a Changing World
ASP Conference Series, Vol. 389, © 2008
C. Garmany, M. Gibbs, and J. W. Moody

Plans in Canada for the International Year of Astronomy 2009

Jim Hesser

NRC-HIA, 5071 West Saanich Road, Victoria, BC, V9E 2E7, Canada

Jayanne English

Department of Physics and Astronomy, University of Manitoba, Winnipeg, MB, R3T 2N2, Canada

Rémi Lacasse

Fédération des astronomes amateurs du Québec, 4545, ave Pierre-De Coubertin, C.P. 1000, Succursale M, Montréal, QC, H1V 3R2, Canada

Scott Young

The Manitoba Museum, 190 Rupert Avenue, Winnipeg, MB, R3B 0N2, Canada

John Percy

50 St. George Street Room 101, Toronto, ON, Canada M5S 3H4, Canada

Abstract.   Professional and amateur astronomers in Canada are working together to strengthen - and form new - partnerships with the formal and informal education communities, as well as Aboriginal, arts and cultural, and other organizations: "To offer an engaging astronomy experience to every person in Canada, and to cultivate partnerships that sustain public interest in astronomy." Our ideas have much in common with those of other IYA nations, especially our US neighbour with whom we enjoy close liaison through the AAS, but we seek to exploit unique Canadian opportunities.

1.   Broad Themes and Philosophy

Some dozen specific programme ideas are grouped under three broad themes with strong emphasis on connecting with young people. These themes are:

- **Reconnecting With The Sky:** star parties, material for educators and kids, visiting dark sky sites and creating new ones, etc.

- **Canadians at the Frontiers:** national planetarium shows, national lectures by outstanding researchers who are also gifted public speakers

- **Astronomy in Society:** First Nations and Inuit traditional knowledge, astronomy in Canada's multicultural society, collaborations with arts and entertainment organizations

The ways that we support these themes include the following:

Raising pride and awareness: Canadians (are) exposed to more news and entertainment from the US than from home. We want more Canadians to appreciate the high world impact of their astronomers and educators, while encouraging greater awareness among our youth of future S&T opportunities.

Bilingual activities: Parallel structures ensure comparable access in both French and English.

Legacy: Wherever possible activities include legacy or sustainable components for impact beyond 2009.

Volunteer based: All efforts led by volunteers. Seeking funding for individual programmes, as well as for a paid assistant throughout 2008-2009.

Grassroots emphasis: Depending upon and encouraging individual initiative within the broad context provided by the National Committee and the IAU.

2. Our Organization

The Canadian Astronomical Society (CASCA), the Royal Astronomical Society of Canada (RASC) and the Fédération des Astronomes Amateurs de Québec (FAAQ) partnered to develop Canadian activities in strong collaboration with the planetarium and science centre communities, the national broadcaster (CBC), Canada's Aboriginal communities, the National Research Council (NRC) and the Canadian Space Agency (CSA). All organizations have been involved from early days in planning and decisions.

3. Astronomy Elements

Teams across Canada are working on funding proposals to implement focussed astronomy outreach through various approaches, including:

- A proposal led by the RASC for ¿1M Canadians to enjoy "Galileo moments", and to promote astronomy as widely as possible with help from their centres and other outreach programs (Guides, Cubs, Scouts), with associated handouts and resources.

- "Galileo Live" with actors and new material proposed for Canada's 5 major planetaria.

- A fully scripted 4-hr miniseries connecting astronomy with history, art, and literature, as well as promoting the end-to-end value to society of "dark skies" and reconnection with the night sky is under review by broadcasters.

- National lecture series by top researchers who are also excellent public communicators.

- Postal stamp proposal awaiting Canada Post decision in 2008.

- Early stages of thinking about lesson plans and supporting material for distribution via education sites such as http://www.cascaeducation.ca

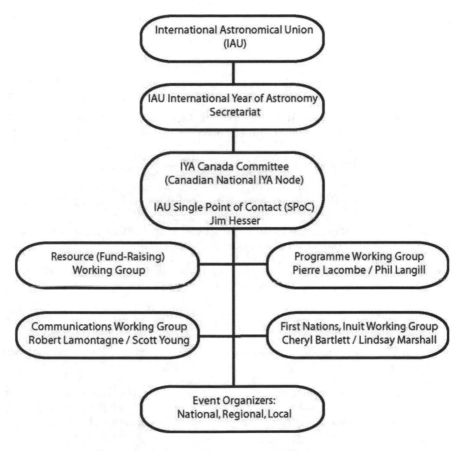

Figure 1.   Canadian IYA 2009 Organizational Chart

4. Two Complementary Thrusts

Offering engaging experiences to all Canadians requires a broadly cast net. Two examples of early success attracting outstanding new partners are:

First Nations and Inuit Outreach: Cape Breton University's Integrative Science Programme and the Mi'kmaq College Institute are energetically leading efforts to create a deeply meaningful Aboriginal component, including:

- Formal engagement with their local Membertou First Nation and the Unama'ki Institute of Natural Resources to create the essential basis for national outreach and planning with the diverse First Nations communities

- Goals include:
  - strong, participatory "eyes on" dimension locally and within the K-12 school system(s) in Aboriginal communities across Canada
  - fostering broadened awareness and understanding of the pathways to higher education in conjunction with the values of Aboriginal traditional knowledge
  - encouraging dark sky preserves on Aboriginal lands
  - national collection of indigenous stories about the night sky in conjunction with local ecosystems to be published in book form

Collaborations with the arts communities: Early exploration has focused on classical music organizations, with encouraging results:

- At least two musical organizations of national repute are commissioning new music based upon Galileo and astronomy.

- encouraging responses from most major symphonies about performing Holst's The Planets accompanied by astronomical imagery.

- The Victoria Symphony has committed to offering a series of concerts including:
  - Educational concerts written by Music Director Tania Miller about Galileo and astronomy, with lesson plans including astronomy, for performance in February 2009 to elementary and middle schools (about 9,000 children).
  - Kids concerts based thereon open to the public in Sept. 2009 and to be performed in Vancouver and Toronto.
  - An original quartet by a Composer in Residence based on astronomical themes performed in schools in partnership with Starlab Planetarium shows.

The encouraging lesson so far is how appealing IYA 2009 opportunities are proving to be to new partners and how modest initiatives by individuals pursuing personal interests can create far-reaching impact.

Andrew Fraknoi - Richard H. Emmons Award Winner

Andrew Fraknoi with Richard & Phyllis Emmons at the Vancouver ASP
Meeting

Part VI

Summaries

EPO and a Changing World
ASP Conference Series, Vol. 389, © 2008
C. Garmany, M. Gibbs, and J. W. Moody

ASP Networking Sessions Summary

Lindsay Marie Bartolone

Adler Planetarium & Astronomy Museum, 1300 S. Lake Shore Drive, Chicago, IL 60605

Abstract. In response to evaluation conducted during the Annual Meeting of the Astronomical Society of the Pacific in 2006, "Engaging the EPO Community: Best Practices, New Approaches," loosely structured networking sessions were added by the program committee in an effort to assist conference attendees in achieving their stated conference goals. The co-chairs of the 2007 conference invited registrants to serve as facilitators for twelve networking sessions. This work aims to summarize the conversations that took place during those sessions, based upon notes and artifacts provided to the author by the session facilitators.

1. Introduction

In preparing the program schedule for the Astronomical Society of the Pacifics 2007 Conference, "EPO and a Changing World: Creating Linkages and Expanding Partnerships," the program committee examined results from the evaluations that had been distributed to registrants at the conference the previous year. One hundred of the two hundred responses listed Networking as the most useful aspect of the conference and sixty-five responses included aspects of networking in their statement of primary goal for attending the conference. The program committee felt that providing more and varied opportunities for networking would be beneficial for the conference attendees.

To that end, twelve networking sessions were added to the schedule. Six took place on Wednesday, September 5, 2007 for thirty minutes and six were held on Thursday, September 6, 2007 for forty-five minutes. Session topics and frequency were determined based upon survey results completed as participants registered online for the conference. The conference co-chairs invited registrants whom they believed possessed excellent facilitation skills and knowledge in the topic area to lead the networking sessions.

The scheduled sessions and session facilitators are described in Table 1.

1.1. Session Descriptions

The facilitators designed and created the format and products of the sessions at their discretion. The sessions took many formats including small round table discussions about starter topics suggested by the facilitator, or "speed-dating," where participants were encouraged to have short one-on-one discussions with many members of the group. Session sizes were small, ranging from one session that had no participants to several that had groups of ten to fifteen. Sessions on Wednesday had fewer participants due to the placement as the last session of the day. Announcements were made on Thursday morning during the general session, and those sessions were better attended.

Table 1.   Schedule of Networking Sessions and Facilitators

Date	Duration (minutes)	Session Topic	Facilitator(s) & Organization(s)
9/5/2007	30	Research in Learning	Karen Carney, Adler Planetarium
9/5/2007	30	Partnering with Museums and Science Centers	Lucy Fortson, Adler Planetarium, and Erika Reinfeld, Harvard-Smithsonian Center for Astrophysics
9/5/2007	30	Underserved and Underrepresented Audiences	Sanlyn Buxner, Lunar & Planetary Lab, University of Arizona
9/5/2007	30	Working in the World of Formal K-12	Bernhard Beck-Winchatz, DePaul University
9/5/2007	30	Partnering with Youth and Community Groups	Irene Porro, MIT Kavli Institute for Astrophysics & Space Research, and Alan Gould, Lawrence Hall of Science
9/5/2007	30	Telescope Networks for Education	Vivian White, Astronomical Society of the Pacific, and Mary Kay Hemenway, Univ. of Texas at Austin
9/6/2007	45	Research in Learning	Karen Carney, Adler Planetarium
9/6/2007	45	Partnering with Museums and Science Centers	Lindsay Bartolone, Adler Planetarium, and Erika Reinfeld, Harvard-Smithsonian Center for Astrophysics
9/6/2007	45	Web 2.0 and Educational Technology	Nancy Ross, Adler Planetarium
9/6/2007	45	Working in the World of Formal K-12 Bernhard	Beck-Winchatz, DePaul University
9/6/2007	45	Partnering with Youth and Community Groups	Irene Porro, MIT Kavli Institute for Astrophysics & Space Research, and Alan Gould, Lawrence Hall of Science
9/6/2007	45	Creating NASA Products	Denise Smith, Space Telescope Science Institute

Research in Learning This format for this session centered around organizing questions posted on sheets of paper around the room that participants responded to by making tally marks indicating if they knew possible answers to those questions or wanted to know answers. They then had discussions about the questions and at the end indicated if they had learned answers. Overall, 48 of tally marks made by participants were listed under the questions as things participants wanted to know and 15 tally marks were listed indicating that participants had found answers to their questions. Almost every question or topic had at least one participant who had found an answer to that question, indicating perhaps given more time in the session more participants could have found answers to more of their questions. The questions from both sessions are included in Table 2.

Table 2.   Questions and Topics from Research in Learning Sessions

Question Number	Organizing Questions
1	What's out there now and how do I find out?
2	Can I conduct research through my EPO?
3	What is the difference between research and evaluation?
4	How do I apply research to my practice?
5	How can I form a partnership to use or produce research?
6	What has been done to use education research in informal settings?
7	How do I make a useful partnership with an educational researcher?
8	How can I find out about the effectiveness of my programs?
9	What are current educational research initiatives in informal learning?
10	Employment opportunities for education research in physics/astronomy

Partnering with Museums and Science Centers These sessions asked participants to identify their goals for attending the session and then attempted to group participants based upon shared goals. At least twenty-two individuals attended one of these sessions. Small group discussions were held and many productive interactions occurred according to participant surveys. Participants indicated that they had between 1 and 10 productive interactions with other group members. Discussion topics included: exchange of professional job knowledge between an expert and novice in the field, how to reach museum communities through networks and how museums can receive materials from agencies.

Participants from these sessions overwhelmingly indicated that ASP should have this topic as a networking session again in future years.

Working in the World of Formal K-12   One of the two sessions on this topic was canceled due to lack of interest, however, the second session had at least eleven participants. Conversation topics between participants included essential knowledge versus extension knowledge, the challenges that are faced by school teachers and EPO professionals who want to teach astronomy topics in schools, and resources that are available for teaching astronomy content in grades three through eight. Ten participants completed exit cards that described one thing they had learned and one way they will implement something as a result of this session. The majority of implementation strategies involved investigating and sharing new resources, specifically the Space Science Sequence from Great Explorations in Math and Science (GEMS.)

Underserved and Underrepresented Audiences   This session was offered only once and had fifteen participants. The session began with group introductions and then participants separated into three discussion groups, two that focused on sharing ideas and experiences and one that discussed the nature of how to think about audiences served by programming. This discussion included the topics of dominant culture and individuals who are different from a "usual audience." The participants also discussed their various funding agencies and what the terms underserved and underrepresented meant in those contexts and from their personal experiences. Overall, the group concluded that there is no single way to reach everyone, and that it is necessary to target specific groups and work with them to discover the best ways to communicate. Other strategies suggested by the group included using the advice and experiences of others who have done similar work and partnering with community organizations. Participants indicated that perseverance is important to reach new communities.

Partnering with Youth/Community Groups   This session was offered twice, once with two participants and once with ten. Although the groups were small, eight participants felt they had enough time and people available to have "enough" productive interactions. Many of the participants listed that they found new products, possible partnerships and networks to help them in their work in this area. Seven participants suggested that this session topic should be offered again by ASP, however it was recommended to have representation from youth or community groups at the sessions and/or to hold the networking sessions more informally over breakfast with tables designated for various topics.

Telescope Networks for Education   This session was offered once with around fifteen participants. Many of the participants represented current telescope projects rather than interested novices. Discussion was extended from a meeting that had occurred the previous day at Adler Planetarium. The challenges of providing this type of resource to teachers were discussed including finding qualified teachers and designing programs that meet the needs of teachers and students. There was some discussion of the effectiveness of remote telescope networks for reaching both critical thinking skill goals and affective goals. The remainder of the session was spent discussing strategies for synergy between remote telescope communities. The participants felt that identifying the underlying common elements in the various interfaces was important to achieve universal access.

Web 2.0 and Educational Technology This session was offered once with at least nine participants, including NASA representatives, school planetarians and university staff. First, participants discussed the definition of Web 2.0. They provided several examples including Wikis, RSS, Mashups, and Tagging. There was no complete common definition, however they indicated that Web 2.0 includes more collaborative development of content, whether by community contribution or the ability to manipulate and combine data from multiple sources. Participants shared examples that they were aware of or had worked on. They also discussed the process of design for a new feature, including questions about their audience, the access the audience has, and how to really reach the audience they had in mind. The group also had a discussion about learning in these environments and upcoming reports on IMLS and NSF funded projects in these areas. Concerns held by this group for this type of work included funding, staffing and keeping data (personal and scientific) safe.

Creating NASA Products This session was offered once with approximately fifteen participants. Group members were asked to write down a question that they had about NASA product creation and then participants held discussions in an effort to answer each others questions. Some of the questions included, "Does a product have to be nationally applicable or can it be regionally specific?" "Who are the reviewers and what criteria are they looking for?" "What are the required reviews?", and "What are the basic requirements?" Participants provided some suggestions for formative evaluation, and also for using technology for tracking product use, including YouTube and SecondLife. They also discussed the importance of creating products that can be formatted for more than one audience, i.e. make the same product in more than one language or a planetarium show in a size appropriate for large and small planetaria. Some additional information about the creation of NASA products can be found on the Institute for Global Environmental Strategies website: http://www.strategies.org/education/index.aspx?sub=education&sub2=productevaluation.

2. Conclusion

The networking sessions provided an opportunity for small groups of participants to interact, learn from one another, share resources and ask and answer questions. This article provides a summary of those interactions and can perhaps serve as a springboard for future ASP sessions, networking topics or articles for the community.

Acknowledgments. The author would like to express her sincere gratitude to the facilitators who agreed to accept the task of leading these networking sessions. They shouldered the additional responsibility during what was already a very packed conference, with many side meetings and opportunities. Their dedication to the advancement of the EPO profession should be commended. Without them, these sessions would not have been possible.

Meade Telescope Raffle Winner, Jose Alonso

Rapporteur Robert Hurt

EPO and a Changing World
ASP Conference Series, Vol. 389, © 2008
C. Garmany, M. Gibbs, and J. W. Moody

Summary-Innovative Partnerships and Delivery Methods: Creating Linkages and Expanding Partnerships

Robert L. Hurt

Spitzer Science Center, MS 220-6, Pasadena, CA 91125

Abstract.   This paper summarizes the conference presentations on "Innovative Partnerships and Delivery Methods"

1.   What Are "Innovative Partnerships and Delivery Methods"?

Of all the conference threads at the 119th annual meeting of the Astronomical Society of the Pacific, this arguably casts the widest net, encouraging participants to look to non-traditional outlets for astronomy communication. The thread summary from the website offers a sampling of the challenge to go beyond the ordinary:

"How do we effectively communicate science in the information age? This strand looks at current research, challenges and emerging best practices in using innovative delivery methods and settings, ranging from iPods to children's books and from shopping malls to the National Parks. How can we partner more effectively to deliver science content through non-traditional channels? What new types of community partnerships can be formed?"

In the field of astronomy outreach, there are a number of established venues and methods for education. These reach into the classroom, as content is adapted to fit national standards and offered as curriculums to teachers. These encompass informal educational experiences outside of the classroom. Museums, and in particular, planetariums, are long-established venues for exposing the public at all ages to the universe. The challenge posed in this thread is to find new ways of collaborating both within and beyond these traditional venues and to develop methods of delivering con-tent to new audiences.

2.   Topics in the "Innovative Partnerships" Thread

This thread encompasses 14 workshop sessions and 28 posters. While the goal of in-novation tends to run counter to "categorization," it is still possible to identify six different subtopics running through this thread. The general thrust of each area will be described below; for more information on specific threads readers are directed to consult the corresponding contributions in these proceedings from the individual authors. Talks will by cited by their authors and posters by their session numbers.

Figure 1.   Acting out the parts of water, dust, and clouds to make a rainstorm

2.1.   Innovating in the Classroom

The classroom remains a critical venue for reaching young people at an age where there curiosity in the world around them is ascendant. Traditional programs based around teaching standards that deliver core science understanding will always be an essential part of the mix, but is it possible to do more?

There is a much broader set of opportunities to reach students of all ages in a way that provides engagement and can help stimulate advanced interests in science careers. A broad sampling of such efforts was presented in the poster contributions in this thread.

Introducing science topics that would traditionally be considered too "advanced" for general school audiences was one recurrent theme. The lesson was generally to find key related standards and overarching topics that bridge advanced disciplines and general science knowledge. Results covered such areas as nuclear astrophysics (WE03), quasars (WE16), and multiwavelength galaxy studies (WE10). Such outreach projects spanned students ranging as far as K-12.

Addressing the needs of teachers was also a key element in this thread. Enthusiasm and understanding is stimulated from the top down by delivering more advanced tools and curricula into the hands of teachers (WE06, WE21).

The workshop addressing the classroom demonstrated the innovative activities in the "Zula's Ready, Set - Science!" program (A. Thompkins, A. Vedder, & D. Manchester). Participants here experienced "kinematic learning" first hand, showing how activity and interaction can transform science processes (like the rainfall cycle) into a dynamic and interactive group performance.

2.2.   Beyond the Classroom

Possibilities for reaching and engaging students do not end with the school bell. Just as the school system provides an outreach partner for the astronomy educator, there is a rich infrastructure available to reach students outside of the academic classroom. This can include national organizations like scouting, 4-H clubs, etc. (sometimes dubbed "OST," or Out of School Time, Networks), as well as organizations local to a community or neighborhood.

The primary lesson of each of the three workshops covering this topic was to identify partnerships with organizations that can work to everyone's mutual benefit (H. Gibbons & J. Lutz; J. Lutz et al.; A. Krishnamurthi et al.). Organizers for after-school clubs are always in need of rich and educational content to maintain vibrant programs and so will welcome the chance to partner with astronomy educators. The mutually beneficial relationship can provide willing and interested audiences for the educators and increase the value of the clubs experience.

The challenge for an educator is to identify these community opportunities and to learn to work as collaborators addressing the specific needs and structures within a given group. The reward is to tap into existing infrastructures efficiently and easily develop astronomy content to reach a wide cross section of children through High School and beyond.

2.3.   Museums & Exhibitions

Museums will always play a critical role in reaching children and adults alike in an informal education environment. Specific examples of successful museum content can help everyone produce more effective exhibits in any venue.

Three posters in this session highlighted specific exhibits for museums and planetariums. These spanned the production of planetarium shows for a multilingual audience (WE07), an exhibit experience demonstrating black hole science (WE07), and a video game to help students understand the formation of the moon (WE29).

2.4.   Internet-Enabled Activities

While the internet has been an established tool for so long that it is hard to remember a time without Google, the possibilities for education and engagement evolve dramatically every year. In this theme, posters and workshops highlighted useful technologies for educators to develop innovative content for learning.

The three posters covering the internet spanned technologies, opportunities, and evaluation of the educational impact. Specific examples included a laundry list of easily accessible tools to get your message across (WE17), or standards to bring astronomy imagery into the modern internet era (WE12). An innovative study (WE09) tracked the educational experiences of users of a popular astronomy web forum, demonstrating positive long-term learning effects correlated with such participation.

The workshops on this topic introduced participants to specific technologies to enable education and reach new audiences with content. Online courses were shown to be a powerful and effective means to reach a broad cross-section of educators wishing to reinforce their knowledge, giving opportunities to learn when attending physical classes would be impractical or impossible (A. Hurst et al.). A tutorial on videoconferencing technology demonstrated the possibilities in providing eye-to-eye contact between remote locations cheaply and effectively (D. Zevin et al.). An outline of two video podcast production workflows demonstrated how anyone could set up their own internet show and reach a worldwide audience (R. Hurt & L. Christensen).

2.5.   Community Partnerships

Interest in astronomy is not limited to school kids, and reaching a diverse audience of adults and families should also be a key agenda for educators. Arguably one of the most effective techniques for reaching people is to engage them in and around their community. We are surrounded with a surprising array of opportunities for partner-ships throughout our communities, and sometimes it takes a moment of reflection to recognize the possibilities. However, by exploiting diverse, and even unexpected partnerships, you open up a broad set of possibilities for reaching people throughout both local and global communities.

Three posters on this topic highlighted opportunities vastly different in scope but all rich in potential. Such partnerships may be as simple as "just asking" local authorities (WE05). Astronomy institutes and observatories may find ways to bring in local populations and interest them in the sky in rural areas especially if the events are designed with the audience in mind (WE19). Even partnering with other cities across the globe with astronomical institutions can stimulate local interest in both communities (WE01).

The National Park Service has a long tradition of engaging visitors in local history, culture, and nature, and there are many possibilities to reach out to the sky through this venue as well. Two workshops helped participants understand more about the Park Service's tradition of "interpretive" storytelling and how they could work within this framework to bring certain kinds of sky stories to park visitors (A. Davis, R. Paglierani, & D. Hutson; M. Bahr, C. Tsairides, & C. Morrow). Likewise, amateur astronomers have a long tradition of community involvement and can make great partners as agents of education (M. Berendsen et al.).

Would you expect to learn about the universe in a bar? Perhaps the most innovative kind of partnership was discussed in the "Science Café" workshop (B. Wiehe & S. Gurton). This growing program of informal lectures and discussions set at local bars and café's provides a fun and innovative way to bring people actively into the process of learning in a social, comfortable setting.

2.6.   International Year of Astronomy 2009

One of the greatest opportunities for moving the sky under the public eye is the rapidly approaching International Year of Astronomy (IYA) in 2009. This collaborative event will provide educators worldwide a wonderful chance to tap into an international network of activities and apply them at the local level. For maximum impact, everyone in the astronomy community should try to get involved at whatever extent possible in this grass roots attempt to get the world to look up and think about the universe.

An ongoing dialog will benefit IYA activity development. Posters showed developing plans in countries like Canada (WE11) as well as institutions like

Figure 2.   Building a telescope from lenses and styrofoam cups

NASA (WE23). A case study of a similar effort for the International Polar Year helps see the effect of similar activities in other related fields (WE24).

Of course the IYA should be a hands-on and eyes-on experience for everyone. One workshop explored how to partner with your local newspaper to develop an astronomy-themed supplement for it (J. Harvey). Another provided the opportunity to try a hands-on optics kit that gets people involved with the ideas of optics and telescopes in a way that is cheap and fun (S. Pompea).

Ultimately educators in the US have a lot of resources available to them as well. By coordinating through the American Astronomical Society it is possible to be part of this global effort (D. Isbell & S. Deustua).

3.   Summary

People love to look at the sky, and virtually everyone will experience a sense of wonder when seeing the universe revealed in images and words. In that sense astronomy educators are in a position to be envied by many other science disciplines. By exploiting that natural interest, and throwing in a bit of imagination and creativity, it is possible to find exciting new ways to put the sky in front of people's eyes. The sessions in this thread are but a teaser of the possibilities to find new partnerships and to deliver astronomy to everyone to enjoy.

References

All references in this paper refer to other papers in this volume.
Sessions are referenced by the day of the week and session number (e.g. WE07, WE12)

Rapporteur Phil Sakimoto

Rapporteur Jordan Raddick

EPO and a Changing World
ASP Conference Series, Vol. 389, © *2008*
C. Garmany, M. Gibbs, and J. W. Moody

Towards Broadening the Audience

Philip J. Sakimoto

Department of Physics, University of Notre Dame, Notre Dame, IN 46556

Abstract. The strand *Towards Broadening the Audience* was intended to seed thoughtful conversations about building bridges for outreach programs across cultural barriers. Many participants spoke about progress in increasing the diversity of their outreach audiences, but it was new voices from time-honored sources that offered fundamentally new wisdom. From the religious traditions and tensions that mark the Holy Land came the simple concept of bringing unity through teaching the commonalities found in basic concepts of the observed sky. From Mayan traditions, both contemporary and ancient, came the reminder that the sky is intimately connected to all aspects of our lives. Astronomy outreach should therefore be a part of much larger family and community celebrations. Ideas such as these offer renewed hope for major advances in bringing space science outreach to much broader audiences. They tell us about the importance of learning from voices with perspectives different from our own, and of building partnerships based upon genuine cross-cultural understanding and mutual love of the sky.

1. Introduction

Decades of concerted efforts to expand space science outreach activities to an ever-widening variety of audiences have brought some successes, but, on the whole, progress has been frustratingly slow. Significant gains seem to require major new approaches, but what are they? Could fundamentally new insights lie hidden behind cultural barriers, seen and unseen? Could such insights increase our effectiveness in reaching new audiences? These are the questions that motivated the conference strand *Towards Broadening the Audience.*

The strand's stated intent was to provide "insights into successfully working with a broader diversity of audiences and understanding the cultural influences on engagement with science. How do you work effectively in cultural settings that are different from your own? How does culture influence science? How can effective partnerships be formed?" Various presenters took a wide variety of approaches to meeting the challenges posed by these questions. To some, the challenge was best met by taking a very broad approach: if you find ways to significantly increase the numbers of people reached by your outreach activities, then a broader diversity of people will naturally be drawn in. To others, the interpretation was more focused: if you wish to work successfully with a particular target group, then you must find ways to embrace and honor the other's culture. Invariably, there is much to learn from listening to cultural views different from one's own. New approaches can emerge, and true partnerships can be born.

With time and attention, the divisions between "we" and "they" can meld into a new "us."

2.   Broadening the Net

Efforts aimed at increasing the numbers of people reached by outreach activities fell into two basic categories: those using new communications technologies to reach greater numbers of people, and those using partnerships with other institutions and organizations to leverage larger audiences. Both approaches promise to extend the reach of the outreach programs involved.

2.1.   New Technologies

We now live in an age of instant communications. Podcasts, text messaging, online communities and blogs have become the norm among the younger set, while email and passive Web sites have become old fashioned. Clearly there is much to be gained by bringing space science outreach into these new communication arenas, and there is much to be learned about how to do so. The overall impact of new communication technologies on diversity is not yet clear. They undeniably help reach larger audiences, but it is too early to discern the impact they might have on reaching traditionally underrepresented groups. Given the newness and the inherent anonymity of such approaches, assessing their true impact is a difficult task.

Social Networks   For the dinosaurs among us, a much-needed introduction to online social networking was provided by Pamela Gay and Tom Foster of Southern Illinois University Edwardsville in a lively workshop called *Your Face(book) and MySpace: Let's Hook Up.* In the workshop, they recounted the history of Facebook (a legacy from Ivy League universities that continues to cater to college students and college graduates) and MySpace (a large open network that caters to a much broader audience), and they walked participants through the process of defining an online personality, collecting friends, and starting groups.

The potential uses are quite varied. You can use networks of friends or groups defined around common interests to send invitations to Web events or live events. "Friends bring friends," and more than 5,000 MySpace members list astronomy as an interest. You can establish groups centered on specific outreach themes or events, or you can make a personality for your own space mission. Indeed, the Swift and GLAST missions already have their own MySpace personalities. At the time of this writing, little brother GLAST is extremely jealous of big sister Swift because she is already in orbit. Lest the ASP feel left out, a Facebook group "ASP Rocks Astronomy" was created during this workshop.

Using social networks is not without difficulties. The writing style can be hard for oldsters to penetrate (hint: hire a high school student to do your writing), inaccurate information may propagate, and inappropriate materials might be encountered. The latter problem, coupled with concerns about privacy, limits the use of online communities for outreach to adult audiences. Nevertheless, EPO practitioners can make significant contributions by getting their messages out into such communities, and by serving as kind and gentle cyber-police politely correcting any misinformation that might be out there.

Green Screens and Podcasts   In a set of mini-tutorials, Elaine Lewis, Troy Cline, and Lou Mayo from NASA's Goddard Space Flight Center provided introductions to green screens and podcasts as new delivery technologies for outreach. The context of their workshop was the upcoming March 20, 2008, event *Sun-Earth Day-Space Weather Around the World*. This annual celebration of the Sun and its effects on Earth has a large and dedicated audience that the organizers are hoping to expand by using these new information dissemination technologies. The applicability of the technologies, of course, extends to a wide range of other outreach activities.

Podcasting is a rapidly growing phenomenon that can be easily put to use. A roving microphone and readily available audio editing software are all that you need to produce your own podcasts. In conjunction with Sun-Earth Day, podcasts are being used to capture the sounds and excitement of events like solar eclipses and to provide a continuously updated source of information on space weather and related phenomena. Among the advantages of podcasts are that they can be made available over the Web and that interested users can receive new content automatically via direct subscriptions.

Green screens can be used to allow students to star in their own TV programs. For Sun-Earth Day, students pose in front of an "invisible" green screen and use a computer video camera and teleprompter to give space weather reports. The computer superimposes the student's image upon a background showing a space weather map or a suitable remote location. The net effect is that of a professionally produced TV weather report. The technology is easy to acquire. A computer video camera, readily available software, and a green cloth backdrop are all that are needed to replicate this activity in any classroom.

2.2.   Partnerships

EPO involves partnerships. The very nature of bringing frontline science to classrooms or the public implies a relationship between those who acquire the knowledge and those who disseminate it. For many people on the street, learning about astronomy means visiting the local planetarium or encountering a sidewalk astronomer. Expanding relations with such providers is a good way to expand the reach of out-reach programs.

Planetariums   Jeanne Bishop of the Westlake Schools Planetarium in Westlake, Ohio, along with a cast of planetarians and planetarium partners too large to list here, provided a panel discussion entitled *Partnerships with Planetariums to Broaden the Audience and Communicate Advances in Astronomy*. Among the roles that planetariums can play are serving as a venue for local Science Olympiad events focusing on constellation identification, producing programs featuring the work of contemporary astronomers, and bringing programs to schools and community settings by using digital projection technologies in portable planetariums.

A unique international collaboration between the Adler Planetarium in Chicago, Illinois, the Beijing Planetarium, and the Liberty Science Center in Jersey City, New Jersey, was also described. This project is aimed at producing a *Sesame Street Sky Show* for audiences in both China and the United States with the goals of introducing astronomy, promoting positive attitudes toward science, and fostering cross-cultural understanding among Chinese and American children. The project also promotes bilateral collaboration among science educators and institutions in both countries, even to the point of joint funding provided by the National Science Foundation of the United States and the National Science Foundation of China.

Amateur Astronomers   Many societies of amateur astronomers are interested in providing public outreach. As the ASP has shown through its Night Sky Network, amateur societies can make excellent partners for getting people acquainted with objects in the real sky. The Sun-Earth Day organizers are seeking astronomy club partners to set up solar observing opportunities to promote Sun-Earth awareness. Astronomy clubs can also make natural partners for planetariums by complimenting the programming inside the dome with outdoor observing sessions.

3.   Targeting Specific Audiences

Efforts aimed at broadening the audience by working with communities of specific interest took many forms. A number of posters and workshops addressed issues and reported progress in working with a particular underrepresented group. Others looked closely at ideas and methods that can come from making deep connections across cultural boundaries.

3.1.   Underrepresented Groups

Providing resources for special needs, ensuring gender equity, and working with urban and underrepresented minority groups were highlighted in workshops and posters. In these areas, significant progress has been made, yet much more needs to be done.

Special Needs   The progress in providing outreach materials and activities for people with special needs was highlighted by the ASP's selection of Noreen Grice, President of You Can Do Astronomy LLC and Planetarium Coordinator at the Museum of Science in Boston, to receive the 2007 Klumpke-Roberts Award for out-standing contributions to the public understanding and appreciation of astronomy. Through her pioneering book, *Touch the Universe: A NASA Braille Book of Astronomy*, Ms. Grice brought the world of astronomy to the entire community of people with visual disabilities, and she made the words "tactile images" part of the everyday vocabulary of EPO professionals. In so doing, she set a new standard for providing services to students and others with disabilities: new methodologies that foster true inclusion of persons with special needs are the now the goal. A variety of workshops and posters focusing on special needs projects followed suit. Among the issues receiving attention were special education; sonification of data, balloon projects, and tactile learning experiences for the visually impaired; and wheelchair accessibility at observatories. The clear message was that, by paying attention to special needs and working closely with people to have and serve those needs, innovative and effective outreach activities that serve all levels of "able-ness" can be developed.

Gender Equity In a workshop entitled *Equitable Classroom Practices*, Deborah Jensen of Rice University and Elizabeth Jensen of the University of California, San Diego, modeled methods for promoting gender equity in the classroom. Their work over the past nine years has sought to find ways to increase the representation of females in science, engineering, and mathematics. One important aspect is to use classroom techniques that consciously invite females to participate on an equal basis with males. Such techniques include emphasizing cooperative learning groups and the student use of manipulatives, ensuring equity in the amounts and quality of teacher attention, and developing teachers' skills in questioning students and using multiple types of assessments. The take-home message was that paying attention to equity issues can make a substantial difference in the interests and performance of females in science activities, and that a solid research base of knowledge on such issues is readily available.

Urban and Minority Working with various urban and underrepresented minority groups was a focus of many sessions. Posters reported on leveraging partnerships with museums and schools, forming after school or community groups, using Spanish language media outlets, and working with Native American colleges. Tying much of this together was a workshop, *Strategies for Diverse EPO Partnerships*, led by Sanlyn Buxner, of the University of Arizona and the Phoenix mission. In this workshop, a variety of issues that might arise when conducting activities that involve audiences from cultures and settings different from those of the organizers were raised and discussed. Differences in expectations over such issues as commitments to attend, the availability of languages other than English, and the of sharing information on grade and age levels can easily lead to problems with no-shows, overbooking, mismatches in ability levels, and communication difficulties. Suggested remediations centered on two basic principles: in the short-term, go out of your way to accommodate unexpected circumstances; in the long-term, build ever-tighter relation-ships with your partners and communicate frequently in order to head off problems before they occur.

3.2. Cultural Connections

Some of the most important messages in this strand came from modern-day connections with ancient cultures of the Middle East and Mesoamerica. Carefully listening to and fully embracing the customs and cultures of others can lead to remarkable insights and methods for devising outreach programs. It takes time and patience, but the rewards can be immeasurable.

Sunrise and Sunset A reminder of the importance of the most basic of astronomical observations came in a workshop led by Taha Massalha of the Academic Arab College for Education in Haifa, Israel, on *Multicultural Astronomy Learning Using Sunrise and Sunset Phenomena: Sun and Moon Cycles in the Holy Land*. Dr. Massalha's institution is a college that exclusively serves future teachers. Consequently, they focus on teaching the most basic concepts very thoroughly. In the case of astronomy, this means careful attention to the observed cycles

of the Sun and Moon. They are part of everyone's daily lives, and they are
the basis of the calendars of all the dominant religions in the Holy Land. In
a classroom full of students from different religious traditions, the phenomena
of sunrise and sunset provide a common theme that unifies the students. The
teaching methods are familiar, based on the National Science Teacher Association's "Astronomy on a Stick" activity, but using them in the Holy Land give
them new meaning. A hand drawn representation of sunset locations and times
over a year, as seen by a student from his home in Nazareth, gives a new sense
of the most basic connections to the sky that unite all of us. (For a reproduction
of this drawing, see the article by Taha Massalha elsewhere in this volume.)

Community and Family   The true meaning of transcending cultural boundaries
when conducting outreach was amply demonstrated in a workshop on *The Living Astronomy and People of the Mayan World Today: Traditions of the Sun
Through Time and Culture.* The workshop was jointly led by Isabel Hawkins
of the University of California, Berkeley, and Felipe Tapia of Orgullo Yucateco,
a community-based group in San Rafael, California. Mr. Tapia and his extended family are part of the Mayan community in Northern California, and
they maintain close ties with their relatives in the traditional Mayan communities in Mesoamerica.

Speaking in their Native Yucatec Mayan language-and translating that into
Spanish and then English-they described their work in recapturing the sky
knowledge of their ancestors and melding it with knowledge from current NASA
space science. Dr. Hawkins described her work in building partnerships with
the Maya, traveling to the historical Mayan astronomical sites and communities
in Mesoamerica and to the Mayan community in San Rafael, California. In the
process, she immersed herself in the Mayan culture, learning about their history
and current lives as well as about their interests in the sky. In return, the Maya
adopted her into their community and family. Their mutual goal was to give
the Maya a voice with which to speak about their own lives and customs, while
gifting their youth with introductions to both traditional Mayan and contemporary NASA astronomy. The evidence of having achieved that goal was clear
when the entire Tapia family came in person to share in the presentation of their
work at the ASP conference.

Science in the Mayan culture is a natural part of all aspects of life. It is
therefore natural to devise astronomy outreach activities as a part of broader
celebrations of family and community life. This is exactly what Dr. Hawkins
and Mr. Tapia do in California, with family-oriented celebrations of Mayan
food, music, dance, and astronomy. It is also what they did in their workshop.
Attired in traditional Mayan dress, the Tapia family described their clothing,
demonstrated traditional dances, and responded to questions about various aspects of their lives and their relationships with the sky. It gave a fully connected
picture.

4.   Conclusion

The picture that remains in my mind from the ASP conference is that of the
Tapia family sitting with the many EPO professionals in the audience while I

Figure 1.   The inaugural Adler-Mansfield Prize for best presentation was given to Felipe Tapia and his extended family, who brought insights into Mayan astronomy and culture to the ASP Conference. Front Row (left to right): Ramon Diaz, Eric Diaz, Arturo Diaz, Felipe Tapia. Back Row (left to right): Claudia Diaz, Rosa Diaz, Stephanie Diaz, Isabel Hawkins, Maria Diaz, Maria Oliva.

gave this rapporteur's summary of the *Towards Broadening the Audience strand*. Looking out upon the audience, I saw a picture of what the future of space science outreach could be like:

> *Imagine a future in which all of us who are engaged in outreach are intimately connected with families and communities from a multiplicity of cultures and settings. Imagine, too, that all of our partners and families came to the ASP Conference. Imagine how different-and how appropriately diverse-the audience at that conference would be. Imagine a future in which this genuinely broader audience is the ASP.*

Rapporteur Edna DeVore

Wrap-up session

EPO and a Changing World
ASP Conference Series, Vol. 389, © 2008
C. Garmany, M. Gibbs, and J. W. Moody

The Evolving Nature of Astronomy Research and its Implications for EPO

M. Jordan Raddick

Johns Hopkins University, 3400 N. Charles St., Baltimore, MD, 21218, USA

Abstract.   Like all sciences in general, astronomy has experienced unprecedented changes in just the last few years. As the total volume of data continues to double each year, we struggle to collect and interpret all the data - and as EPO professionals, we struggle to bring this data to learners in a meaningful way. This rapporteur paper will review some of our community's reactions to the "Evolving Nature of Astronomy Research" thread. These reactions include strategies for learners to access real astronomy data through visualization and resources like the World Wide Telescope, for remote telescope access, for collaborative environments, and for citizen science projects. These resources come together in a variety of activities for learners in all settings, at all levels. As these activities are deployed and evaluated, astronomy education will continue to benefit from its rich interconnections with astronomy research.

1.   The Evolving Nature of Astronomy Research

Astronomy research today is experiencing unprecedented changes. Astronomy in the early 20th century was a data-poor science, where researchers had to wait months or years for data to advance their studies. Today, astronomy is a data-rich science, where researchers can conduct groundbreaking studies quickly, with millions of objects at a time, combining data from multiple wavelengths to build a more complete understanding of the universe (Hanisch 2001). The volume of data collected in astronomy - and all sciences - is now doubling every year (Gray et al. 2005), meaning that each year, we collect more scientific data than had ever been collected in human history.

Since a key goal of astronomy education is to communicate to learners the excitement of modern scientific research (Partridge and Greenstein 2004), our work as educators must be informed by the process of research as researchers conduct it. But with astronomy research changing so fundamentally and so quickly, we must change our practices equally quickly. This rapporteur paper will review some of the community's ideas and methods along the thread of "The Evolving Nature of Astronomy Research," and will detail some of the ways in which the EPO profession is changing in response to the way that astronomy research is now done

2.   Access to Real Astronomy Data

Over the past decade, astronomy data has increasingly been moving online. For example, the Sloan Digital Sky Survey (SDSS) now offers its entire 2-terabyte dataset on the Internet, free of charge, to professional astronomers, teachers and students, and the general public (Sparks, Stoughton, & Raddick 2004). This access to professional-quality data of gives learners unprecedented ability to conduct scientific inquiry, asking their own questions and seeking their own answers.

The downside of such data access, however, is that learners can easily be over-whelmed by the size and complexity of the information available to them. To best use these resources, learners must be able to access data simply and intuitively. This means that visualization - showing data as visually appealing representations - must play a key role in how the learners interact with data.

2.1. Visualization

With the amount and complexity of astronomy data increasing so quickly, it is no longer possible to display data to learners in simple graphs - complex visualizations are needed to discover and interpret patterns. The day before the meeting, a "visualization brain trust" meeting was held at Adler Planetarium; SubbaRao (this volume) reviews the results of that meeting in this volume.

Participants at the meeting discussed ways of producing photos and videos that are engaging and accurately represent science content. They also discussed ways to promote visualization videos, such as producing them in high-definition and making them available as downloads from iTunes. Participants gave demonstrations of videos, web-based tools, and planetarium shows that use visualizations of astronomy data, and discussed new technologies that could impact visualization in the near future.

2.2. Data Visualization and Search Tools

A number of tools are now available, or soon to be available, to provide learners with easy access to astronomical images and simple interactive visualizations. These tools include:

Sky in Google Earth   A common tool to view astronomy data is Sky, a new feature of the popular mapping software Google Earth (introduced in version 4.2). Sky allows you to look up from any point on Earth and see what the sky looks like at that point, right now. You can type in an object name to fly there, or pan and zoom through the sky. The tool includes placemarks that provide information about astronomical objects from Wikipedia and the Hubble press release archive.

World Wide Telescope   Microsoft Research is developing a prototype interface to astronomy images and data called the "World Wide Telescope (WWT)" (Wong this volume). When WWT is released, it will be a free downloadable application that lets users fly through the sky, following hyperlinks from one celestial object to another. The tool is aimed at a variety of audiences, including lifelong learners, K-12 and college astronomy students, and amateur astronomers.

WWT's design philosophy is that learners should always view data in context, and the tool allows EPO developers to program this context through "tours" of the sky. For example, one tour might show a selection of beautiful planetary nebula; another might teach stellar evolution by showing a succession of different stars in different stages of their evolution.

WWT will be released first as a community resource for EPO developers. Once a critical mass of tours has been created, the tool will be released to the public. Astronomers and EPO staff interested in creating tours of the universe within WWT should contact Curtis Wong at curtis.wong@microsoft.com to suggest a tour that they would like to create, and to provide the title and outline along with information about themselves and their organization.

Virtual Astronomy Metadata Project (VAMP)   Sometimes, all astronomy instructors need is a good picture of a single object to show to learners. However, finding images of sky objects can often be a challenge - a web search can often return images unrelated to astronomy, or can return the same famous image over and over again. To illustrate the problem, try searching for "M16" in Google Images.

To provide an easier way to find astronomy images, image providers must develop some way of making the content of the image searchable - what the image is about. The Virtual Astronomy Metadata Project (VAMP) is developing a system to make images searchable in this way. They have already created a hierarchical structure for categorizing images; for example, an image of a Martian volcano could be tagged as Planet → Satellite → Surface → Volcanic Feature. These tags can then be searched, along with other tags that describe the image's wavelength or the mission that it is associated with, in a search engine that returns only astronomy images.

3.   Remote Telescopes

The Internet allows learners access to professional astronomy data, but it also allows them to take their own data with remote, robotic telescopes, controlled over the Internet. Making an observation for oneself can be a memorable experience for a student, more so than viewing even the most beautiful image made by someone else (Sadler et al. 2001). Remote telescopes in other parts of the world can offer additional advantages - students in school during the day can view real-time pictures from telescopes at night, and students or museum visitors in the Northern Hemisphere can see the Southern sky.

Existing telescopes can be turned into remote telescope systems with the Remote Telescope Markup Language (RTML) standard (Pennypacker et al. 2002). In this volume, White et al. (this volume) review a number of remote telescope projects now available or coming online soon:

National Optical Astronomy Observatory Robotically Controlled Telescope (NOAO RCT)   NOAO RCT is part of the Research-Based Science Education (RBSE) program. Students of teachers who have graduated from the program can apply for time (which NOAO has purchased) on New Mexico Skies Observatory's network of 14-inch Celestron telescopes to conduct research projects.

Real Astronomy Experience (RAE)   RAE, an outgrowth of the Hands-On Universe project (Ferlet & Pennypacker 2006), has placed controls for a remotely-controlled telescope in a museum exhibit at the Lawrence Hall of Science in

Berkeley, California, USA. The telescope is in Perth, Australia; there is a replica telescope next to the exhibit that follows the same visitor control. Visitors can use the telescope to conduct a series of activities, and can E-mail their results home.

MicroObservatory   MicroObservatory (Sadler et al. 2001), started about 20 years ago by the Harvard-Smithsonian Center for Astrophysics, offers a network of five telescopes around the U.S. and Australia that were specifically designed for education. These telescopes have provided more than 250,000 images, free of charge, to schools, out-of-school groups, and science museum visitors.

Slooh.com   Slooh.com is a for-profit remote telescope website. Anyone can buy telescope credit, or can join the program for $99 per year, for unlimited access. The program has four 14" remote telescopes in dark-sky conditions atop Mount Teide in the Canary Islands. Users reserve the telescopes for live or queue-based observing. The site includes a community of more than 40,000 members from 70 countries, with member galleries and astronomy tours. The site has been very popular with amateur astronomers, and has school members as well.

Las Cumbres Observatory Global Telescope Network (LCOGT)   LCOGT is an emerging network of remotely controlled telescopes that currently includes the two 2-meter Faulkes Telescopes in Hawaii and Australia (Clery 2006), which students in the U.K. have access to. LCOGT plans to add a network of about 28 0.4-meter telescopes all over the world, devoted primarily to education. Because LCOGT will have telescopes all over the world, the network will be able to provide learners access to any sky object, 24 hours a day.

4.   Collaborative Environments

Analysis of existing data and new observations are both important parts of student research projects, but both are challenging. Learners often feel overwhelmed by available data and tools, and instructors often feel underprepared to teach astronomy content. Instructors clearly need additional ways to help them develop their knowledge and confidence in using the resources described here. Scientist mentors can help with expertise in science content and process (Fortson 2004), and teacher mentors can help with implementation advice, but providing teachers with good mentoring requires overcoming many logistical problems.

One possible solution to the problem of getting quality mentoring to instructors and learners is online mentoring and collaboration within structured environments. In this volume, Fortson, SubbaRao, and Greenberg (this volume) review the benefits of collaborative environments, and discuss two types: general-purpose and project-specific.

General collaborative environments are environments with a single interface that can be used for multiple types of learning experiences - not just astronomy, nor even just science. The *Collaboratory Project* (http://collaboratory.nunet.net/) offers an environment used by K-12 teachers nationwide in nearly all subjects. The Collaboratory's new *Research Journal* offers a template in which to store data and student observations, and for learners to reflect on observations and conclusions. It also offers a structure for mentors and other learners to comment on work. The advantage of general collaborative environments is that learners must learn the interface only once to engage in multiple projects.

Specific collaborative environments are environments where the interface is unique to each project. *Interactions In Understanding the Universe* (I2U2; http://ed.fnal.gov/uueo/i2u2.html) is a specific collaborative environment where K-12 students are given access to scientific data and the tools to interpret that data. These "e-Labs" include grid tools and processing, and physics and astronomy data. The advantage of specific collaborative environments is that EPO developers can create environments best suited to the specific tasks that learners will engage in.

5. Citizen Science

In Citizen Science projects, researchers from the general public work with professional scientists to conduct scientific research that is meaningful to both groups. The idea is not new - amateur astronomers in the American Association of Variable Star Observers (AAVSO) have been doing excellent variable star research since the organization's founding in 1911. But with the advent of the Internet and the instant communication it allows, the learning curve to citizen science participation has been lowered, allowing millions more to participate in meaningful scientific research. The idea of citizen science has many features in common with the idea of "collective intelligence," in which a large group of strangers collaborate online to accomplish a task (Weiss 2005). In this volume, Mendez reviews several recent Internet-based citizen science efforts.

The most successful Internet-based citizen science project in recent years has been *SETI@home* (Anderson et al. 2002), from the Search for Extra-Terrestrial Intelligence (SETI) project. *SETI@home* participants downloaded a screen saver onto their computers that searches through radio telescope data for possible signals from alien civilizations. The software was released in 1999; by 2002, nearly 4 million people had downloaded it. Although the software created much excitement about science, participation was passive - users simply downloaded the screen saver and waited.

Inspired by *SETI@home*'s success, NASA's Stardust mission began the *Star-dust@home* program (http://stardustathome.ssl.berkeley.edu/), in which citizen science volunteers use an online "virtual microscope" to search through scanned aerogels containing a few tracks formed by tiny grains of interstellar dust. The *Stardust@home* user that discovers each particle will be a co-author on the scientific paper announcing its discovery. *Stardust@home* has taken steps to measure each user's reliability, including providing "calibration frames" known to have dust particle tracks (or not). About 20,000 users have signed up, and they have already found about 50 dust particles.

The newest citizen science effort discussed here is the Galaxy Zoo project (http://www.galaxyzoo.org), in which users classify galaxies from the Sloan Digital Sky Survey as spiral or elliptical. By doing this, volunteers are building the most complete database of human-classified galaxy morphologies in the world. These classifications can then be compared to other galaxy properties such as redshift or color to learn more about how galaxies evolve. More than 100,000 volunteers have signed up with Galaxy Zoo in four months.

As the numbers of volunteers show, these citizen science projects have generated much excitement about scientific research, but there have been few studies about the projects' effects on participant knowledge, skill, or attitude toward science. One notable study outside astronomy is a summative evaluation of the Cornell Laboratory of Ornithology's *The Birdhouse Network* (TBN) project (Brossard, Lewenstein, & Bonney 2005). That paper concluded that although TBN increased participants' knowledge of bird biology, it had no measurable effect on their knowledge of science process or attitudes toward science. The study concluded that citizen science projects must make participants explicitly aware of the process of science that they are engaging in.

6. Learning Activities and Evaluation

The materials listed above are resources for learners to engage in the process of doing astronomy, in the way that astronomers do. But of course, these resources must be put into a context that is both feasible and meaningful for the learner. Discussing best practices for creating learning activities is beyond the scope of this paper, particularly since best practices vary so widely by audience and venue. Instead, this paper will review some of the learning activities presented in this volume, with particular emphasis on those that have been evaluated.

These activities come in three general types: student and teacher workshops, formal education activities, and informal education activities.

6.1. Student and Teacher Workshops

In a workshop approach, students or teachers are trained on-site in how to use a set of tools to access data or take observations. Usually, participants receive more training online as they practice using the tools. Participants develop and conduct an astronomy research project, often over the course of the following academic year.

NOAO's *Teacher Leaders in Research-Based Science Education* (TLRBSE) has been a highly successful workshop program for teachers. Dussault et al. (this volume) describe two other workshop programs that give teachers access to data from space telescopes. The *Chandra Astrophysics Institute* invites area high school students to work with MIT scientists and Chandra X-Ray Observatory data to complete a year-long astronomy research project. The Spitzer Science Center sponsors a student and teacher re-search program where TLRBSE graduates and their students use observing time and archived data from the Spitzer Space Telescope to complete astronomy research projects. Another workshop discussed here is *MARSFEST* (Shaner, Buxner, & Keller this volume), in which teachers travel to Alaska to conduct investigations using instruments like those on the *Phoenix* lander. The project is now conducting a 5-year longitudinal study to measure changes in participants' teaching.

The advantages of a workshop approach are that participants can be trained in detail, and can engage with learning activities on a deep level. The disadvantages are that because they require so much training time per participant, that they can only reach a limited audience, and that they tend to attract only the most knowledgeable and enthusiastic teachers and students.

6.2. Curricula for Formal Education

EPO professionals have a history of writing high-quality formal education activities; a number of such activities are discussed here. However, as Slater et al. report in this volume, even the most qualified teachers face many barriers to incorporating space science data and activities into their classrooms - difficulty finding appropriate data and tools, insufficient time to complete inquiry-based activities, and a lack of infrastructure and mentoring. Curriculum developers must develop materials that address these challenges.

Dussault et al. describe formal education activities that use space telescope data. *Teacher HERA* is a simplification of research software used by x-ray astronomers; the software includes learning activities for high school and college students. The Office of Public Outreach at the Space Telescope Science Institute is now producing several new activities, including one that uses orbital parameters of Solar System bodies to teach about how to classify them, building off the 2006 controversy about Pluto's status as a planet.

One well-known set of NOAO-developed materials is *Astronomy Village* (Pompea & Blurton 1995), in which students use NASA images and data to investigate the solar system and universe. *Astronomy Village* materials have been heavily field-tested and evaluated (McGee & Howard 1998), have been deployed in classrooms, and have been the source of original research into student cognition. Another NOAO effort, still in a pilot stage, is *Wilderness of Rocks* (Croft, Sparks, & Pompea this volume), which uses student telescope observations to characterize asteroid composition.

Solar astronomy data is also represented in formal education activities. EPO programs of two NASA solar physics missions collaborated on a program to place magnetometers at 12 schools in 10 northern U.S. states (Peticolas, Odenwald, & Walker this volume), and to develop teacher guides, which have been field-tested and evaluated in the schools where the magnetometers were deployed. A separate project, part of the International Heliophysical Year, puts space weather monitors in schools (Scherrer, Burress, & Ross); that project also includes teacher guides.

6.3. Informal Education Activities

Astronomy EPO also provides many resources for informal education. Because visualization plays such an important role in these venues, results from the visualization meeting (SubbaRao) are important for developing informal education resources.

One effort to bring space science into informal education is a program, conducted through the NSF's Internships in Public Science Education (IPSE) program, to put data and visualization tools from the Sloan Digital Sky Survey into a local science center exhibit (Raddick et al. this volume). An evaluation of that project is now being conducted with the goal of developing a method for creating a sustainable partnership between a research university and a local science center.

One of the most exciting recent developments in informal education is the *Astronomy Learning in Virtual Environments* (ALIVE) project (Yu & Sahami this volume). The project is developing real-time, interactive "virtual environments" in digital planetariums for teaching concepts from Astronomy 101. These virtual environments will then be evaluated, using tools from education research and compared to control groups using the same virtual environments in a classroom setting and using traditional instructional materials.

7. Conclusions

As data volumes continue to double, the discoveries of astronomy research will continue at a faster and faster pace. The EPO profession will continue to bring this data to all public audiences, but to do so it will need to continue to develop innovative ways to make the data understandable and meaningful to learners, and to allow learners to follow up on that data with their own observations.

But most importantly, the EPO profession must continue to develop learning materials that respond to realities of the learners' situations, and to aggressively field-test and evaluate these materials. In addition, working more closely with the education research community will help us make our efforts contribute more deeply to knowledge of how people learn science. The EPO community has done an excellent job of adapting to changes in the way astronomy research is done, and will continue to make use of astronomy research to teach and inspire learners far into the future.

References

Anderson, D.P., Cobb, J., Korpela, E., Lebofsky, M., and Werthimer, D., Communications of the ACM, **45**(11), 56 (2002)

Brossard, D., Lewenstein, B., and Bonney, R., International Journal of Science Education, **27**, 1099 (2005)

Clery, D., Science, **306**, 216 (2006)

Ferlet, R. and Pennypacker, C. R., in *Organizations and Strategies in Astronomy 6*, ed. A. Heck (Astrophysics and Space Science Library vol. 335), 275 (2006)

Fortson, L.F. 2004, in *NASA Office of Space Science Education and Public Outreach Conference*, edited by C. Narasimhan, B. Beck-Winchatz, I. Hawkins, and C. Runyon (ASP Conference Series vol. 319), 221 (2004)

Gray, J., Liu, D. T., Nieto-Santisteban, M., Szalay, A., DeWitt, D., Heber, G., ACM SIGMOD Record, **34**(4), 34 (2005)

Hanisch, R. J., in *Astrophysical Sources for Ground-Based Gravitational Wave Detectors*, ed. J.M. Centrella (AIP Conference Proceedings vol. 575), 45 (2001)

McGee, S. and Howard, B., Journal of Universal Computer Science, **4**, 273 (1998)

Partridge, B. and Greenstein, G., AER, **2**, 46 (2004)

Pennypacker, C., Boer, M., Denny, R., Hessman, F. V., Aymon, J., Duric, N., Gordon, S., Barnaby, D., Spear, G., Hoette, V., A&A **395**, 727 (2002)

Pompea, S. M. and Blurton, C., Mercury, **24**(1), 32 (1995)

Sadler, P.M., Gould, R. R., Leiker, P. S., Antonucci, P. R. A., Kimberk, R., Deutsch, F. S., Hoffman, B., Dussault, M., Contos, A., Brecher, K., and French, L. 2001, Journal of Science Education and Technology, **10**, 39 (2001)

Sparks, R., Stoughton, C., Raddick, M. J., in *NASA Office of Space Science Education and Public Outreach Conference*, eds. C. Narasimhan, B. Beck-Winchatz, I. Hawkins, & C. Runyon (ASP Conference Series vol. 319), 394 (2004)

Weiss, A., netWorker **9**(3), 16 (2005)

EPO and a Changing World
ASP Conference Series, Vol. 389, © *2008*
C. Garmany, M. Gibbs, and J. W. Moody

The EPO Profession: A Changing World

Edna K. DeVore

SETI Institute, 515 N. Whisman Road, Mountain View, CA 94043

Abstract.   The EPO Profession was a strand within the September 2007 ASP conference, "EPO and a Changing World: Creating Linkages and Expanding Partnerships." This paper presents synopsis of the opening address, "Is There Room for Space?" by George Nelson, and discussion of the major themes that emerged in the workshops, sessions, and posters of the EPO Profession strand.

1.   The Education and Public Outreach Profession: Looking to the Future

The Education and Public Outreach (EPO) profession is new, but evolved from the ancient human activity of teaching and learning. I think that EPO professionals find common ancestors in ancient people sitting around campfires sharing stories about the Sun, Moon, and stars. Today, EPO professionals work with scientists, engineers and technologists to communicate to the public scientific discoveries and explorations of the natural world. EPO professionals are found in formal institutions such as universities and colleges, research organizations, science centers, observatories and research ships; they are found where scientific research is being conducted and communicated to the public.

This article provides an overview of the presentations and posters that were grouped together under the conference strand: The EPO Professions: A Changing World. The program organizers challenged presenters to respond to the call for papers: "As EPO programs are being held to higher standards of accountability, how can we improve our practice, develop new approaches for developing products and programs at all stages and in both formal and informal education settings: from writing a proposal, to assessing audience needs, to applying research on how people learn to product/program design, to evaluation and dissemination."

The Astronomical Society of the Pacific's 2007 national conference, "EPO and a Changing World: Creating Linkages and Expanding Partnerships," focused upon education in all environments and venues. This paper is an overview of the EPO Profession strand at the meeting. Altogether, there were twenty-nine presentations and posters within the strand. I hope that this overview serves as an appetizer to whet your appetite for the detailed papers by the original session and poster authors elsewhere in this volume.

2.   The Big Picture: Is there Room for Space?

George "Pinky" Nelson opened the conference by reflecting upon a key question: "Is there Room for Space: EPO and the Big Education Reform Picture." Currently, Nelson is Director of Science Mathematics, and Technology Education Western Washington University. Formerly, he was President of the ASP Board of Trustees, co-chair of Project 2061 at the American Association for the Advancement of Science, and a NASA astronaut and astrophysicist. One might say he had a keen and well-informed perspective on education, public outreach, science, and space exploration.

His reflections on the role of EPO in the larger world of education challenged attendees to consider how EPO professionals working outside of formal education (K-12 schools, colleges, universities) can make a difference. He remarked that our profession's fantasy is public astronomy literacy, while our reality is that EPO reaches the groupies. Can we change this? How can we make a difference? He asked in the description of his talk:

> Can we improve student learning of astronomy without simulta-
> neously improving all science education? Can we improve science
> education without also improving the teaching of mathematics, so-
> cial studies, reading, and writing? Can we improve teaching in gen-
> eral without changing how schools are structured i.e. how time and
> resources are used, how curricula are designed and materials are se-
> lected, how professional development is conceived and implemented?
> Can we change school structure without improving how new teachers
> and administrators are prepared in the colleges and universities? Can
> we improve teacher preparation without improving student learning
> of astronomy? The education reform challenge is so huge and astron-
> omy is such a small part of the curriculum. Yet, I will argue, unless
> we collaborate to develop the best standards, the best curriculum
> materials, the best assessments, the best professional development
> - in astronomy - all while becoming deeply engaged in the larger
> education reform, we might as well stay home. When it comes to
> the schools, EPO is not an avocation; it is important, serious work.
> There are some great things happening, there is room for more. (Nel-
> son 2007)

Nelson recommended that EPO professionals pursue partnerships and col-laborations with formal educational institutions to provide quality professional development for teachers, to promote space science in schools, and to evaluate new astronomy/space science materials for effectiveness and impact before they are published. Finally he urged EPO professionals to pay close attention to research on learning and teaching. Interestingly, these ideas were reinforced as EPO principles and best practices in the individual oral presentations, work-shops, and posters throughout the meeting's subsequent activities.

3. Major Cross-Cutting Themes

The EPO Profession strand anticipated proposals on funding/grant writing, as-sessment and accountability, EPO as a profession, and best practices of partner-ing and collaborating. Only three of these were addressed in the workshops and posters; presentations on funding and grant writing were largely absent. Four major themes emerged: fundamental principles of excellent EPO, best practices to achieve excellence, challenges and lessons learned, and views on the status and future of the EPO profession.

3.1. EPO Principles

The core principle that emerged throughout the strand was that effective EPO is founded on understanding learning and teaching, and applying this knowledge effectively as an EPO professional. Presenters urged participants to dive into How People Learn (Bransford, Brown & Cocking 1999), National Science Education Standards (National Research Council 1995) and Benchmarks for Science Literacy (American Association for the Advancement of Science 1993) to enhance their understanding and skills in developing and implementing curriculum and teacher professional development: align with national standards, assess the needs of your selected audience, and learn what works based upon research. Sessions presented basic information on learning and memory, learning cycles, knowledge construction and preconceptions, ethical considerations and regulations in educational research, and bridging the gap between educational research and practice. Posters described the application of learning research and educational design research to EPO activity development.

3.2. EPO Practices

Best practices could be summarized in two words: "standards" and "evaluation." Always and everywhere, the mantra of "align with standards" was heard and seen. At least at this meeting, the EPO professionals understood that if educational programs are to find a place in K-12 classrooms and K-12 teacher professional development, the programs must align with national standards. Workshops and posters provided introductions to the National Science Education Standards (Standards) and how to employ them in EPO work, as well as how to extend beyond the Standards in creative and appropriate ways. The Standards are a base, not a ceiling or barrier to excellent EPO, and building on the foundation provided by Standards allows teachers to use novel materials and programs in classroom instruction.

Evaluation was the second best practice evident in several presentations. From the first steps taken to understand the audience through needs assessments, to defining goals and objectives, to formative evaluation in beta-testing materials and requesting feedback from participants, to summative evaluation to understand the longer-term impact of programs and projects, evaluation is seen as a key tool for the EPO professional. Workshops and posters addressed evaluation cycles formally-as a discipline-and via application of evaluation principles in specific programs and projects. Evaluation helps EPO professionals understand whether they have achieved goals and objectives, not simply feel good about their work, but understand and demonstrate that it is useful and valuable.

Several posters and workshops referred participants to Astronomy Education Review (http://aer.noao.edu) as a resource for further information on best practices in astronomy education research and evaluation.

3.3.   Challenges and Lessons Learned

Several posters described individual projects or the EPO programs for particular NASA Missions. In the past, similar presentations were a recitation of what has been accomplished, a menu of achievements. The organizers of this conference invited a more thoughtful presentation of these programs and projects. As a result, these projects and programs were more like case studies: what worked, what didn't work, who was involved, what was the impact, and how future improvements will be implemented. The challenges and lessons learned spanned many audiences: school children and teachers, community members, amateur astronomers, and adult learners including scientists. Reading through the posters and chatting with authors was a day-long seminar in professional training and program improvement. It was an excellent experience for the EPO professional who wished to enhance knowledge and skills.

3.4.   The Profession

Finally, there were several sessions that considered EPO as a profession. Sessions delved into the role of the alphabet soup of federal research agencies (NSF, NOAO, NASA, DOE-energy, not education-NIST, etc.) in spawning and sustaining the EPO profession. Many people were nervous about the future at this meeting as a consequence of changing directions at NASA with respect to EPO. Even so, there were considered discussions in workshops on the development of professional standards for EPO certification, on development of master's degrees in astronomy/space science EPO, on building a database of information and tools for the EPO practioner, and on developing effective collaborations with scientific researchers. These discussions point to a more enduring future than the uneasy climate at NASA might otherwise portend.

4.   Final Thoughts

Recently, I was asked, "What, exactly do you do?" Before this conference, I had described myself as an astronomy educator. I taught astronomy and directed a planetarium for two decades. Over the past 15 or so years, I have participated in the development of the EPO profession within NASA's science research program. (Today it is known as the Science Mission Directorate.) I have also worked with the National Science Foundation and private foundations to develop and conduct EPO projects and programs. My career has evolved from astronomy educator to EPO professional. Personally, I consider it a good second career.

The EPO profession has grown and matured in the past 15 years, responding to the wider implementation of EPO within NASA's SMD and other Federal agencies and the growing number of people joining the ranks of EPO professionals. In Science Education Partnerships (Sussman 2002), Dr. Bruce Alberts compared EPO professionals to messenger RNA in the cell which is the key communicator between the nucleus and the rest of the cell. Like messenger RNA, EPO professionals serve as an essential link between the dedicated community of researchers and engineers, and the interested public. The challenge remains as to how to effectively span the gap, and this conference explored the educational research base and thoughtful strategies needed to build the bridges.

The EPO Profession: Is it easy? No. In the words of Pinky Nelson, "Education is not rocket science. It's much harder."(Nelson 2002) Is it worthwhile? I'm confident that the conference participants would reply with a resounding "Yes!"

Acknowledgments. The author wishes to acknowledge the ideas and freely shared information, computer files and thoughtful comments from the 29 workshop presenters and poster authors in the EPO Profession strand.

References

Nelson, G. D., in *EPO and a Changing World: Creating Linkages and Expanding Partnerships*, ASP Conference Program (2007)

Bransford, J. D., Brown, A.L., and Cocking, R. R. (Eds.) *How People Learn: Brain, Mind, Experience, and School.* (National Academy Press, Washington D. C., 1999)

National Research Council, *National Science Education Standards* (National Academy Press, Washington D. C., 1995)

American Association for the Advancement of Science, *Benchmarks for Science Literacy* (Oxford University Press, New York, New York, 1993)

Sussman A., (Ed.) *Science Education Partnerships: Manual for Scientists and K-12 Teachers* (University of California, San Francisco, CA, 2002)

Nelson, G. Quoted remark: *Education is not rocket science - it's much harder.* Shaping the Future Conference, (University System of Maryland, College Park MD, Nov. 30, 1998)

Chicago Skyline from the Conference Venue

ASTRONOMICAL SOCIETY OF THE PACIFIC
(ASP)

An international, nonprofit, scientific and educational organization
founded in 1889, established the

ASP CONFERENCE SERIES (ASPCS)

in 1988, to publish books on recent developments in
astronomy and astrophysics.

A list of recently published volumes follows. For a complete list of all
volumes published please see our web site at
http://www.astrosociety.org/pubs.html

For electronic versions of volumes please see our e-book site at
http://www.aspbooks.org

All book orders or inquiries concerning

ASTRONOMICAL SOCIETY OF THE PACIFIC
CONFERENCE SERIES
(ASPCS)

and

INTERNATIONAL ASTRONOMICAL UNION VOLUMES
(IAU)

should be directed to

Astronomical Society of the Pacific
390 Ashton Avenue
San Francisco   CA   94112-1722   USA

Phone: 800-335-2624 (within USA)
Phone: 415-337-2126
Fax: 415-337-5205

E-mail: service@astrosociety.org
Web Site: http://www.astrosociety.org
E-book site: http://www.aspbooks.org

PUBLISHED: 2003

Vol. CS 300   RADIO ASTRONOMY AT THE FRINGE, A Conference held in honor of Kenneth
I. Kellermann, on the occasion of his 65th Birthday
eds. J. Anton Zensus, Marshall H. Cohen, and Eduardo Ros
ISBN: 1-58381-147-8   e-Book ISBN: 978-1-58381-243-3

Vol. CS 301   MATTER AND ENERGY IN CLUSTERS OF GALAXIES
eds. Stuart Bowyer and Chorng-Yuan Hwang
ISBN: 1-58381-149-4

Vol. CS 302   RADIO PULSARS, In celebration of the contributions of Andrew Lyne,
Dick Manchester and Joe Taylor – A Festschrift honoring their 60th Birthdays
eds. Matthew Bailes, David J. Nice, and Stephen E. Thorsett
ISBN: 1-58381-151-6

Vol. CS 303   SYMBIOTIC STARS PROBING STELLAR EVOLUTION
eds. R. L. M. Corradi, J. Mikołajewska, and T. J. Mahoney
ISBN: 1-58381-152-4

Vol. CS 304   CNO IN THE UNIVERSE
eds. Corinne Charbonnel, Daniel Schaerer, and Georges Meynet
ISBN: 1-58381-153-2

Vol. CS 305   International Conference on MAGNETIC FIELDS IN O, B AND A STARS:
ORIGIN AND CONNECTION TO PULSATION, ROTATION AND MASS LOSS
eds. Luis A. Balona, Huib F. Henrichs, and Rodney Medupe
ISBN: 1-58381-154-0

Vol. CS 306   NEW TECHNOLOGIES IN VLBI
ed. Y. C. Minh
ISBN: 1-58381-155-9

Vol. CS 307   SOLAR POLARIZATION 3
eds. Javier Trujillo Bueno and Jorge Sánchez Almeida
ISBN: 1-58381-156-7

Vol. CS 308   FROM X-RAY BINARIES TO GAMMA-RAY BURSTS
eds. Edward P. J. van den Heuvel, Lex Kaper, Evert Rol, and Ralph A. M. J. Wijers
ISBN: 1-58381-158-3

PUBLISHED: 2004

Vol. CS 309   ASTROPHYSICS OF DUST
eds. Adolf N. Witt, Geoffrey C. Clayton, and Bruce T. Draine
ISBN: 1-58381-159-1   e-Book ISBN: 978-1-58381-244-0

Vol. CS 310   VARIABLE STARS IN THE LOCAL GROUP, IAU Colloquium 193
eds. Donald W. Kurtz and Karen R. Pollard
ISBN: 1-58381-162-1   e-Book ISBN: 978-1-58381-245-7

Vol. CS 311   AGN PHYSICS WITH THE SLOAN DIGITAL SKY SURVEY
eds. Gordon T. Richards and Patrick B. Hall
ISBN: 1-58381-164-8   e-Book ISBN: 978-1-58381-246-4

Vol. CS 312   Third Rome Workshop on GAMMA-RAY BURSTS IN THE AFTERGLOW ERA
eds. Marco Feroci, Filippo Frontera, Nicola Masetti, and Luigi Piro
ISBN: 1-58381-165-6   e-Book ISBN: 978-1-58381-247-1

ASP CONFERENCE SERIES VOLUMES

Published by the Astronomical Society of the Pacific

ASP CONFERENCE SERIES VOLUMES
Published by the Astronomical Society of the Pacific

PUBLISHED: 2004

Vol. CS 325 THE SOLAR-B MISSION AND THE FOREFRONT OF SOLAR PHYSICS, The Fifth Solar-B Science Meeting
eds. Takashi Sakurai and Takashi Sekii
ISBN: 1-58381-187-7   e-Book ISBN: 978-1-58381-260-0

Vol. CS 326 Never Submitted by Editor
ISBN: 1-58381-188-5 LOC#: 2004118371

Vol. CS 327 SATELLITES AND TIDAL STREAMS
eds. F. Prada, D. Martínez Delgado, and T. J. Mahoney
ISBN: 1-58381-190-7   e-Book ISBN: 978-1-58381-261-7

PUBLISHED: 2005

Vol. CS 328 BINARY RADIO PULSARS
eds. F. A. Rasio and I. H. Stairs
ISBN: 1-58381-191-5   e-Book ISBN: 978-1-58381-262-4

Vol. CS 329 NEARBY LARGE-SCALE STRUCTURES AND THE ZONE OF AVOIDANCE
eds. A. P. Fairall and P. A. Woudt
ISBN: 1-58381-192-3   e-Book ISBN: 978-1-58381-263-1

Vol. CS 330 THE ASTROPHYSICS OF CATACLYSMIC VARIABLES AND RELATED OBJECTS
eds. J.-M. Hameury and J.-P. Lasota
ISBN: 1-58381-193-1   e-Book ISBN: 978-1-58381-264-8

Vol. CS 331 EXTRA-PLANAR GAS
ed. Robert Braun
ISBN: 1-58381-194-X   e-Book ISBN: 978-1-58381-265-5

Vol. CS 332 THE FATE OF THE MOST MASSIVE STARS
eds. Roberta M. Humphreys and Krzysztof Z. Stanek
ISBN: 1-58381-195-8   e-Book ISBN: 978-1-58381-266-2

Vol. CS 333 TIDAL EVOLUTION AND OSCILLATIONS IN BINARY STARS: THIRD GRANADA WORKSHOP ON STELLAR STRUCTURE
eds. Antonio Claret, Alvaro Giménez, and Jean-Paul Zahn
ISBN: 1-58381-196-6   e-Book ISBN: 978-1-58381-267-9

Vol. CS 334 14TH EUROPEAN WORKSHOP ON WHITE DWARFS
eds. D. Koester and S. Moehler
ISBN: 1-58381-197-4   e-Book ISBN: 978-1-58381-268-6

Vol. CS 335 THE LIGHT-TIME EFFECT IN ASTROPHYSICS: Causes and Cures of the $O-C$ Diagram
ed. Christiaan Sterken
ISBN: 1-58381-200-8   e-Book ISBN: 978-1-58381-269-3

Vol. CS 336 COSMIC ABUNDANCES as Records of Stellar Evolution and Nucleosynthesis, in honor of Dr. David Lambert
eds. Thomas G. Barnes, III and Frank N. Bash
ISBN: 1-58381-201-6   e-Book ISBN: 978-1-58381-270-9

Vol. CS 337 THE NATURE AND EVOLUTION OF DISKS AROUND HOT STARS
eds. Richard Ignace and Kenneth G. Gayley
ISBN: 1-58381-203-2   e-Book ISBN: 978-1-58381-271-6

ASP CONFERENCE SERIES VOLUMES
Published by the Astronomical Society of the Pacific

ASP CONFERENCE SERIES VOLUMES
Published by the Astronomical Society of the Pacific

ASP CONFERENCE SERIES VOLUMES
Published by the Astronomical Society of the Pacific

ASP CONFERENCE SERIES VOLUMES

Published by the Astronomical Society of the Pacific

PUBLISHED: 2008

Vol. CS 388 MASS LOSS FROM STARS AND THE EVOLUTION OF STELLAR CLUSTERS
       eds. Alex de Koter, Linda J. Smith, and Laurens B. F. M. Waters
       ISBN: 978-1-58381-644-8   e-Book ISBN: 978-1-58381-645-5

Vol. CS 389 EPO AND A CHANGING WORLD: CREATING LINKAGES AND
       EXPANDING PARTNERSHIPS
       eds. Catharine Garmany, Michael G. Gibbs, and J. Ward Moody
       ISBN: 978-1-58381-648-6   e-Book ISBN: 978-1-58381-649-3